6 00.

Profitable Sheep

THE MACMILLAN COMPANY
NEW YORK · CHICAGO
DALLAS · ATLANTA · SAN FRANCISCO
LONDON · MANILA

IN CANADA
BRETT-MACMILLAN LTD.
GALT, ONTARIO

Fig. 1.   Profit on the hoof.

Will C. Minor, Fruita, Colo.

Profitable Sheep

SPELMAN B. COLLINS, B.S.

Sheep Specialist
California State Polytechnic College
San Luis Obispo, California

Illustrations by

RICHARD F. JOHNSON

Animal Husbandry Department
California State Polytechnic College

THE MACMILLAN COMPANY · *New York*

Preface

It has long been felt that a book concerning the successful operation of the business of raising sheep was much needed. Particularly now, when increased interest in the beast is apparent, high-school and college students and practicing sheep operators alike have need for guidance and instruction in this profitable field.

This book is designed to provide answers to questions that students in all classes may face in the progress of the sheep enterprises they carry on through the year. Enough factual material is provided to give background to instructive material thought desirable in carrying out jobs with sheep. In the latter respect this book differs from the usual text. It is built around the thesis that a good manager often is such because he knows "how to do things" rather than just "what should be done."

Written from a background of thirty years of experience with sheep, this book, the author hopes and believes, will find a welcome place in the libraries and classrooms of colleges and high schools and on the bookshelves of practical sheepmen. This experience has included several years in business as a range sheep operator in the valleys and mountains of California, as a producer and exhibitor of purebred sheep, as a camp tender and foreman in extensive field-fattening operations and as a high-school and college instructor.

The plan of this book is to carry the sheep owner or student through a complete year of activities with commercial ewes producing market lambs and wool. Thus, first treated, are the problems that arise in purchasing breeding stock and acquiring land to run them on. This is followed by discussion of problems concerning breeding, maintenance of the ewes through gestation, preparations for lambing, etc., until the cycle is complete. Additional sections on equipment and disease control that do not fit into a particular spot, chronologically, are also included.

It is thought that such a treatment of the subject may enable the student to capture a strong feeling of the requirements for the successful operation of this business. It is well known that at all times some sheepmen are succeeding financially, others are losing, and still others are on the border line. These variations, more often than not, are due simply to the fact that men have not seen the whole picture, often do not know the consequences of their actions, and so cannot fully manage their affairs. Successful management of the sheep business includes breadth of viewpoint as well as skilled knowledge and energetic attention to detail. It further presupposes a real understanding of the nature of the animals worked with.

This book is designed to provide that breadth of viewpoint necessary to start the business on a sound basis. Further, it provides instruction in many of the skills an operator finds himself called upon to perform in the course of his sheep activities. The author has attempted to provide instruction in detail and has implemented the text through the use of "action pictures" and diagrams. He sincerely hopes that the sheep industry of the future may prosper in the hands of understanding livestock owners.

SPELMAN B. COLLINS

Foreword

The sheep population of this country has dropped from 49 million head in 1942 to 27 million today. We produced about 450 million lbs of wool then, while our production of shorn and pulled wool totaled only 260 million lbs this year. Strange as it may seem, this great reduction in sheep numbers came about while we in this country were consuming two or three times as much wool as we produced. The impact of these figures becomes apparent when one takes into consideration the fact that the economy of so many counties in the western states depends to a great extent on a thriving and prosperous sheep industry. The vast empire in the mountain area of the West is suitable only for grazing purposes. The livestock that day in and day out gather the grass from the ranges of the West constitute a free labor force contributing substantially to the economy of the country as a whole. The decline in our sheep population during the war years occurred largely because of the difficulty in securing competent help. In addition, the price of wool was maintained at a low level all during the war, while labor and other costs increased by leaps and bounds; as a result, the growers had great difficulty making both ends meet.

If the sheep industry is to survive in this country it must be prepared to meet competition, not only from the low cost foreign producers, but from the rapidly expanding synthetic industry here at home as well. Someone must point the way toward more efficient methods in every segment of the sheep industry. To my way of thinking, we should look to our colleges to do that job for us.

I do not profess to be experienced in school work, although I gained a little knowledge of the intricacies of higher education when I was a member of the Board of Trustees of the University of Wyoming a number of years ago, and later when I was an ex officio member of that Board while I was Governor of the State. I became well acquainted with the late John A. Hill, who was Dean of the College of Agriculture at the University of Wyoming, and who was one of the outstanding authorities on wool in the country. I worked very closely with Dean Hill during my tenure of service in the Congress. It is now thirteen years since I first served in Congress, and during all of that time I have been concerned with legislation affecting the sheep industry. I was engaged in the sheep business for more than a quarter of a century, although my partner was the active manager of the ranch. With the experience gained from that background I have read *Profitable Sheep* with a great deal of interest.

In my opinion this should prove an ideal textbook for training our young men so they can be prepared to weather the storm in the new era in the sheep industry that lies ahead. Out of a wealth of practical experience Mr. Collins lays down the rules which one must follow if he expects to run sheep on a profitable basis. The illustrations are admirably done and help materially to present the situation in a practical manner. I have heard many a woolgrower say that if you take care of the sheep they will take care of you. I think that Mr. Collins' treatment of the care of the ewes before and during breeding and gestation and of the lambing operations is a solid, down to earth exposition of an extremely intricate business.

The information contained in the book will prove of great value to all woolgrowers, young and old alike. Each of the different phases of the sheep operation is handled in a masterful manner. Our entire domestic sheep industry is going to face fierce competition if it is not to wither on the vine. Such a fate would not only endanger the security of our country but would threaten the economy of our western states. That must not happen. We need highly trained men to carry on in the industry. *Profitable Sheep* will help immeasurably in that regard.

FRANK A. BARRETT
United States Senate

Contents

Chapter 1

Entering the Business

Before entering the commercial sheep business for the production of wool and milk-fat lambs, the prospective sheepman would do well to survey the field very carefully and to assure himself of his chances for success. The history of the industry during the past few decades gives conclusive evidence that just liking sheep is not enough to assure success.

A commercial sheep business is acquired by inheritance, by purchase, or by building it up from a small start. The first of these, of course, is the simplest, and often the inheritor already has had considerable experience in the business. This is not always true, however; many who have inherited sheep and grazing lands have been inexperienced and have subsequently lost their holdings. The person who buys sheep, with or without a ranch or grazing rights, certainly cannot afford to do so without a careful survey of his chances for success. The third person, who builds for himself a business that will support him, probably pursues the safest road, but of course it is the slowest, and even he will need breadth of vision and plenty of ability and skill to assure his final goal.

It is the purpose of this chapter to survey the points that any sheepman should cover before embarking on his career.

What Sort of Man Is Most Likely to Do Well with Sheep?

The answer to this question is more important than might be imagined, offhand. As in any other business, the attributes that make for success are largely personal. These personal traits are made up of work habits and habits of the mind, or managerial ability, and the man most likely to be on top is the one who likes his work naturally, and can see far enough ahead in any circumstance. Particularly is this true with farming and even more so when farming with livestock.

A Personal Score Card. If a prospective sheepman wished to check his personality to determine whether it might fit him for success, he would do well to prepare himself with the following "ideal" sheepman:

1. I love animals; I hate to see them suffer.

Contact, of course, is the only means by which this inherent love of sheep can be determined. Persons who have worked with sheep for any length of time usually develop an affection for the beasts, and many a "cowboy" has been "won over" after a few months of work with them. It is most likely that a good rating on this point would mean that the sheep would have excellent care.

2. I am observant; I readily notice signs of illness or discomfort in animals.

This quality of being observant is perhaps more important in a sheepman than in any other type of stock owner, not only from the standpoint of prevention of loss of life from disease, but also because of the great importance, as

Don Tomlin

Fig. 2. Herder and dog make a team.

far as maximum returns are concerned, of rapid, uninterrupted growth if top-quality, fat lambs are to be marketed. Sheep and lambs are extremely sensitive to changes in feed and show quick changes in condition when the feed varies.

3. I put the proper care of stock above personal pleasure and comfort.

Although it is not advised that a man's health should be sacrificed to ensure comfort for his sheep, nevertheless the owner should so manage his affairs that his stock is properly cared for. The owner who lies abed when his "drop band" needs tending, who fails to rustle feed when his ewes are losing flesh, is not the sort likely to succeed.

 4. I am patient: I do not "fly off the handle."
The sheep is a beast that requires patience, and she will suffer in the hands of an impatient herder or owner.

 5. I would rather herd the sheep on foot, and let them move quietly, than see them crowded or rushed by dog, man, or horse.
Owners who run large numbers of sheep and employ several herders give ample proof of the value of this trait. A herder who follows another onto a particular piece of feed, and is therefore handicapped by less fresh grazing, may put more gains on his charges because he is a more careful herder. Of course, injuries to the sheep are less likely, too.

 6. I like to get up at sunrise.
The sheep is an early riser. Her nature demands feeding early, resting while the sun is hot. If her tendency is not recognized, she will not do as well.

 7. I consider before I act; I do not rush into business propositions blindly or simply because of sentiment.
Perhaps more failures in the sheep business have been due to this one failing of man than to any other cause. The person who can fully assess his prospective operations and determine the possibilities of his actions is surely less likely to fail than another who engages in an enterprise because "a friend is doing it" or because "I think I like it." Every sheep-raising setup is a unit by itself, and each needs close scrutiny to determine the likelihood of its profitability. (This point is developed further on in this chapter.)

What Types of Lands and Feeds Are Suited to Sheep?

 Sheep are grazers or browsers by nature. They do best and return the most profit when the greatest part of their year's feed is grass or brush. On the other hand, they will survive and do well under some confinement and on hay and grain or prepared feeds, though usually uneconomically and at a sacrifice of health.

What Sheep Like to Eat. There is a distinct difference in the character of natural feeds that will make lambs grow fast and those needed for mature sheep. Not that the ewe does not like what is good for her lamb, but when she is not suckling a lamb, she can be maintained on feeds not suited to lamb growth. Lambs are more fastidious than ewes and the ewes too are quite particular. Lamb feed must be palatable, tender, and fresh, and this means a man-

Calif. Woolgrowers Assn.

Fig. 3.   Lambs do their best on hard, clean, sweet feed.

agement of feeding grounds that will maintain the better natural varieties and keep them in balance. (The means by which this may be accomplished are discussed later.) Many varieties of grass and browse are used by sheep. The thing to investigate in purchasing feed or feed-growing land is whether it maintains a sufficient growth of the palatable varieties, commensurate with cost, and whether that feed can be maintained in such a manner as to be suited to lamb growth, or whether it is of a sort that can never be more than dry-ewe feed.

Every locality grows different varieties of feed according to climate, altitude, and latitude. In California and other far western states the favorite natural grasses for sheep are bur clover and alfilaria ("filaree"), and the range owner is fortunate if a large part of his cover is the former. It will be noted that these are low-growing grasses—not rank—which are especially desirable for lambs. Many other succulent weeds, not so widely found, are relished by sheep; some of these weeds, such as yellow star thistle, are

Don Tomlin

Fig. 4. Alfalfa and similar pastures fill the ewes but are not best for their lambs.

certainly pests as far as farming is concerned. Foxtail (one of the varieties of brome) is palatable when quite young but more so to ewes than to lambs. Nevada and the desert areas grow other varieties, and also brush such as sage, which sheep relish at certain stages. Chaparral brush and young mountain lilac and birch brush are very much desired, but such brush as mesquite, poison oak, and manzanita will never provide gains.

Of course many of the cultivated or irrigated grasses such as Alfalfa, Ladino clover and other clovers, Sudan grass, etc. are relished by sheep, but it is usually a mistake to think of these as making up any major portion of the year's food for a strictly commercial lamb-producing business.

Good natural-grass range, possibly supplemented by browse and adjacent to stubbles or other wastes, make up the most suitable feeding combination for sheep.

Above all, as far as the growth of young lambs is concerned, *fresh* pasture is desirable. The layout should provide for herding

Calif. Woolgrowers Assn.

Fig. 5.   Steep lands suit sheep ideally.

or fencing to make it possible to move lambs daily onto fresh areas, there to enjoy a variety of palatable grasses, clovers, and browse.

Where Sheep Like to Graze. Sheep are run under fence or are herded in open country. In Australia, New Zealand, parts of Texas, and other western states large bands are run strictly under fence. Of course, all small farm flocks, where numbers are too few to support the cost of herding, are likewise maintained under fences. In broken country, or where sheep are moved from place to place onto rented pastures or into the public domain or national forests, they are commonly in the care of herders. They delight in hillside feeding, like to "camp" or "bed down" on high, dry places, but are not averse to feeding on low, swampy ground occasionally. However, generally speaking, the sheep likes best, and does best under, rather arid conditions, on well-drained land where part of its year's feed is green and part dry, and where mountains or slopes can afford natural protection from storms. Sheep are run successfully under conditions just the opposite to these, but usually at greater expense and under less healthful circumstances. The prospective sheepman makes a mistake in running sheep where artificial protection is necessary and where costly feeds (cultivated and irrigated)

Fig. 6. Sheep do best where shade is provided.

must be used, unless perhaps he is in the purebred business, selling highly valued individuals. Here also, unless he "teaches" his ram produce at some time to use dry and rough feeds, they are often unsatisfactory breeders for range sheepmen. Sheep should be thought of as rustlers on their own, and as users of grass and waste in rugged surroundings.

How Sheep Like to Be Handled. The foregoing paragraphs have conveyed some idea of how sheep should be handled. Further, it can be said that quiet, patience, and regularity of attention are quite valuable in getting returns. This means doing such things as the following: refraining from unnecessary corralling; providing supplemental "feeding" instead of "driving" from field to field or from one part of a grazing area to another; limited use of dogs, which should be well trained; regularity in salting and watering;

and daily observation (particularly so under fenced conditions) as to the comfort and feed needs of the sheep. In other words, best returns will be had by catering to the habits of the beasts: feeding early in the morning and late in the evening in summer heat, and resting undisturbed under shade during the middle of the day.

How Much Pasture Do Sheep Need?

This is a question that cannot be answered directly. Natural grass ranges in arid lands support from as many as three ewes (and their offspring) to the acre, year round, to as few as one ewe to perhaps ten acres or more, depending on varieties, cover, and percentage of waste area. The only way to determine what a given range will support is by trial, or the observation of similar ranges nearby, and this observation should be in terms of normal growth, normal climatic conditions, and a normal amount of grasses allowed to seed. Also, this observation should be made when normal sheep husbandry is being practiced. In other words, if a lamb-raising setup was the ultimate desire, it might be very difficult to secure a good picture if the particular area was being used only for the "growing out" of ewe lambs for replacement purposes.

The needs of sheep for pasture, of course, are greatest when the ewes are suckling lambs. If the location is one that allows a good lamb crop and fast growth (such as the early lambing sections of California, Arizona, and other states), the motto should be "Feed to the point of extravagance at this time." Pasture must be bountiful, fresh, *never* restricted if the lambs are to grow and make best returns; therefore the stock must be moved to other areas for freshened feed or, as a second choice, it may remain on the inferior feed if supplemental "creep" feeding of the lamb is provided.

If ewes are in good condition after the lambs are weaned and if they are not too old, their need for feed is very much less. In fact, many owners have found it very remunerative actually to partially starve the fatter ewes until just before breeding again, as they will breed more quickly and produce more twins.

Pasture should never be allowed to become so restricted that the sheep suffer for any length of time. This will result in lowered wool clip of inferior value.

Are Wastes from Other Crops Available to Lower Costs?

Many areas where sheep are run are close to the wastes from farming operations, and stubbles of various sorts support them during summer and fall months. If a range is located within even as much as 75 to 100 miles of such feeds, they can greatly lower the costs of operation.

Calif. Woolgrowers Assn.

Fig. 7. Wastes of crops such as this barley stubble help cheapen sheep costs.

Desirable wastes are the stubbles of barley and wheat, beet tops (for fattening—lambs only), bean and pea straw, vineyards after the crop is removed, almond hulls, melons, morning-glory growing on fallowed fields, rice stubble, ditch-bank, and roadway weeds, etc.

Usually standard prices on an acre or head per day basis are asked for such feeds in a given locality. For the inexperienced, a payment per head per day is probably safest. If some experience has been had, purchases of blocks of such feed on an acre basis may be cheaper, if the buyer can judge values closely.

Where such feeds are available, the sheepman certainly makes a mistake to hold sheep at home on too poor feed in the fall or on soiled, overgrazed areas in the spring. It is often possible for small owners (and they are often the most needy ones in this respect) cooperatively to purchase feeds away from home and run flocks together, under fence or herded, at times of the year.

Could the Land Support a More Profitable Crop than Sheep?

Sheep are run on land valued from twenty-five cents to perhaps two hundred dollars or more per acre, but in the latter case they are invariably high-class purebreds where individuals have a high sales value, and usually much of their feed is the waste from other crops. Do not expect commercial sheep to pay taxes on valuable farming land and return much profit. On the other hand, many farm flocks, using wastes from farm crops and requiring labor when that needed for the crops is slack, have been the real source of income above expenses on valuable farming land.

Again, about the only way to determine whether sheep are the more profitable source of income is to budget operations and compare them with those for other crops, of course not losing sight of the differences in labor needs and the varying percentages of that labor that can be done by the operator or his family.

Generally speaking, sheep are most profitable on land that is not usable for crops (or on land from which crop wastes are consumed).

Which Branch of the Industry Most Suits My Setup?

There are several rather distinct types of sheep raising. These may be listed as follows:

1. Farm flocks, selling fat lambs and wool.
2. Farm flocks of purebreds (usually unregistered ewes), selling range rams.
3. Farm flocks of registered animals, selling purebred stock for stud flocks and exhibition; also generally selling range rams.
4. Farm lamb feeding (using home-grown feeds); sometimes in combination with a flock of ewes.
5. Large commercial bands of ewes. Producers usually own or lease a "home place," generally the lambing grounds, and move about the country following the feed, either stubbles

Calif. Woolgrowers Assn.

(*a*)

(*b*)

Fig. 8.   Branches of the Sheep industry.

    (*a*) A farm flock just after spring shearing.
    (*b*) Produce of a purebred flock; yearling **Corriedale rams raised** by Leslie Crane, Santa Rosa, Calif.

11

(c)   *Frank Nissen, Esparto, Calif.*

(d)   *Will C. Minor, Fruita, Colo.*

Fig. 8 (cont.).   Branches of the sheep industry.

      (c) Replacement yearling ewes ready for sale just shorn.
      (d) A range band summering in the mountains.

(e)

(f)

Fig. 8 (cont.). Branches of the sheep industry.

(e) Dry lot fed lambs about ready to be marketed.
(f) Clover fattening of lambs.

Some lambs do not get fat enough to be butchered directly
off their mothers.

or mountain feed. Some produce primarily wool and replacement ewe lambs, others largely fat market lambs.

6. Raisers of replacement ewes, almost always *purchasers* of ewe lambs that are carried through the first winter and resold as yearlings for breeding.

7. Commercial dry-lot feeders of the lambs that do not get fat enough to market off their dams.

8. Commercial field-feeders who use similar lambs on alfalfa pasture, clover, beet tops, and similar types of growth.

The choice of one or another of these types of sheep raising should be based (aside from inclination) on experience, land values, and location of the ranch or farm. On the other hand, if the selection is limited to one branch, the operator would be wise to seek out a setup that suits it.

The Effect of Location. The advantages that certain locations may offer is more apparent where rams are being raised to offer to the trade and where lambs are being fattened in dry lot than perhaps where the other types of production are in effect.

The *raiser of rams* (stud animals or range rams) is best located somewhere near the center of a commercial range or farm-flock growing area. If his location is too far from such a center, his sales "at home," which are usually most numerous, will be lessened because buyers will not travel greater distances if rams of similar quality are closer to their operations. Then too, a farm location easily reached and on a generally traveled road, where advertising is constantly seen, has its advantages. Many rams are sold at public sales some distance from home, but the beginner needs to gain a reputation before he can get best returns at such sales, and his best chance is to sell good animals at first to his neighbors. Therefore he had better locate his business centrally.

It is naturally an advantage for a *lamb feeder* to be located as close as possible to markets (both for feeders and for fattened animals) and to cheap feeds, as well as where weather conditions are conducive to good gains.

As far as location for a ewe and market lamb-raising business is concerned, there is less need for consideration of such things as mentioned above. Where natural grass is the chief source of lamb and sheep maintenance, the character of this item is paramount. Also climatic conditions will greatly affect the product.

As examples of what may be expected in locating in different areas the following points, cited from Californian sheep experience, are interesting: "Early" lamb raisers, of necessity, are located where precipitation is early, where grass-growing temperatures come early, and where soil makes growth vigorous. These areas are restricted to the great valleys, more especially those to the south. Growers locating in the higher foothill areas must lamb later because of more rainfall, later grass-growing temperatures, and less vigorous feed growth in the shallower soils. Also such areas usually have a shorter growing season for grass, necessitating moving the sheep higher into the mountains as the feed grasses dry or else selling lambs at light weights off their mothers or as feeders later. Such practice may still be as remunerative as the first because operations are carried on upon cheaper land.

The home ranches of some growers are located in high mountain valleys requiring extensive winter feeding and late spring lambing. Some growers move their sheep from these headquarters onto desert areas, using the cheap feed there as long as patches of snow remain for water.

It can readily be seen how location affects operations, and it is useless to attempt to circumvent the restrictions imposed by environment. In partial contradiction, however, it should be stated that in border-line areas it is possible, through supplementary "creep" feeding of lambs, to market portions of the crop earlier than would seem possible in view of location.

The Effect of Soil. This factor has been partially indicated in the above discussion as it relates to the time and vigor of green growth of feeds. One further point should be made: Very likely, stud flocks and farmer-feeding setups will be most successful where soil types are of the better sort. Purebred flocks located on such farms have the advantage of usually being in a setting that allows better development of their qualities. Good soil may mean that natural grasses grow more luxuriantly, and such farms usually are the ones that best can grow temporary (irrigated) forage grasses so useful in "growing out" purebred breeding stock without overfattening it.

Lamb-feeding setups are more lucrative when located on good soil because the greatest advantage can be gained there from the use of the fertilizer produced. Increased yields of hay, grain, and other lamb feeds (as well as other produce) are most often the chief "income" from lamb feeding, and the feeder who raises his

own feeds on good soil is more likely to make this profit than one
located where the manure cannot do as much.

Raising Replacement Ewes. This practice, listed above as number
6, requires a location somewhat different than the others. If ewe
lambs are to be purchased and grown suitably for sale as breeding
yearlings the next summer, they need different treatment than older
ewes. Naturally, the owner of such stock wants to operate as eco-

Fig. 9.   Manure from fed lambs, applied to good soil, is a profitmaking combination.

nomically (commensurate with proper growth) as he can. The
buyer of replacement ewes wants them well grown but not overly
fat, and a location providing enough grass plus exercise is desirable.
Typical operators find the following a profitable setup: A winter
range of the more rugged type, not necessarily growing the best
types of grasses (cheap land), near farms which offer wastes from
crops that can be used during the fall months and to which the
flock may possibly be returned the next spring for new green
growth.

What Effect May the Breed of Ewes Have on Profitability?

Very few *commercial* ewes are purely of one breed (though a
predominance of the blood of one is usual), and as a result there
are many "types" of ewe flocks with differing natural lambing

Fig. 10. Grade range ewe types. (*a*) A typical grade Rambouillet (*b*) The crossbred ewe, shears less, lives fewer years (*c*) Merinos— best suited to wool growing areas (*d*) The "Crossbred-Wool" type has advantages.

dates, growth patterns of lambs, types of wool, reactions to environment, and so on.

It is extremely important that an owner fit his "breeding" to the locality he is in or to what he desires as a product if he is to get maximum returns from his investment.

Predominantly, the ewes of western range bands carry the blood of the Rambouillet, Merino, or "Crossbred-Wool" breeds. This is necessary to provide an animal with gregariousness—the flocking instinct so necessary to herding in open country. Under fence, however, the "wool" type of sheep may often be more profitably supplanted by crossbred-wool types or breeds of the longwool varieties, and where mutton breed rams are used to produce market fat lambs a wide variety of such ram breeds exists, their choice depending on the environment under which the sheep run.

Areas Suitable for the Various Breeds. It is not the purpose of this section to describe the breeds or recount their history. These topics are fully covered in other publications. But the items that should govern the selection of breeds have not been strongly pointed out, and they are very important to prospective sheep owners.

In a district suitable for raising market lambs capable of growth, it is folly to run a straight band of merinos, even though their wool is probably the most desirable kind, because more income per ewe under such circumstances comes from the sale of lambs, and merino lambs are not very desirable for market purposes. Yet such sheep setups are known. The owner would be much better off with different ewes.

On the other hand, the merino very likely would be more profitable than a ewe with more mutton in her make-up in an extremely rough area, isolated from markets, where rainfall was extreme and the grass-growing season short. Under such circumstances the larger, more muttony breeds might not flourish as well, and the wool income would be the larger.

The breeds used in the United States for the ewe flock are commonly different than those used for sires. This is advantageous for dual production of wool and fat lambs and also exploits hybrid vigor, resulting in larger lamb crops, greater viability, and more rapid gains. Most circumstances where lambs are marketed fat off their mothers demand the use of a "mutton" type of ram on a "wool" type or "crossbred-wool" type of ewe for maximum income from both sources. (There are undoubtedly ranching or farming setups where this does not hold.)

Ewe Breeds. These are Rambouillet, Merino, Corriedale, Romeldale, Panama, Columbia, Targhee, and crosses of Romney, Lincoln, and Cotswold on Rambouillet ewes, commonly.

Many range ewes that are of the "blackface and Rambouillet" cross type seem to be sufficiently gregarious for herding, but they

Don Tomlin

Fig. 11. Grade Rambouillet ewes such as these are profitmakers.

are generally not as desirable as the above-mentioned types from several standpoints, namely: livability, uniformity, and wool-producing ability.

The *Rambouillet,* in pure form, or as a high grade, to date constitutes the greater proportion of ewes run. The most desired type is a large, smooth, open-faced ewe carrying a uniform fleece with length of staple over 2 1/2 inches for 12 months' growth. She is long-lived, will come into heat early in the summer, and of course is extremely gregarious. These characteristics indicate her most

(a)　　　　　　　　　　　　　(b)

Courtesy J. W. Maillard, Yorkville, Calif.

(c)

Fig. 12.　(a) Small Merino ewes belong in woolgrowing areas.
　　　　　(b) Merino wool is dense, bright, and shows character.
　　　　　(c) A top Merino ram that sheared over 23 lb in his two-year-old
　　　　　year.

profit-producing environment: foothill and mountain pasturage under herded management in areas not extremely rough nor on the other hand too open and easily grazed. Her lambs may be born "early," but she is not the best milker and the lambs do not quite compare in form with those from a more muttony type of ewe, nor do they mature as fast. She therefore is most profitable in a setup where advantage can be taken of her ability to lamb early, but where feeding grounds are not of the best type and the lambs require 5 to 6 months to be fat enough for market. Rambouillet ewes are bred to Rambouillet, Hampshire, and Suffolk rams, commonly. The circumstances governing a choice between these breeds are given in the discussion below of the "Ram Breeds."

The *Merino,* in its various subforms, fits essentially the same type of environment as the Rambouillet. However, because of its small size and extreme "wool" type there are some differences. As indicated above, it finds itself suited to the more rough, steep, rugged ranges and in naturally clean areas where this finest of wools can be grown to best advantage. Such a place would be where burs and stickers that might get into fleeces are not too prevalent and where rain or snowfall keep dust down for a long period in the year. In other words, lambs for market must be a minor possibility for income. Because of the smaller size of the breed the rams used are Merino and the smaller mutton breeds, Southdown and Shropshire, though the small-headed Suffolk may fit some of the better grazing areas.

The *"Crossbred-Wool"* breeds, namely Corriedale, Columbia, Panama, Romeldale, and Targhee, find favor under slightly different setups than the Rambouillet. Although there are not very many purebred ewes of these types, there are now many range ewes in the West that have a percentage of these bloods or are the result of crosses on straight Rambouillets of Lincoln, Cotswold, and Romney, the progenitors of these "Crossbred-Wool" breeds.

These breeds are essentially alike in that they all produce a fleece of longer staple than the Rambouillet, somewhat coarser and much lighter shrinking. Further, they lean more to the mutton type, are somewhat better milkers, and lamb but slightly later. The pure breeds mentioned above have been bred long enough for them to approach the degree of uniformity of the Rambouillet. However, because of the scarcity of these ewes, many operators have simply

(a)   (b)

(c)   (d)

Fig. 13.   (a) The Lincoln: his blood helped found the "Crossbred-Wool" breeds.

      (b) "Crossbred-Wool": A champion Corriedale ram owned by Wesley Wooden, Davis, Calif.

      (c) "Crossbred-Wool": A champion Columbia ewe exhibited by Mark Bradford, Spanish Fork, Utah.

      (d) "Crossbred-Wool": A. T. Spencer's Romeldale.

crossed onto their own Rambouillet type of ewes either rams of these breeds or those of the other longwools mentioned, resulting in bands of ewes not as uniform as to fleece or form as they might be. It can readily be seen that as a result of all these types of crossing, many ewe bands in the West range from a half to an eighth (or less) of longwool blood, each probably fitting into a little different setup as far as the particular range is concerned.

These breeds and crossbreeds, because of their closer approach to mutton form, plus their heavier yield of clean although coarse wool (if carefully bred and selected), may be more profitable than the Rambouillet where the country upon which they are to be handled and its location are suitable for the marketing of early lambs that mature and are ready to sell at 4 to 5 months of age. It must be made clear, however, that these ewes must be carefully selected to maintain this advantage over the Rambouillet.

One other consideration often found necessary in deciding between these breeds or types is the character of brushiness found on the ranges upon which they graze. A ewe with a denser fleece will lose less of it on the brush if she is forced to travel and feed through such cover than will an open-fleeced ewe.

Rams used on this type of ewe have been generally limited to the Rambouillet and the larger mutton breeds, the Hampshire and Suffolk. In some cases rams of the Corriedale, Romeldale, and similar breeds, have been used.

Mutton breeds of ewes—the blackfaced Hampshires, Suffolks, Shropshires, etc., and the longwooled Lincolns, Cotswolds, and Romneys—can seldom return the income that the aforementioned breeds do under commercial range conditions. They are not gregarious, the blackfaces shear fewer pounds of less valuable wool, and the longwools produce lambs less desirable from the maturing and packer standpoints. They must be run under fence. This does not infer that as purebred flocks they cannot be just as profitable as the others.

Ram Breeds. Those commonly used have even more distinct placing, or usefulness according to environment, than do ewes.

The Rambouillet, Merino, and "Crossbred-Wool" rams have their place where it is thought desirable to raise ewes for replacement purposes, that is, when they are bred to ewes of the same

types. These surroundings, of course, will be the same as those best
suited to the ewes as described above.

However, such ewes are often run where the production and sale
of replacement ewes is not economically advisable. Where milk-fat
lambs can be sold to market at prices equal to, and sometimes ex-
ceeding, the price that can be obtained for (or must be paid for)

Western Livestock Journal

Fig.14.   Hampshire ewes showing excellent type and style.

yearling ewes of replacement type, a grower might be foolish to
raise replacements either for himself or for sale.

Still again, there are border-line situations where a man *should*
raise his own replacements and where, if he does, he obviates the
necessity of keeping two types or breeds of rams, and consequent
breeding inconveniences. He sometimes can do a better job of
"breeding up" his flock or band himself than can be done by depending on improvement through purchases of replacements, but
he should carefully compare the cost of raising replacements with
that of buying them before deciding on one or the other course.
(This topic is further discussed later in this chapter.)

Mutton breeds of rams in the United States in probable order of usage upon range bands of ewes and farm flocks are Suffolk, Hampshire, Shropshire, Southdown, and Oxford, plus minor use of the Dorset Horn, Cheviot, and crossbreds of Hampshire and Suffolk breeding.

The *Hampshire* ram has been the most popular sire of market lambs but is of late years finding much competition from the Suffolk in fields where that kind of sheep best fits.

He belongs where feed conditions are excellent, where the ewes are large-framed, and where a milk-fat lamb ranging in sale weight up to 90 to 100 lbs is not discriminated against. Therefore he is best suited for use on Rambouillet and "Crossbred-Wool" ewes run in lamb-growing areas in country where grass is fast-growing and luxuriant. In such a setup the Hampshire-cross lambs will reach a salable condition in from 4 1/2 to 6 months at heavy weights and bring in a maximum income. If, on the other hand, the Hampshire is the sire of lambs grown on sparse feed, they will grow so much as far as frame goes before they are in a sufficient condition to sell that they will be overweight, from the packers' viewpoint, or will never get into fat enough condition on their mothers. This is equally true of the other large mutton breeds as sires: the Suffolk and Oxford. In areas where summer rains are not usual, where natural feeds dry up after 4 to 6 months of growth, it is very desirable to grow a lamb that will be finished in that time, otherwise he will suffer from heat, burs, stickers, etc., and be relatively unprofitable.

The *Suffolk* ram is finding favor in similar environments and in addition, particularly, where feed may be rank and plentiful but scattered, as in many mountainous summer ranges. The Suffolk-cross lamb is recognized as being a more aggressive feeder than the Hampshire and is able to make better use of such feed. He will also be a large lamb when in marketable, matured condition, perhaps even larger than the Hampshire, which brings out the admonition that this breed should be used with caution in an area where short seasons or feed failures are at all common. Also the degree of excellence of rams of this breed must be constantly improved if they are to compete with the Hampshire.

Both these breeds, as well as the *Oxford*, are most profitable if their lambs can be marketed fat off their mothers rather than as

(a)

(b)

Fig. 15. (a) A top-selling Suffolk ram lamb produced by P. J. Rock and
Son, Alberta, Canada.
(b) A champion yearling Suffolk ewe exhibited by Howard Vaughn,
Dixon, Calif.

feeder lambs. Although such feeders are excellent users of feed—good gainers—they are likely to be the oversize kind when finished and therefore are discriminated against by the bulk of lamb buyers.

Incidentally, this breed has found considerable favor as the sire of lambs from yearling ewes. The newborn lamb sired by a Suffolk is more slender, with a relatively small head and shoulder, than one

Calif. Woolgrowers Assn.

Fig. 16.   Shropshire: Used in farm flocks.

sired by a Hampshire. Therefore it is born quite easily, and growers report less trouble with first lambers. Though born small, the lamb grows fast.

The *Shropshire* ram is not greatly used as a sire of market lambs from the range flocks of the West. He finds his greatest use in farm flocks, largely on ewes of similar breeding where ewe lambs are retained for replacement. The Shropshire has the top fleece of the mutton breeds and produces excellent though slower-growing lambs than the larger breeds mentioned. Under "average" feed condi-

tions, then, he will find his "profitable" place. Where more luxuriant, dependable feed grows, the profits from the larger breeds of
rams are greater. "Average" conditions are usually "farm pasture"
conditions where every effort is usually *not* made to provide fresh,
clean lamb feed and to force lambs for fast development. Also farm
pasture will often supply green feed for a longer period, either
through irrigation of permanent pastures or growth of summer
greens.

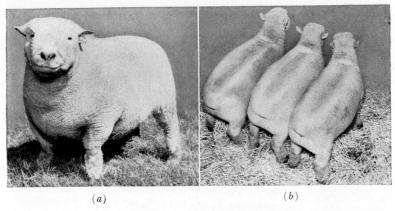

(a)   (b)

Fig. 17.   (a) A toppy Southdown yearling ram.
           (b) The beauty of the Southdown fat lamb is unsurpassed. A Severa
           Wilford Grand Champion pen.

It should be kept in mind that this discussion presupposes the
use of ewes such as described in the section on "Ewe Breeds" and
the crossing of these breeds of rams for lambs.

The Shropshire is often used on Merino ewes in bands where
only a portion of the ewes (the better half or third) are bred to
Merinos for replacements, while the remainder of lambs can get
to market fat or semifat. Being smaller, it is more suited to such
ewes than the Suffolk or the Hampshire ram, which sires lambs that
have a tendency to "grow away" from the milking ability of the
ewe—in other words to grow frame without fat and therefore end
up largely as thin feeder lambs at market time.

Perhaps the one feature about the Shropshire that has limited
its use, even in suitable places, has been excessive wooling about the
eyes, causing extra worries for the owner in lambs that can't see their

feed. Further, such wooling means easy targets for foxtail stickers and beards, a great problem where such grasses grow.

The *Southdown* ram is usable most profitably under pretty exacting circumstances. He cannot compete with the bigger breeds where feed is luxuriant and lambs can make a big weight in a short time; but when he is crossed on the right type of ewe *in areas where feed is likely to be sparse* because of limitation of rainfall, his lamb has a much better chance of coming through to a marketable condition *fat* than a lamb sired by bigger rams. Only in areas where such lambs are sold at a premium, such as has been the case in Kentucky and Tennessee, can the Southdown as a sire provide a greater income than the larger sires as a result of more poundage. To date, possibly owing as much to the small number of such lambs available as to anything else, lamb buyers in other sections have not paid a sufficient premium for Southdown-sired lambs. They, especially as crossbreds, are certainly worth a premium because of their higher dressing percentage.

The place for the Southdown ram is in an area where feed may be limited and where lambs as a result may have to be marketed at light weights. Even light, they will carry "killing" flesh, and they will more likely be marketable as older lambs under such conditions than will lambs of the larger breeds. Short-season "foothill" country most completely fits this picture.

Summary of the Mating of Breeds for Market Lamb Production

The most important item concerning the selection of a ram breed to be used upon a certain type of ewe for the production of market lambs is tied up with the *milk production* that can be expected from the ewes. If a ewe is a rather inferior milk producer *either* because of her breeding (which may be dictated by her location) or because of the lack of milk-making feed normally grown in the area, she had best not be mated to a ram breed that grows very fast. The lambs will be feeders or will be badly hurt, whereas, if sired by smaller type or a quicker finishing breed, they may get to market fat.

Therefore a sheep owner should recognize the limitations of his feed and breed of ewe and find the ram that can produce a maximum under those circumstances.

(a)

(b)

Fig. 18. Recommended ewe-ram combinations suited to the milking ability of the ewe.

(a) A fast-growing mutton breed ram: the Suffolk (shown is a Chicago International Grand Champion lamb exhibited by Fred Coble of Winters, Calif.)
(b) "Crossbred-Wool" type ewes: Columbia, Corriedale, etc.

The author's ideas concerning crossbreeding under range conditions are as follows:

1. *Crossbred-Wool ewe* and *Suffolk ram* for a setup where spring feed is excellent but somewhat short in duration.

Here the good milking ability of the Corriedale, Columbia, etc., type of ewe will match the natural growing ability of the ram and combine to produce much weight before the feed dries.

2. *Rambouillet ewe* and *Hampshire ram* for a setup where the ewes can be bred *early.*

(c)   (d)

Fig. 18 (cont.). Recommended ewe-ram combinations suiting the milking ability of the ewe.

(c) A large thick mutton breed ram: Hampshire.
(d) A large fine-wool ewe: a grade Rambouillet.

Where early growing strong feed is available and places where the lambs can be carried for a long time on either natural or planted feeds. The fair-to-good milking ability of this ewe will match the Hampshire rate of growth and produce a high percentage of extremely desirable fat lambs at 5 to 6 months of age. If such ewes are bred later and run to the mountains in summertime, so that the green-feed season is long, the same results obtain.

3. *Merino ewe* and *Southdown or Shropshire ram.*

The relatively poor milk-producing ability of these ewes must be met with the natural slower growing feature of these smaller rams. Extreme weights will not result, but a good percentage of the lambs will sell fat rather than as feeders.

Calif. Woolgrowers Assn.

(*e*)

(*f*)   *J. W. Maillard*

Fig. 18 (cont.). Recommended ewe-ram combinations suiting the milking ability of the ewe.

    (*e*) A small-scale mutton breed ram: Southdown (or Shropshire).
    (*f*) Small-frame fine-wool ewes: Merino.

(g)   (h)

Fig. 18 (cont.). Recommended ewe-ram combinations suiting the milking ability of the ewe.

    (g) "Whiteface" rams of a blood line suited for replacement production (This a Mark Bradford Columbia)
    (h) "Whiteface" ewes of a blood line suited for replacement production.

How and Where Should I Purchase Ewes?

In buying ewes to be used for commercial fat-lamb production, aside from a decision as to which type of ewe or ram fits the farm or range where they are to be located, other considerations need attention. Either the beginner or the more experienced sheepman should consider which age of ewe is best to buy, what points should be noted in selecting the individual sheep, the season of the year, and the effect upon the sheep of a change in their location.

What Age Ewe Should I Buy? Four general age classes of ewes are purchased: ewe lambs, yearlings, middle-aged ewes (2's to 5's) (2 years to 5 years old), and aged ewes.

It is often advisable that a beginner, or an operator going onto a new farm or range, *purchase ewe lambs.* Before he is required to experience, in his new surroundings, the critical lambing period, he will have the opportunity to run these ewe lambs for an entire 12 months, discover the real carrying capacity of his holdings, and regulate his operations or numbers to conform to the place. If he purchases older ewes, which will lamb within a few months, such a beginner, on a strange place and without knowledge of the needs for lambing equipment may be confronted with a perplexing situation.

Of course such lambs should be selected carefully. If early born, they may be quite growthy when purchased and there is a possibility (especially with ewes carrying quite a bit of mutton blood) that they *should* be bred as lambs, at 9 to 10 months of age, to prevent subsequent shy-breeding due to overfatness as yearlings. Not all of such a group will breed, but 40 to 50% may. However, proper management to prevent overfattening is more often the proper course with this type of ewe. The ewe lambs should be as uniform as to age, wooling, and body form as possible. This will mean profit in the end, as will be discussed later.

Some range men, all of whose own (blackface-cross) ewe lambs go to the butcher, now are purchasing their whiteface ewe replacements in terms of ewe lambs rather than as yearlings. This is advantageous only if a separate setup suited to cheaply growing the lambs to the yearling (breeding) stage is available. More usually, the yearling, ready to breed, fits the rangeman's setup.

Yearling ewes are more often purchased than those in any other age class. They will usually command top prices as they have all their life ahead of them and may have stood a culling. Again, uniformity should be emphasized, and overly fine-boned, undersized ewes, or those with overshot or undershot jaws, should be discarded. Yearling ewes, of course, will have been shorn once or twice but not have lambed, so inspection will not disclose spoiled udders, though some teats may be closed or injured by the shearing. If the ewes are too fat before breeding time, they will not breed to lamb as uniformly as is desirable, and also, a larger percentage will not breed at all. A lambing of from 85% to 90% with yearlings is about normal.

In purchasing yearlings it should be kept in mind that they are yet to experience their first lambing; as first lambers they will lamb at a lower rate and are more temperamental than older ewes, and more difficulties will be experienced.

Middle-aged ewes, from 2 to 5 years old, should supply the easiest lambing, best quality animals if they are properly culled as to spoiled udders and health. Ewes up to 3's probably should command as good a price as yearlings, and 4's and 5's should cost less.

(a)

(b)

Fig. 19. Age classes of ewes that can be purchased.

(a) *Yearling* ewes out of the wool are the most commonly bought replacement.

(b) *Aged* ewes thrive when on soft feed.

(c)   *Will C. Minor, Fruita, Colo.*

(d)

Fig. 19 (cont.)   Age classes of ewes that can be purchased.

(c) *Mixed-age* ewes should be "mouthed" when bought.
(d) *Ewe lambs* will need to be run separately.

A knowledge of how to tell the age of sheep is very important when buying ewes and is discussed below.

Old ewes, usually from 6 to 10 years, may under exacting circumstances be bought at prices that may make them profitable. Such ewes either are on the verge of losing their incisor teeth or have already done so; as a result they need softer food and more protection and can stand less privation and travel than younger sheep. If such ideal conditions can be provided and the ewes are not "shelly" but still have considerable vigor and body, a purchase can often be made that will bring from one to three lambings, with a resulting profit. Some sheepmen having luxuriant feed such as alfalfa or clover pasture have purchased such ewes, bred them, and sold them to the butcher the next summer, very shortly after their lambs were sold. Of course the 8-year-olds and up probably would not keep fat enough to allow such a practice.

Buyers should be cautioned against a heavy purchase of old ewes if they are to be run with younger ewes, trailed a great deal, and forced to suffer short-feed periods such as the younger ewes can readily withstand. They will quickly break down and become useless or die if so treated.

If aged ewes are bought that have "broken mouths" (or missing teeth in front), it is good practice to pull the snags with pliers and let the ewe pluck her feed with her gums rather than to suffer the inconvenience those snags cause in taking food.

Where Should I Buy Ewes? (The Effect of a Change in Location). Sheep require "acclimatization" before they will do their best in a new region. The amount of such treatment needed and the effect of such relocation vary according to the severity of the change, but no purchaser of sheep should disregard this fact since to do so may result in serious consequences. Most serious losses occur if sheep are moved from a mild-climate area in which they have been raised into a more rigorous one. The opposite movement is not so bad. However, if sheep have been raised in a mild, cool climate such as along a coast line or in higher altitudes, they will suffer when taken to hot interior valleys, and deaths or poor health and poor production result.

It is safe to buy ewes from an area pretty similar in climate to the place where they are to be kept permanently. In some regions this fact alone has largely been responsible for the establishment and growth of "replacement-ewe-raising" businesses. Lambs bought in some far-distant area are "acclimated" *as lambs* close to where they will finally serve their years and seem to stand this change better than if they came the same distance as older sheep.

The various State "Woolgrowers" associations in the United States either carry advertisements of ewes for sale or have lists of sources of purchasable ewes. Small bunches may often be bought from larger operators in the neighborhood.

Ewes are usually purchased from early summer to late fall—after the spring clip of wool has been removed and usually before breeding time. During this period they are bought at the lowest price. After breeding, and as they get closer to lambing, their value increases. A prospective purchaser had best see his ewes before the spring shearing, when he can see their fleeces, and then buy them "out of the wool," when he can see their bodies more surely. Wool income, varying with breed and location, amounts from one-fourth to one-half of total income and cannot be disregarded or treated lightly when brood ewes are to be purchased. In lieu of actually giving the buyer an opportunity to see the sheep in the wool, larger producers should be able to provide statements from their wool handlers indicating the variance in grades of wool grown and in poundage per ewe. The shrinkage should also be indicated. Such figures will of course not cover the few individual sheep that are far off the average.

Of late years many purchases have been made of "pairs" of ewes and their suckling lambs. Especially has this practice often occurred when drought or threatened drought has worried owners concerning their ability to finish the crop of lambs already produced. Such pairs have been bought relatively cheaply by those who controlled abundance of lamb-growing feeds. Often the sheep when offered for such sale were in relatively poor condition and also the lambs were not in bloom. A proper judgment of the "hurt" of the lambs, the condition of the wool on the ewes, and their probable conformation under better circumstances would need to be considered by the buyer in offering a price.

Incidentally, in shipping such a band or group of ewes and small lambs, it would be well to heed the experience of those who have done it often. Most such shipments would at least require close to a full day of travel in which time, improperly handled, some of the younger lambs might be disowned by their dams and would become "bummers." Shippers of "pairs" state emphatically that the lambs should *not* be separated from the ewes if as old as six to eight weeks but rather should be shipped together in relatively light loads in trucks or cars. Of course, very few of the lambs will be with their own mothers in any given car or on any particular deck, but they are less frightened, stampede less, and end up in better shape than when put into separate compartments from the ewes.

Perhaps needless to say, when unloaded the ewes and lambs should all be held up closely for perhaps ten hours for the lambs to "mother up." The ewes should have a chance to feed during this time, too.

How and Where Should I Purchase Rams?

The buying of range rams to be used to produce market lambs should be approached with caution. Rams that must perform their function under trying conditions as far as feed and climate are concerned are highly expendible creatures, and if good service is to result, rams must be bought that can perform.

The rams needed should be bought early in relation to the breeding season for the area where they are to be used. The reason for this advice is that the more vigorous, mature rams owned by a breeder and sold at his farm naturally would be chosen first by buyers. Those that are not taken early would be the less desirable ones and often when finally purchased would have had more weeks or months on grain or on soft pasture feeds, which does not help their chances as breeders. Then, as a further result of this extended feeding, their natural poorer constitution and conformation would have been veiled by the extra condition put onto them. This makes it difficult, even for the most experienced judge, to detect their deficiencies.

Such rams furthermore are the ones most likely to be poor breeders because if put onto much different feed (with the ewes they are to breed) than they have been accustomed to, they take longer to acclimate themselves, or to get to work, and then lose condition and vigor fast. Many such rams have died in the first breeding season.

Buy rams that are in a condition suited to the requirements of

the area where they must work. Some rams fitted as heavily as those
that appear at high-class ram sales will not perform under rugged
conditions (of high temperatures and much travel or poor feed)
until this extra condition has "melted away." Owners of ewes
might suffer two or three weeks or more of poor breeding where
the rams work under this handicap. On the other hand, well-grown
young rams that have been grained, if they have had sufficient exercise and variation in pasture, do perform well when they are put
with the ewes where climate and feed are not too much different.

Buy purebred rams. These animals are much more homozygous
than grade sires and are more homozygous than crossbred rams.
Though they will probably cost more initially, they may be cheaper
in the long run because they can be expected to breed more true
to their own merit and their produce may have more uniformity,
which means better prices.

Buying at ram sales should generally ensure a purchaser the best
bred rams. The ram sales are the show places for breeders, and they
do bring their top individuals to these sales. Too, many such sales
places employ unbiased persons to "sift" the rams consigned to
them, and these people eliminate through close inspection rams that
exhibit features that might hinder their service or affect their prog-
eny. The items that most often bring this elimination about are
overshot or undershot jaws, crooked legs or legs too straight just
above the hocks, turned-in eyelids or other eye afflictions, defective
testes or evidence of past injury at that point, and evidence of
disease (notably of caseous lymphadenitis or "boils"). This list
might well be kept in mind by a ram buyer contemplating purchase
of rams at a breeder's farm.

Whiteface rams (wool breeds) are generally always sold at ram
sales with a full fleece, as buyers wish to see the character of the
wool on animals they are to use to produce replacements. Such rams
should be shorn before they are put to the ewes.

At all ram sales the buyer will find variation in the quality and
the fitting of consignments from various breeders. A good judge may
be able to purchase rams at lower prices that can do him as much
good as others that command top figures if he can see "breeding"
in the cheaper group. Further, a knowledge of the conditions under
which these rams were raised may assist in properly evaluating them.
Then too, later born rams coming from a particular location to the

sale may not have as mature an appearance nor be as fat as others; they can generally be purchased safely by persons who do not need to place the rams with their ewes immediately and who can condition them further.

Telling the Age of Sheep

The purchaser of sheep should *almost always* inspect their mouths for age. With a little practice it is simple to distinguish lambs and yearlings without "mouthing," but if a mixed-age bunch is being bought, it may be extremely profitable to be able to tell ages, especially if different prices are to be paid for different ages. Many beginners have been cheated by unscrupulous sellers who realized that they could not tell ages or see indications of worthless ewes, such as spoiled udders. If the buyer doesn't feel himself well enough versed in "mouthing," he should surely have with him, when making a purchase, someone who can tell ages and whom he can trust.

Mouthing is much simpler with sheep than with horses and can readily be learned if the shape and size of teeth of various ages can be observed. The uninitiated would do well to inspect the teeth of several ewes of ages from lambs to 8 or 10 years and familiarize himself with the differences. It is generally thought that the change from "milk" teeth to permanent incisors and the changes later in shape of teeth and the losing of teeth vary somewhat among breeds or types. In other words, the "blackface" types change their teeth earlier, or seem to be older for their actual age than do the whiteface (Rambouillet) types. Thus, a Hampshire ewe that was actually but 2 1/2 years old might already have her 3-year teeth, whereas a Rambouillet would still have her 2-year teeth and seem younger. This is only *generally* true.

The tooth-changing habit is as follows: a lamb soon after birth uncovers eight small "milk teeth" across the front of its lower jaw. At 12 months of age (or thereabouts) the center pair of these generally drop out and are replaced by two permanent teeth easily two or three times the size of the milk teeth. At 2 years of age two more milk teeth drop out and are likewise replaced. These two are the ones on each side of the center pair. At 3 years the next pair go, and at 4 years the sheep has eight permanent teeth. It is sometimes difficult to distinguish accurately between a 3- and a 4-year-old as the last (or "corner") permanents are not much larger than the milk teeth. After 4 years the gums begin to recede and the teeth seem to get longer and to spread apart, and only considerable acquaintance can very accurately determine the age from the teeth. Most sheep keep a "full mouth" of eight permanents until they are 6 or 7 years old, some longer. Most, however, lose some or all eight

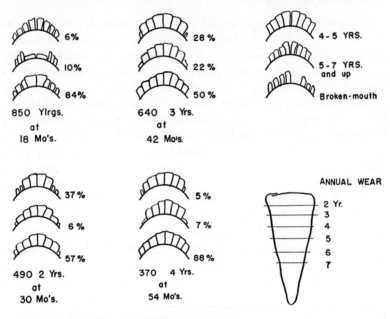

TEETH CHANGES IN SHEEP

Fig. 20. Tooth changes in Rambouillet ewes.

by 7 or 8 years of age. Sheep feeding on brush rather than soft grasses lose their teeth earlier. When a sheep has lost all her permanents, she is called a "gummer." Some old ewes whose mouths are shaped so as to make it possible wear down their teeth as their gums recede and seem to have a "lamb mouth" when they may actually be 7 to 10 years old.

The Montana Experiment Station has recorded the actual occurrence of tooth change in a large group of Rambouillet ewes whose actual age was definitely known. Among 850 yearlings examined at 18 months' average age, 6% still showed a "lamb" mouth, 10% were just changing the middle pair to permanents, and 84% showed the typical yearling mouth: one pair of large teeth in the center and three pairs of "milk" teeth. The examination of 490 two-year-olds at 30 months showed only 37% of typical 2-year mouths, 6% starting with the 3-year mouth, and 57% having the actual 3-year mouth. In other words, someone "mouthing" this group might have considered over half of them to be a year older than they actually were. Examination of 640 three-year-old ewes at 42 months (or 3 1/2 years) revealed that only 28% had 3-year mouths, another 22% were starting their 4-year teeth, and 50% showed the full 4-year mouth. The 4-year picture was that of 370 examined at 54 months: 5% showed 3-year, 7% starting 4-year, and 88% the full 4-year mouth. These figures no doubt would vary between sheep on differing types of feed and of differing blood lines, but the evidence is sufficient to indicate that the pattern tooth-change picture is somewhat irregular.

How Should I Finance This Start?

Once a decision is made to enter a certain branch of the sheep business and to borrow money or use savings for that purpose, no greater mistake can be made than to spend that money without first gaining a pretty clear idea of what is going to happen to it and what returns are going to result from its investment.

With such knowledge a prospective operator can determine approximately what his net income will be and whether that figure will be sufficient to allow the standard of living he thinks he needs. Thus, if $1,500 of labor-income is thought necessary and the sheep enterprise will provide only $1,000, other activities will have to supply the remainder.

With no knowledge of the real need for a proper use of income to pay such items as interest, replacement of ewes to replenish losses due to death, etc., a beginning sheepman may often be inclined to use his wool and lamb money unwisely. Therefore the value of a correctly planned budget cannot be overrated.

Aside from budgeting the year's activities, the prospective sheepman should make some attempt to determine whether the particular year when he contemplates a start is the best one to make that start. It is well known that sheep prices go up and down in cycles and when at their height can go no other way than down. Although prices may be very good at the time, the downswing may occur before the enterprise becomes self-sustaining. Purchasing a beginning at top prices with the hope that he could beat the downswing has caught many a sheepowner in the past. A discussion of deciding when to start follows in a section below.

Returning to the question of financing and budgeting, it is not our purpose to advise as to the source of money. The important thing is to be able to foresee fully how that money should be disposed. Simple but complete bookkeeping should be maintained by every farmer.

What Are the Essentials of a Sheepman's Budget?

In order to see completely the financial picture incident to entrance into the sheep business, no item that bears upon costs or income should be missed. If some items are not accounted for, figures will be misleading and may indeed result in disaster. Again it must be emphasized how extremely important it is to a beginning sheep owner, especially one with limited financial backing, to know what net return he can expect for his efforts, and a complete budget, even though only estimated, is the only safe answer.

To determine profit or loss, you must know four things:

1. What you have at the first of the year
2. What you have spent during the year
3. What your income was during the year
4. What you have at the end of the year

These four statements can well be used as the titles of sections of your books. Itemized somewhat further they will include the following:

1. *What you have at the first of the year*
   a) *Your assets* (at the beginning of your year)
      (1) Livestock on hand (numbers, description, values)
      (2) Equipment on hand (values—if owned *completely*)
      (3) Real estate (values less mortgages)
      (4) Other assets (cash, value of feed purchased, notes and bills due)
   b) *What you owe at the start of your year*
      (1) Notes you owe (other than on real estate, noted above)

     (2) Bills you owe

     (3) Labor unpaid

     (4) Advances received on contracts, etc.

Subtract the total of 1a from 1b for *net assets.*

2. *What you have spent during the year*

   a) Expenditures having *inventory value*

     (1) Livestock purchases (date, kind, values)

     (2) Equipment purchases

     (3) Real-estate purchases and permanent improvements

(Total (1), (2), and (3).)

   b) Expenditures having *no inventory value* (operating costs)

     (1) Feed raised or bought (hay, grain, pasture)

     (2) Labor charges for operation of sheep

     (3) Supplies bought for sheep

     (4) Shearing, wool handling, taxes, insurance

     (5) Interest and loan charges on sheep

     (6) Automobile: gas, oil, repairs, taxes, depreciation

     (7) General and other expenses on sheep

     (8) Wages or salary allowed yourself

(Total the above.)

   c) Notes and bills you owe (include record)

3. *What your income was during the year* (gross receipts)

   a) Income from lamps, sheep, wool, pelts, etc.

   b) Notes and bills owing you (include record)

4. *What you have at the end of the year* (net assets)

   a) Livestock on hand (inventory)

   b) Equipment on hand

   c) Real estate on hand

   d) Other assets (cash, credit in checking account, feed on hand
paid for, notes due from others, bills due from others, etc.—
less notes, bills, and labor and other liabilities)

By subtracting the net assets at the end of the year from those
for the first of the year the net profit or loss on the year's operations
(on an inventory basis) may be computed.

How Can I Decide If Now Is the Best Time to Start?

If this question could be answered without qualification, many
prospective sheepmen would be saved losses, or would benefit more

than they would otherwise, but of course the answer is not possible. However, there are certain indications which history affords us and which experience tells us are worth noting. They concern seeming "cyclical" price movements and the reasons for them.

Since 1880 in the United States there have been six complete cycles in prices in each of which prices for sheep, lambs, and wool about doubled and then lost all their gains. This has meant that persons who have gotten into the business at the peak have often not been able to pay their debts and accumulated interest on money borrowed nor have been able to keep up with their running expenses and maintain a standard of living, and consequently have lost all. It has meant too that some long-established sheepmen have stepped beyond the border line of conservative expansion when the price structure was high and have found themselves in straits during the lean years.

These great changes in sheep prices have not been due so much to changes in sheep numbers as to consumer demand and general price levels. In other words, "spring lamb" is considered a relative delicacy by many people in relation to other meats. Therefore, whenever world economy has toppled the financial well-being of the American public it has promptly restricted its use of "delicacies" and lamb prices have had to drop to sell. As far as wool goes, again, domestic prices have fluctuated because we are an importing nation. As world-wide conditions became straitened at intervals, foreign wools were sold to American mills at lowered prices, pulling down domestic prices.

These conditions seem to be inevitable, and the prospective sheep owner should by all means determine for himself "where the business is" before spending his money. If he can enter the business when prices are near the trough of the wave, it would seem that he would have a far better chance to succeed, even though his income per head might be small at first. At least he would have experienced "the worst," and if he survived he might have several good years and be better able to survive a returning slump because he had experienced just what that means.

The advice of the "old-timer" is still very sound: "The man who wins is the one who stays with it." But in order to stay at all the man must get started right.

What Is the Effect on Operations of Raising vs. Buying Replacement Ewes?

Although this subject may not seem to belong in a chapter on entering the sheep business, it does require consideration by a beginner if he is properly to budget his operations. Of course it is of interest too to the established sheepman.

Probably more often than any other item, the replacements figures are slighted or disregarded in estimating the possible returns from a sheep setup. The whole story is not told when simply returns from lambs and wool are checked against labor, feed and rentals, interest, etc. Ewes get older each year—get nearer their end and depreciate in value—and the true returns from the business must be determined with this fact in mind. The business cannot be "bled" dry of the producing medium (the ewes) and no account be taken of that occurrence.

The Case Where Replacement Ewes Are Raised. The average commercially productive life of range ewes is 7 years. The average death loss is about 5%. This means that 20% of the ewes must be replaced each year, or at least money must be set aside to provide for them if the flock is not to diminish. Of course, if all the ewes are yearlings at the start, only loss by death need be made up yearly until the sheep become aged (5 or 6 years).

The simplest operations, in which the replacements are raised, will result in a flock that uses ewes and rams of the same breeding— for instance all Corriedales or all Hampshires. However, the most income from commercial lamb production is more often likely, when the ewe flock differs from the rams. To maintain ewes of high standard means using two breeds of ram, a mutton and a wool type, and suffering the inconveniences of separation of ewes at breeding time; it also means, perhaps, a lesser income from the sale of the fat wether lambs sired by rams (wool type) producing the replacement ewes. More specifically, the ewe flock *may* be of the crossbred-wool type (or Corriedale, or Rambouillet) upon which rams of the crossbred-wool type and Hampshires will be used, half of the ewes bred to each. Usually the ewe band will be carefully culled over and the better ewes bred to the replacement-ewe sire.

Aside from considering these inconveniences, the owner must

make financial comparisons between this practice and that of *buy-ing* replacements, and then draw his own conclusions as to which practice is the more profitable.

An argument in favor of raising replacements is that, theoretically at least, the owner can produce ewes exactly to his liking. In other words, if an owner is satisfied that he has a very profitable type of ewe *and that he can breed that type* or improve upon it, he has a greater chance to do so than if he buys. (On the other hand, it may sometimes be possible to buy better ewes than an inexperienced breeder can produce, but that is a matter for the individual to decide.)

In raising replacements, extra feed or pasturage will be required for carrying the ewe lambs from weaning until 14 to 18 months of age (the normal age when yearlings would have been bought). This extra land (or feed) will not be needed if yearlings are pur-chased and brought in just before breeding season. Furthermore, during the breeding season, when the lambs are only 6 to 9 months old, fields other than those needed for the breeding ewes must be available for them if they are not to be bred too young. Wool shorn from the lambs will reduce costs.

If an owner is located in an area where his market lambs of necessity may have a lesser value in comparison to wool income than in another area, he will likely have more excuse for raising his own replacements than will owners in the other area. The decision is an individual problem.

The Case Where Replacement Ewes Are Purchased. This is prac-tically the opposite of the above. Not more than one breed of ram is needed—that which produces the best type of market lamb for that area. No provision need be made for caring for weaned ewe lambs. All lambs will be sold when milk fat (presumably) at their highest value per pound, and in many early-lamb raising districts this value may equal or even exceed the cost of a yearling ewe. On the other hand, there will be no wool income (from lambs), and there will be expenses in locating, buying, and transporting the yearlings purchased. The main items, however, are the relative in-come from the ewe lambs sold for the market as compared with the cost of the yearling replacements, and the relative quality of those replacements as compared with the quality of ewe which a man believes he can produce.

Chapter 2

Pre-Breeding and Breeding Management of Ewes

The importance of proper care of ewes and rams previous to and during the breeding season needs some emphasis. The sheep owner is interested in as large a crop of lambs as is suited to his location, and he wants these lambs to be uniform in type and condition when they become of salable age. To accomplish these goals means planning, perhaps over several years, and good management through the breeding season.

Previous to Breeding, at What Physical Condition Should Ewes Be Maintained?

This is an important question and one requiring, if the most satisfaction is to result, the best of a sheepman's managerial ability. Involved in the answer is a discussion of the proper growth of wool, and the lambing percentage.

Concerning wool growth, a ewe condition is necessary that will not jeopardize the strength of the wool fibers. It is possible to reduce the condition of a ewe to such an extent that the diameter of the fibers grown during the pre-breeding season will be greatly decreased—even to the point where they will be so weak that they will break apart at a very slight pull. This of course lowers the value of the fleece because, in effect, it may reduce a "combing length" fleece to short "clothing" wool, which is less valuable per pound. Furthermore, too lengthy a period of reduced condition will result in shorter fiber length, lighter fleeces, and reduced income. The sheep owner should make certain that his ewes are not so treated, and here experience alone is the teacher. Each year's wool clip should be carefully studied, and defects, in the light of the past year's history, should be accounted for and corrected, if possible.

This discussion is important because both a quick completion of the breeding of the flock and the percentage of lambs produced

University of Calif.

Fig. 21. Ewes may shed their fleece after a fever "break."

depend pretty much on a reduced condition of ewes for a short time previous to breeding. In other words, overfat ewes do not "buck up" quickly or produce many twins, nor do they come into heat on time.

The degree of fatness necessary for proper breeding and unimpaired wool growth, therefore, must be most carefully watched.

Many ewes, when their lambs are weaned in the spring, will have been "suckled down" in condition to a point where they are quite thin. Others in the same band will be quite fat, and still others, by the time the rams should be placed with them, will have regained condition because their lambs were weaned or sold earlier than were others. Then too, dry ewes will be excessively fat and aged ewes too thin unless they are segregated early and handled differently. Probably the average period between the time a ewe weans a lamb and when she is rebred is six weeks to two months. In that time she needs conditioning to respond to breeding in the ideal manner.

Very fat ewes should be almost starved to get them anywhere near the condition to breed. They will carry enough body fat to prevent their fleeces from suffering unduly. They should be run on fields that were heavily fed during the spring and are not too well supplied with nutritious seeds or the better portions of plant growth. In other words, such ewes should be forced to clean out corrals and otherwise to exist on the poorest feed to get them down in condition.

Constant pasturing on irrigated feed is very risky for breeding ewes because of its effect on their possibilities with the lamb crop. Though this pasturing is not a practice common with range opera- tors, many small farm flocks in the West, of late years, have been maintained on such feed with the result that ewe lambs retained for replacements and the older ewes have gotten too fat and become unsatisfactory breeders. From observations it has been noted that (aside from the difficulty in getting yearlings to breed at all—unless

Calif. Woolgrowers Assn.

Fig. 22.   Ewes carried year round on irrigated feed such as this birdsfoot trefoil get too fat.

they were bred as lambs) the lambs from the excessively fat ewes were much smaller at birth, and developed much more slowly than those from ewes that had spent their summers and falls on dry feed. It is advised that if ewes are to use such feed, it should be only in the winter and spring months or until the lambs are weaned. After that, such ewes should be held down in flesh on dry grass, stubble, or similar feeds so that their systems do not become loaded with fat during gestation.

Ewes in medium condition at weaning should be placed in fields where that condition can be maintained and perhaps reduced some-what *gradually*. Complete starvation is not the answer as wool fiber diameter will be affected, but this low condition is required to make "flushing" operations (discussed below) fully effective and to pro-duce uniform lambs and lambing. Merino, Rambouillet, or the crossbred-wool type of ewes should be held at a condition making it fairly easy to "see their ribs" (if shorn). Ewes with more mutton blood probably could not be reduced to that point. The inexperi-enced owner will more often run his sheep to below this point—to emaciation—than will one who has previously carried ewes through this period. Close daily inspection of the flock may be necessary to prevent emaciation.

Very thin ewes, usually the aged ones at weaning, should be built up in condition rather than allowed to run too long in that state. Thus, the goal is to bring all the ewes to breeding time in the *same lean but thrifty, gaining* state.

At this point it would be well to emphasize further the value of maintaining the ewe band on a generally high plane of nutrition throughout the year and from one year to the next. Some very en-lightening figures provided by the United States Department of Agriculture are presented in Fig. 23 and Table 1.

Table 1

EFFECT OF NUTRITION ON LAMBING OVER PERIOD OF YEARS

Range condition	*Year of lambing*	*Lambs dropped per 100 ewes*	*Lambs alive per 100 ewes*	
Poor precipitation the previous year	1925	83	81.7	
	1927	85	70.0	Av., 72%
	1929	78	66.0	
Good precipitation the previous year	1926	93	86.0	
	1928	91	85.0	Av., 91%
	1930	102	96.0	
	1931	109	99.0	

These U.S.D.A. studies, made in Idaho, provide figures for Rambouillet range ewes that illustrate the great effect of simply "enough to eat" upon the size of the lamb crop. These range ewes,

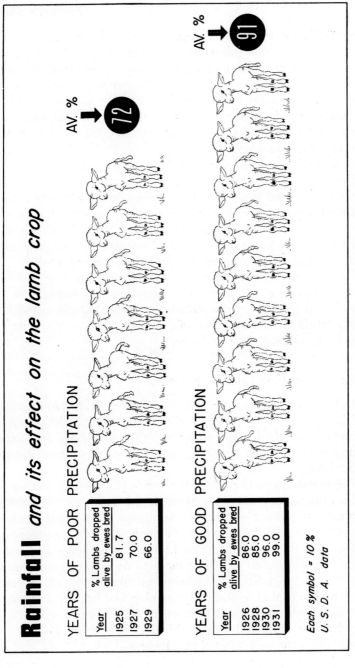

Fig. 23. Good precipitation, giving a high plane of nutrition, fosters the lamb crop.

largely with unsupplemented feed, showed striking differences in their lamb production following years of good and of poor rainfall —a circumstance that would have strongly affected their condition (or degree of fatness) as they suckled the previous year's crop and as they later were bred. For the years shown it will be noted that the lamb crop following years when the rainfall was good was improved by about 20%. Undoubtedly, too, the wool crop was improved to a like degree.

In the author's experience it has been noted that farm ewes that had run on plain feed for several years produced stronger, faster growing lambs and loftier, brighter, heavier fleeces when the owners instituted a program of range fertilization, provision of improved and "stronger" summer feeds, and rotation grazing. In whatever way the general year-to-year plane of nutrition is kept at a high level, it will result in better returns in both lambs and wool.

The inexperienced sheepman too often is unable to "see" beneath the wool covering and accurately determine the condition of his ewes. Sheep are not to be regarded like goats, "capable of existing on the labels of tin cans," but will respond and give manifold returns for excellent feeding and care.

What Summer Care Do Ewes Require?

Aside from controlling the condition of ewes previous to breeding, and later, feeding the pregnant ewe properly for development of her lamb "salt, shade, and water" constitutes the basis of summer management. If she is supplied regularly with these three she will do her best.

The common practice of forcing bands of ewes to stand out in direct sunlight day after day through the summer, even though they seem to come through it in fair shape, cannot but result in shortening the life of those ewes and certainly results in poorer use of feed. Of course it may often be nearly impossible to provide shade, but every effort should be made to do so. It is a well-known fact that sheep under fence, allowed to "shade up" all day near water and to feed at will in early morning and late evening, maintain their flesh on less feed than others herded and corralled and forced to an unnatural regime. Herders of varying abilities can greatly effect the well-being of their charges.

Several other minor but no less necessary duties must faithfully be performed by the sheep owner during the summer. Sheep under fence are probably more neglected than those herded, in some respects. More deaths occur because the flocks or bands are not seen every day. Ewes in fleece in late summer frequently get on their backs in low spots in the fields and quickly die exposed thus to the sun. Of course they will also die if they get in this position in

Fig. 24.   Ewes required to stand in heat suffer.

the shade or in cool weather unless they are discovered within 48 hours.

If a sheep on its back has not died before it is discovered, the owner may find it necessary to spend several minutes working with it when it has been turned right side up, in order to save it. Often the sheep is badly bloated and at the same time partially paralyzed so that it tends to fall to one side as it attempts to move. If the owner runs alongside the sheep, allowing it to lean against him, exercise soon will restore the function of the paralyzed legs. Too, while lying on its back a ewe has generally defecated and urinated and is soaked above the tail and often along the back. This makes a very attractive bed for the deposition of eggs by the blowfly, and this possibility should not be overlooked.

As fields become fed down, sheep often get their heads caught in the mesh of woven wire fences while trying to feed through them, and dogs, near towns especially, may molest them.

In lower elevations especially, the danger from blowfly and screw-worm fly attacks cause the most worry and requires close super-vision to control. The eyes of ewes pastured in foxtail fields are constant targets for the beards from these grasses, and often the sheep must be brought in every day or every few days for the removal of stickers if blind sheep are not to result.

Calif. Woolgrowers Assn.

Fig. 25.   The telltale stain of a blowfly strike.

The ewes themselves will not generally suffer so much from stickers as will lambs, which carry a fleece, are shorter of leg, and are closer to the flying spear-pointed seeds. A discussion of the manner in which lambs, held over into the sticker time, should be handled appears near the end of Chapter 7.

What Is Essential to Breeding for a Large Percentage of Lambs of Uniform Age and Type?

Uniformity in lean ewe-condition previous to breeding has already been discussed. Other practices that will result in a "successful" breeding season, in terms of a large percentage of lambs uniform as to age and type, are listed below and are taken up in subsequent paragraphs.

1. The use of enough vigorous rams
2. Maintenance of ram vigor to assure fertility
3. "Flushing" the ewes
4. Maintenance of a uniformly bred ewe band, or
5. Separation of various breeds or types into groups
6. Unvaried short length of time rams are with ewes, over the years
7. Strict culling of non- or shy-breeders, poor milkers, and late lambers

8. Breeding where temperatures are conducive
9. Proper disposition of late lambers

1. *Proper ram use* can be a great determining factor in regard to both numbers and uniformity of lambs produced. The writer knows of one extreme case where a 20% crop resulted when insufficient numbers and overaged rams were used.

Under rough range conditions at least three young (yearling to 3-year old) rams are thought necessary to each 100 ewes. Under farm conditions one young ram to 50 ewes may be sufficient, and

Fig. 26.   Young, vigorous rams help ensure a good lamb crop. (These are Arthur Grenville's pen that sold at $800.00 per head at the National Ram Sale at Ogden, Utah in 1954.)

if older rams are to be used or young rams made to perform more service, the practice of using alternate rams or of supplemental grain feeding or the employment of "teaser" rams may be desirable.

Where ewes are bred under strictly range conditions it may be impractical to do much about giving the rams especial care, but if possible, and especially when the average age the rams is on the "old" side, the period of heaviest breeding might well be given attention and fresh rams supplied. During the weeks when the rams show no particular activity, the ratio of rams to ewes may be wide, but when considerable numbers of ewes follow the rams about waiting to be bred, extra rams could profitably be supplied.

It is a good practice to place only a third of the rams needed with the ewes until such time as the ewes begin clustering around them. Then the full number of rams is supplied. Even better would be the removal of the original third, their rebuilding with a strong-protein-grain ration, and their return to the band for the final two weeks of service.

In smaller flocks, vigor of the rams can often be well maintained by removing the rams from the ewes during the day and feeding them a good grain ration. Rams can be quickly trained to come out of the flock for their grain, and as most of the breeding takes place at night or early in the morning, no loss in breeding time will take place because of this practice.

Fig. 27. Breast painting a ram to test his fertility.

The length of time during which ewes are in heat or oestrus ranges from 3 to 73 hours, with an average of 29 hours, according to investigation (73% of the ewes checked were in heat over a period of from 21 to 39 hours). in other words, most ewes in good, thrifty condition will be contacted by a ram even though the rams are excluded from the flock during part of a 24-hour period.

The oestral cycle repeats itself every 14 to 19 days if the ewe is not bred.

In prebred flocks or very small, grade flocks where an excellent ram is to be used on many ewes, his energies may be conserved by the use of a "teaser." This is usually a poorer ram, fitted with a canvas apron that will prevent him from breeding the ewe, but the shepherd can detect the ewe in heat and take her to the more valuable ram. The apron fitted to the teaser must be pretty well made to be successful. It should be cut to fit his belly and should hang almost to the ground immediately in front of his penis. It is often necessary to tie it into locks of wool to prevent it from shifting unless it is part of a harness. Instead of such an apron, a sack tied to the ram's belly at the front and rear flanks will do.

2. *To be assured that a new ram is fertile,* a simple expedient and a little careful note-keeping are necessary. Very seldom is a

young, vigorous, range-raised, ram sterile, but some are if they are overfat or have been on the show circuit without sufficient exercise. If there is any suspicion of such a condition, much time can be saved in the breeding program by the use of a "breast paint" on the ram. A good paint can be made of lampblack and raw linseed oil, mixed into a thick paste. Scourable branding fluids, so used, dry too quickly to be as satisfactory. The paint, applied to the ram's brisket with a paddle, will last a week to ten days before needing replenishment. As a ewe is marked on her rump when the ram breeds her, a notation of the date and her identity must be made; then if a considerable number of bred ewes return in heat and are bred a second or third time, the ram is known to be sterile and must be replaced. The colors of the paint may be changed every 18 days to make detection easier, though this is not necessary if the ram is painted every few days so that a fresh marking on the ewe can easily be seen over a faded one. There is now available on the market a marking pad which may be harnessed to the ram. This harness is fitted with a crayon keyed into a metal slot fixed to

Fig. 28. Ram fitted with a marking harness.

the portion between the ram's front legs. It should be fitted carefully so that it will not slip. The crayon should be carried well back on the breast of the ram so that when he mounts the ewe his weight will make a sharp mark on the ewe's rump. If the harness is loose or the crayon not in place, it may be very difficult to detect the mark made on the ewe.

Range men have used this harness successfully to make up their drop bands pretty accurately for lambing. All those ewes marked by the rams over each period of 7 to 10 days are branded shortly afterward, brands being different for each bunch, so that before lambing time five months later each group can be easily dodged out from the flock. As a matter of fact this method of making up the lambing "drop bands" is far more accurate than the "bagging-out" process and is highly to be recommended where the ewes are bred near dodge chutes needed to separate and brand them about every 10 days.

One fault found with the harness crayon has been that it is often too hard or too soft. The owner should make sure that the crayon is fresh because if it is too dry the mark may be too indistinct to

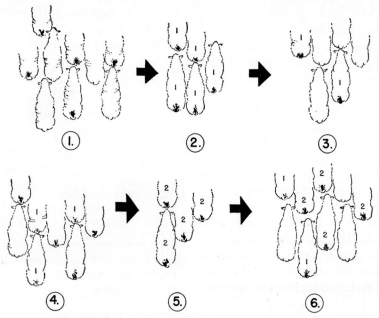

Fig. 29.   The complete "marking harness" program of separating drop bunches.

1. Rams mark some ewes;
2. these are branded after 10 days;
3. and placed back with the band.
4. Others become marked by the rams;
5. these are branded 10 days later;
6. and are returned to the band.

identify. Also, if it is too soft for any reason, the crayon is too quickly worn away or becomes imbedded with gravel and dirt as the ram lies down and rises.

This practice of breast painting (or employing a harness crayon) is especially useful where good but aged rams are being used. A ram over 5 years old is under suspicion concerning fertility and perhaps more often because of inability to get around. A poor or long-strung-out lambing may result if the ram cannot do the work, and for this reason it is considered poor economy to retain too-old rams. One means of detecting fairly accurately whether the old ram is doing the work is noting (through use of breast paint) about the number of ewes he is breeding, then replacing him for a time with a younger ram (breast-painted) and noting whether the number of ewes bred increases greatly. Any ram may be "sterile" for the first *day or two* after being placed with the ewes.

At times ram lambs have been used for breeding at ages of 9 to 10 months. (They have been known to be fertile at as young as 5 months.) This has generally been a practice only when the supply of good-quality yearlings has been used up and extra rams were needed. This practice can be very seriously harmful if the lambs are not properly cared for. On the other hand, a fat ram lamb of good growth, hand bred and heavily fed, is capable of much service.

If ram lambs are to be used in a range band they should, first, *not* be placed in the band with older, heavier rams that will knock them off ewes as they attempt to breed and thus injure them. If used at all, they should preferably finish up the tail end of the season and be allowed to remain with the ewes only two weeks. They should then be removed and fed well—far away from the ewes—or they may be sorry sights as yearlings. Of course a single lamb, properly supplemented, may be used, full season, on a small group of ewes.

3. *Flushing* ewes that have been properly preconditioned to the right degree of leanness does have a strong effect in increasing the numbers of twins dropped. Twins are desirable in setups where the ewes are likely to have plenty of feed to make milk after the lambs are born or where creep feeding of the lambs can be successfully practiced (as described later). Twins are not desirable for year-old mothers or even yearlings or where the lambs usually must spend a good deal of their early months under rigorous climatic conditions, unprotected. In such cases one good single is more likely to live and also will allow its dam to survive in better condition.

Flushing consists in excitation of the ovaries to double-egg production by a sudden increase in physical condition brought on by good feeding. The more usual flushing feed is a green feed such as

Sudan grass or irrigated pasture after the ewes have been held for some time on restricted dry feed. If green feed is not available, grain and good hay may accomplish the same results if fed extravagantly. This will also have the effect of bringing the ewe band into heat more quickly and uniformly. Such increased diet should be started two weeks before the rams are to be placed with the ewes, and to be entirely effective should result in a daily gain of close to half a pound.

Fig. 30. Sudan grass is an ideal flushing feed.

In support of this contention concerning the effect of flushing several sets of figures are provided below.

(a) Investigators Marshall and Potts flushed with grain and with good pasture and produced lamb crops of 128.7% from the unflushed control and 147.4% from the flushed.

(b) Clark showed the effect of fat in flushing as follows:

Thin ewes, unflushed, shed 1.0 ovum each.

Thin ewes, flushed, shed 1.4 ova each.

Fat ewes, unflushed, shed 1.7 ova each.

Fat ewes, flushed, shed 1.5 ova each.

The degree of "fatness" is not described, but the advantage of an improved condition at breeding is clearly shown.

(c) E. H. Pearse (in his book: *Sheep and Property Management*) gives these figures for Merino-Leicester ewes in Australia:

Flushed produced 109.4% (18% twins).

Unflushed produced 91.1% (2% twins).

4. There is a natural difference between breeds of ewes as to the season in which they first come into heat. The Merino and Rambouillet come in early, sometimes in May, but only a few Southdowns or Suffolks ever do until August. The other breeds vary between these extremes. Thus it can be seen that it would be very difficult to have a uniform short-term drop of early lambs if the flock was of very mixed breeding. If the owner desires a two-month period of lamb-drop, he had best keep his ewes all alike as to breed and not attempt to breed earlier than is natural for the particular blood lines represented.

5. The alternative to the above practice would be to separate the ewes (and this would be feasible only where large numbers were owned) according to approximate types, and to operate separate bands or flocks so that the lambs in each would be fairly uniform and thus attractive to buyers and more simply handled.

It is not possible successfully to bring about an earlier lambing date for a given group of ewes very quickly. In other words, it would be almost impossible to get many ewes of a band ordinarily starting to lamb in February to start in December in one year. In purchasing ewes this should be kept in mind because, certainly, a very un-uniform production would result if such an acute change were attempted. Such a band of ewes could be changed to earlier lambing, very completely at least, only by advances of two weeks per year in the date when rams are put with the ewes. This would mean that four years would be needed to affect a two-months earlier average lambing date.

6. One other practice about which successful commercial sheepmen are very particular is the maintenance, from year to year, of an unvaried short length of coupling time. Especially where all the ewes are of like breeding, the rams are with them for only 6 to 8 weeks, and practically all the ewes will conceive and produce lambs in a similar short period. When the longer (4 or 5 months) breeding season is practiced there can be no hope of a really uniform crop. If, subsequently, for the latter group, the breeding season is shortened to 8 weeks or so, a great proportion of the ewes that have habitually lambed later will not conceive. As dry ewes the following spring they will likely get overfat and will not breed that year

either, and heavy culling will be necessary. If properly maintained in lean condition, however, they may well conceive and lamb within the shortened season the next year.

7. *Culling* must accompany any attempt to get a maximum of uniformity in the crop. The usual practice with ewes that do not produce a lamb is to brand them in some way to keep them identified until the following lambing season and then, if they again fail to produce, to market them. If they are 5 to 6 years old when they first do not produce a lamb, it would seem better to market them then rather than to run the chance of keeping them another full year and then getting no lamb. The more perplexing case, however, is the yearling ewe that misses. Undoubtedly it would be more effective and more economic to cull at the beginning of the cycle. In other words, young ewes (raised or purchased) should be carefully scrutinized and rigidly sorted or bought with the thought of uniformity in mind rather than raised or bought as a nondescript bunch that will require a culling program afterward.

Fig. 31.   A sure means of identifying ewes for later disposal is to crop the ears.

By far the greater number of mixed sheep are owned by small-flock operators who have usually "picked up" little bunches here and there, used plain-bred rams, and paid little attention to breeding because to them "sheep were all alike." A person needs only one opportunity to see the offspring and scale weights of the produce of such a bunch in comparison to a uniform, well-bred product run under the same conditions to be easily convinced of the advisability of breeding.

Practices used to identify sheep to be culled are either to brand them or (to make doubly sure that none escapes disposal) to cut one or both ears off close to the head. A spoiled udder may not be detected after it dries up, but if the ewe is immediately marked when her udder is first found in this condition, she will not escape disposal.

Probably the characteristics most commonly leading to culling among ewes where "breeding" is being improved will be along lines of constitution and wooling. The sort generally culled (also, the kind *not* to buy) will be the ewes that have extremely fine bone (an indication of "run-out" breeding), and the narrow, flat, shallow-chested ewes with long, thin necks. This variety of ewe, whose "front legs come out of the same hole," is the sort that produces a long, narrow lamb that can never grade high on the hooks even though it may be reasonably fat. Of course the light, open-wooled ewes, especially those showing coarse hairiness on the britch, also should be culled, as their lambs will not present as nice an appearance or sell as well.

Ewes that are undersized also should be disposed of.

8. High temperatures at breeding time very definitely can affect the success of the breeding season. Not only do ewes fail to come into heat as uniformly as at a cool spot, but also rams lose fertility when temperatures rise.

9. *Ewes lambing late* in relation to the average offer a distinct problem and create a series of circumstances that would seem to make advisable their removal from the flock. Records on purebred ewes where individuals are accurately checked show that ewes that breed early one year do so the next and in succeeding years and that late lambers are generally late every year. If a definite short breeding (and therefore lambing) season is to be adhered to, it will be the late lamber that often will not come into heat before the rams are removed, thus reducing the crop. If such ewes do not lamb, they are in danger of becoming overfat so that their chances of breeding at all the following year will be reduced.

It would seem that an effective way to reduce the chance of lowered lamb crops and an excessive number of dry ewes would be to sell late lambers to the butcher.

Should Ewe Lambs Be Bred?

This is a consideration of much economic importance. The length of life of a range or farm-flock ewe is about seven years on the average. If she can produce six crops of lambs instead of five in that time without injuring her production otherwise, it means more income from her.

Rather conclusive data on this subject is supplied by H. M. Briggs, of North Dakota Agricultural College, who reports on the effect of breeding 122 "blackface crossbred" ewes at 9 months of age and a similar number at 21 months, the usual "yearling" breeding age. These sheep were observed for seven years, and figures were obtained on their production of lamb and wool and upon physical effects.

These things were noted: The ewe lambs that conceived gained in weight until lambing time faster than did the open ewes but weighed less at the time the lambs were weaned then the ewes left open. The ewes bred as lambs were of approximately the same weight as the ewes bred as yearlings by the time they were 31 months old, whereas the late-bred ewes reached their mature weight at 21 months. This indicated that the early-bred group required 10 months longer to get their size, but from then on they maintained their weight as well as the late-bred group. This slowing in the arrival at mature weight apparently had no effect on fleece production. One deleterious effect of early breeding showed up as the ewes reached 6 and 7 years of age. The early-bred ewes then lost their teeth earlier, about 10% more of them having "broken" mouths at that age. This would indicate that tooth development was impaired by early lambing, but this would not be a serious disadvantage chargeable to early breeding as the bad mouths do not show up until an age when breeding ewes are disposed of anyway. If ewe-lamb breeding were practiced, supplementary feeding of bone meal in the lamb year might be helpful in tooth development. To what extent did the lamb crop produced by breeding early improve income? Briggs reports that about 65% of the ewe lambs exposed to rams actually produced lambs (this is about a normal production). Of this 65% only 64% actually raised lambs, and of course these lambs were lighter at birth than those from the later-bred ewes. However, subsequent lambs were equal in size.

A summary at the end of the sixth season showed that the early-bred group had produced 6.72 lambs and a total average weight of 496.36 lb in six lamb crops while the late-bred group had produced 6.03 lambs weighing 465.4 lb, giving 0.69 lamb and 30.96 lb more weight in favor of early breeding.

One other advantage to early breeding not noted by Briggs but generally recognized by experienced sheepmen is that in the case of very early born ewes at least, and especially those carrying any amount of "mutton" blood, the possibility of their becoming barren or not breeding at the yearling stage because of overfatness is lessened by breeding them at 9 months of age. Especially do farm-flock owners that have plenty of good feed often "overfatten" young ewes before they get to the 21-month yearling breeding age where they may become barren or shy-breeding ewes.

It must be kept in mind in breeding a ewe lamb that unless good feeding practices are carried on during the time she is raising her first lamb and until she reaches mature weight at about 2 1/2 years of age, the advantages listed above may not exist.

In commercial flocks there is one other advantage in breeding ewe lambs: The necessity for providing a separate field to run them in at breeding time is eliminated. At least this would be true for crossbred kinds. Perhaps extremely fast-growing Hampshire ewe lambs or others of that type that first come into heat at 5 or 6 months of age would have to be kept separate from the older ewes and rams until they became 9 months old.

Of course, in the case of purebred flocks where sales of breeding stock are made on the basis of the size and appearance of the ewes, it might be a disadvantage to breed ewe lambs and have to show prospective buyers a flock that included undersized yearlings. Also, of course this would create a disadvantage as far as exhibiting was concerned, but for the commercial operator this practice is one to be recommended according to the extent to which feed conditions will allow for good care of the yearlings.

Ewe lambs should not be bred before they become 9 or 10 months old; if they are, they will be longer in reaching their mature weight as set by heredity, or may never be able to do so. A lamb bred at 9 or 10 months will generally be "late" bred in relation to the breeding date of the band of mature ewes. She therefore should not be allowed to nurse her lamb full time if she is to be brought back to the normal date the next year.

Chapter 3

The Care of Pregnant Ewes

To those who have not seen what can result when pregnant ewes suffer improper feeding or management, the care of the ewe from the time she is bred until she lambs may seem to be particularly easy, with little responsibility resting upon the shoulders of the owner. Nothing can be further from the truth, for it is through this gestation period of about five months that the lamb is developed so that it can grow at a normal rate after birth. Further, during this time, proper conditioning of the ewe will strongly influence her milk flow and her own health and also her development and later life. Just a list of the things that can result from improper care is quite impressive: the lamb crop may be extremely light; the lambs may be deformed or "rickety"; there may be losses from abortions, lambing paralysis, and exposure; the wool clip may be light or weak; lambs may be born extremely weak and develop poorly or die; the ewes themselves may be so weakened that they will be inclined to disown their lambs and will require much more attention at lambing time.

Nutrient Content of Feeds

Of first importance through the gestation period is feed. A knowledge of the nutrient content of various kinds of feeds commonly used by ewes through the fall and of their consequent need for supplementary feed is a very valuable asset.

68

The needs of ewes for vitamins, minerals, and protein are less than for such animals as dairy cows producing milk or sows suckling pigs or even for beef cows, but this should not signify that they can do their best on deficiency diets. Except in such areas of deficiency as phosphorus in the soil, for instance, most of the needs of pregnant ewes can and will be supplied by natural feeds, but often the natural feeds used in the fall are not balanced as to make-up but are pretty one-sided, as for instance in a field of barley stubble. The

Fig. 32. Sparse stubble alone is poor gestation feed. These ewes are fat but their lambs will suffer if they continue long on this quality of feed.

barley stubble, if not too closely fed, will provide enough energy material in the leaves and grain that can be picked up and enough protein and Vitamin A in green foul material that may grow among it or nearby, and undoubtedly phosphorus needs will be met by the grain, at least for the early part of the gestation period. But many stubble fields not only are short on grain but entirely lacking in green foul materials and consequently in Vitamin A, protein, and minerals, and this fact should be recognized.

As a consequence, although the ewes, under their coating of

wool, may appear to be well nourished, the effects of deficiencies will appear strikingly and seriously once the ewe lambs. Then a weak milk flow, a slow-growing lamb, a quick falling off in flesh, a ragged, broken fleece, etc., will appear. Further, if bad weather persists, a strong likelihood of death losses in ewes as well as lambs will result. Especially hurt will be the older ewes who ordinarily do not store as much body fat as do younger ewes and whose powers of recuperation after a short-feed period are much weaker.

In support of this latter fact the report of the Extension Service of the University of California in regard to trials run in Mendocino County of that state some years ago is of extreme interest. These trials were conducted on the I. C. Burke Ranch in Anderson Valley, which is in an area subject to heavy rainfall and occasional heavy snows. During the 1936–1937 season severe conditions existed for sheep in this area. Feed-growing conditions in the spring of 1936 were below normal, and the ranges dried up in May. During the next month rains fell on this dry feed, further leeching its nutritive material. Later, when rains would normally have fallen and started another crop of feed, none came; in fact, they were two months late and were then accompanied by very cold weather and heavy snow. Those who heeded the warnings of the Extension Service, including Mr. Burke, did not suffer heavily, but others lost many sheep as well as cattle. This area is rough, open-range country with no barn protection.

Mr. Burke started supplementing feed on September 5 with 1/8 lb of cottonseed cake per head, every other day. Later this amount was fed daily, and when the weather became severe the amount was raised to 1/4 lb. Feeding continued through the winter until March 5. The only other supplementary feed was oat and vetch hay to a few old ewes and to undeveloped yearlings for a short time. Mr. Burke's cost for supplemental feeding was $1.01 per head.

In May 1937 Assistant County Agent Calvin Foote made a survey in Anderson Valley of the effect of the severe season on eight sheep ranches where no supplemental feeding had been practiced or where feeding started late, after sheep had become thin. The survey was made only on ranches similar to Burke's so that comparisons could be made.

Table 2 shows the results of this survey.

Table 2

VALUE OF SUPPLEMENTAL FEEDING IN SEVERE SEASON

Ranch No.	Ewes at breeding time	Ewes at marking	Per cent of mature ewes lost	Lambs raised	Per cent of lambs raised	Supp. feeding
1	2,000	1,600	20.0	550	27.5	Cottonseed (started Dec. 1)
2	4,800	3,500	27.0	900	18.7	Barley, & cott. (started Dec. 15)
3	1,300	800	38.5	94	7.2	None
4	546	304	44.3	16	2.9	Little cottonseed
5	1,150	900	21.7	223	19.3	Hay
6	530	503	5.1	125	23.6	Alfalfa & clover hay
7	800	400	50.0	90	11.2	Little barley
8	300	130	56.6	3	1.0	None
Total or average	11,426	8,137	28.7	2,001	17.5	
I. C. Burke	462	452	1.8	352	76.2	

A comparison of the average and of Burke's figures is self-explanatory. For $1.01 plus some extra labor Mr. Burke got a 60% larger lamb crop and lost some 25% fewer ewes. Figures for a flock of the same size as Mr. Burke's, but giving an "average" performance, would be as follows:

Flock	Bred ewes	Ewes at marking	Per cent of ewes lost	Lambs	Per cent of lambs raised	Cost
Average	462	330	28.7	81	17.5	?
Burke	462	452	1.8	352	76.2	$1.01

If the 352 lambs Mr. Burke raised brought only $5.00 per head (in 1938) this would be an advantage over the average in sale of lambs of $1,355.00 less $1.01 per head for feed, or a net advantage of $889.00. Added to this would be the value of 122 mature ewes at $7.00 per head or $854.00 more, plus the cost of going out and buying or replacing in some way the ewes lost to bring the flock up to capacity. In other words, the timely feeding of supplements in this of course unusual but actual situation was worth to this small range operator some $1,800 to $2,000 in those years. In terms of present sheep values this figure would be tripled. In comparison with the hardest-hit operators this figure would be considerably larger.

Of course, for the great percentage of sheep the above predicament never is met. However, there are many losses, not so strikingly apparent, that are due to an improper judgment of the ewes' condition and state of nutrition through the gestation period, and it behooves the owner to *know* whether his ewes are actually improving in weight and condition through this time or whether the wool cover is deceiving him.

Causes of Death of Sheep

The *loss by death* in ewe flocks is probably about 5%, on the average. Most of this loss results from lambing difficulties, but other losses which occur during the fall and at other periods of the year are to some extent preventable. These losses include those from poisoning, from varmints, and from improper diet.

Losses from Poisonous Feed. Plants that poison sheep vary according to locality, and usually the owner is conversant with them and does what he can to avoid them. On the other hand, many losses are suffered annually when sheep are moved into strange areas or are handled differently than in previous years.

It is a well-known fact that sheep brought up in areas which grow such poisons as milkweed, lupine, loco weed, etc., will not touch them under ordinary circumstances. Other sheep, purchased and brought to the same area, will become poisoned and die. Another situation occurs occasionally when ewes that are accustomed to going to the mountains in summer are for some reason held in the lower country where they do not get their usual summer green feed. Then the green sprouts of milkweed and lupine are attractive to them and they are often poisoned.

Of course, very hungry sheep may consume poisons that they ordinarily wouldn't touch, so it is well to know the identity of poisonous plants and to search out and avoid areas growing them.

Some of those common to the West are, as mentioned above,

milkweed, lupine, and loco weed and poisonous or black nightshade, cocklebur, St. Johnswort, mountain or black laurel, azalea, and death camas. There are many others but not so commonly occurring. Sheep may also be poisoned on the sorghums at certain stages.

An excellent description of these varieties with colored plates, is provided in the University of California Experiment Station Bulletin No. 593 by Arthur W. Sampson and H. E. Malmsten.

Much of the loss from poisons is avoidable; much is associated with overgrazing and with lack of care in searching out and avoiding poison areas. In most cases, little can be done in the way of cure, so the sheepman who would prevent losses is the one who "knows his poisons" and avoids them.

In brief, the facts about the common poisons are as follows:

1. *Milkweeds* often cause serious losses, especially when sheep are driven on roadways and are hungry; also among "mountain" sheep confined to the valleys in summer. Parts poisonous are the leaves, stems, and pods including seeds—the seeds being the most poisonous. Deaths may occur in a few hours. Hungry sheep confined in fields where seeds of milkweed have dropped are most hard hit, so investigation of such fields in spots where milkweeds ordinarily grow should profit the owner. Eradication being impractical and no treatment effective, plenty of feed to satisfy hunger is the answer.

2. *Lupines* are considered to cause heavy losses, the seed again being three or four times as toxic as other parts, and the most serious period being after flowering. Again the best protection is had by providing the sheep with plenty of other feed—not feeding so closely that lupine will be taken.

3. *Death camas* is generally regarded as the most violent sheep poison. These plants are slender, grasslike herbs growing 6 to 20 in. tall, and the seeds and bulbs are the most toxic, though the bulbs are seldom eaten. It is most dangerous early in the spring, pushing up growth before most food grasses do. There is no medicinal remedy; recovery often follows if the animals are allowed to remain quiet.

4. *Cocklebur* is relished by sheep just as the plant sprouts from the ground and before any true leaves have developed. After that, the plant is not eaten as it is extremely bitter. Sheep should be kept out of the damp areas where cocklebur grows at times when the

seed ordinarily sprouts. The seeds too are extremely poisonous. A program of pulling the plants to avoid seed formation should eliminate it as the plant is an annual. Fats and oils administered to poisoned animals have remedial effects.

5. *Black nightshade* grows rather widespread and the consumption of any part, especially the green berries, may cause illness, though seldom death. Grubbing the plant should be the program followed.

6. *Black laurel* is a common poisoner in the mountain areas, where it grows in damp meadows at 4,000 to 8,000 ft elevations. It is unpalatable and generally causes losses only when sheep are on the road and are hungry. Epsom salts dissolved in water as a drench in doses of from 2 to 6 ounces aids in eliminating the poison.

7. *Loco weed* poisoning symptoms do not appear until after the animal has fed on the plant for a good part of the season. Sheep then show a tendency toward paralysis and incoordination. Deaths may occur in a few days, or the animal may live for a year, still showing symptoms. Those that recover should not again be put on loco weed range as they will teach other sheep the habit. Supplemental feeding during periods of feed shortage is in order.

Losses from Varmints. Such losses are, of course, serious at times and are disheartening, and every effort should be made to prevent them, especially during the gestation period when abortions may be caused in ewes run by varmints though not actually killed by them. Coyotes and stray dogs cause the most trouble, though bears, wolves, bobcats, and mountain lions occasionally prey upon sheep.

The *stray dog* has probably caused more damage and hard feelings than any other varmint. Shooting and poisoning of innocent (or guilty) dogs has caused much antagonism between owners. Prevention has been made strongly possible through the enactment and strict policing of laws designed to control unwanted dogs and has been very effective under such regulations.

The California Dog Law, brought about by sheepmen and sympathetic County Boards of Supervisors, is typical.

Section 4C states: "The owner of any livestock . . . killed or injured by any dog or dogs may recover . . . twice the actual value of the animals killed or twice the value of the damages sustained. . . ."

In order to collect, however, it is necessary to file a suit, and any sheep owner is foolish not to do so if only to establish the fact in the community that irresponsible owners and dogs are not going to be tolerated. It is advisable to place the facts in the hands of a lawyer and to follow his advice as to sufficiency of proof to satisfy a court of law.

If the sheepman has killed the dog in a lawful manner, he will have little to fear if a counter suit is brought by the dog's owner

Calif. Woolgrowers Assn.

Fig. 33. Injuries and losses from dogs are constant threats.

for malicious killing. Section 4A of the California Dog Law states: "Any person shall have the right to kill any dog found in the act of killing, wounding or persistently pursuing or worrying any livestock or poultry on land or premises not owned or possessed by the owner of the dog, or if he shall have proof as conclusively shows that such dog has been recently engaged in killing or wounding livestock or poultry on land or premises not owned or possessed by the owner of such dog, and no action, civil or criminal, shall be maintained therefore for killing such dog."

It is always necessary to have the facts clearly stated and impor-

tant to have a sufficient number of witnesses so that there will be
no doubt in the mind of the jury and the judge. It is most important, also, to establish proof of ownership of the dog causing the
damage.

Coyotes present a different problem than dogs. Unwanted by
anyone, they nevertheless are difficult to control entirely. Aggressive
trapping and poisoning campaigns, carried on preferably by the
State, can and have achieved remarkable results, but outlying areas
often never are freed of this varmint, and local trappers are not
always readily available.

One sure way to prevent coyote loss has been observed by the
author with a small flock run in California foothills. The owner,
located in a bad coyote center, never experienced a loss, whereas
neighbors were constantly subject to depredations. His remedy was
bells. Every ewe wore one, and every lamb, as soon as it was able
to carry one (two weeks old), had a small bell beneath its chin.
The cost of these bells and straps was considered cheap in terms of
possible actual losses and in terms of peace of mind for the owner.

Other cases of halting coyote damage through the use of fewer
bells have been observed. (Of course this practice might be impractical for a range band.)

Coyotes do not frequently attack mature sheep. Preferably lambs
are taken, and because it is quite evident that corralling of sheep
(to prevent losses) is an especially poor practice when ewes are
suckling lambs—if they are to be gotten fat—this procedure is not
recommended. Every effort should be made to eliminate the coyote
and to prevent losses without recourse to corralling.

In passing, it might be mentioned that evidence of a coyote killing
is characteristic: The lamb or sheep will have been caught at the
throat, and if it has been eaten upon, its rear flank or belly will
most often have been opened. A lamb sucking its dam will have its
stomach opened and the curdled milk within devoured. Dogs catch
a sheep at any point on their bodies.

Losses from Bloating and Foundering. A third sort of thing that
will produce losses in the flock is *improper diets* or *diets improperly
fed.* Much of this type of loss is accidental but needs discussion for
those whose experience is limited. The deaths are attributed to
bloating and *foundering.* For the most part *bloating* is caused by
such green plants as clover and alfalfa. These plants probably cause

more gas production within the digestive tract than grasses and also, recent evidence seems to prove, because of their softness or smoothness they do not produce a throat reaction that eliminates as much of the gas through belching as do coarser grasses. Many sheep are lost annually in grazing alfalfa. Much of this loss could be prevented, but complete avoidance is not possible.

Don Tomlin

Fig. 34. Bloat on alfalfa pasture is difficult to avoid.

In the West, heavily pregnant ewes often are put on alfalfa fields in late fall as a source of feed, Vitamin A, and protein to lamb on or to give the ewes a "lift" after weeks or months of dry stubble grazing. It is good to approach such grazing with caution and preparation.

Fall-fed alfalfa may or may not have undergone a freeze. If it has, it has stopped growing, is relatively dry, and is not so likely to cause bloat, but freezing alone should not be relied upon. Many hold the mistaken idea that corralling the sheep and allowing them to feed for only a few minutes at a time or up to a certain line or irrigation check will prevent bloating. Too many cases of recurring losses have been observed for such a practice to be recommended. If the sheep are to be saved, some method must be devised to make it possible to turn them loose in the alfalfa field, disturbing them thereafter as little as possible. Ewes can stand a good deal of gas pressure without death if allowed to remain quiet. A case in point is the observation of a band of ewes in a strange alfalfa field alongside a railway. Upon being frightened by an oncoming train, they ran across the field, several dropping dead en route.

Loss is best prevented in feeding alfalfa by "conditioning" the sheep previous to putting them in the field. The best procedure is to let them feed for one to three days on green grasses that will "loosen" the digestive tract, then *toward evening,* after the sheep are quite full of such food, to turn them onto the alfalfa and "go away and forget them." If any losses do occur, they will be light. The admonition to "go away and forget them" is quite important. Sheep will start to bloat, and the owner's tendency will be to go into the flock to see if he can help a certain sheep; thereby he will disturb others and cause more bloat. If *green grass* is not available on which to fill the sheep previous to pasturing in the alfalfa (or clover) field, a good fill of hay will suffice. Straw as a fill will not be eaten sufficiently to serve the purpose. Never put sheep onto such a field when they are hungry or in the morning when it is dewy or wet from rain.

Bloat losses can never be entirely eliminated, and it will always be the best or fattest, greediest sheep that will be lost. Ewes that have been lambed upon alfalfa often die when they have been confined to one end of the field by hours (or days) of storm and then, upon clearing weather, they venture out to fresh feed, eat fast, and bloat.

California Ladino clover feeders find that they suffer fewer losses from bloating if they feed no salt. Other feeders proclaim that their bloat losses are reduced or eliminated simply by providing the lambs with *no shade,* thereby making it uncomfortable for them to lie for many hours through the heat of the day in any one spot, and forcing them to keep eating. If they don't get hungry, they don't bloat.

Abortions. During the five-month gestation period many things can happen to a bunch of ewes that can cause abortions of foetuses.

An abortion means, of course, 12 months of lost productiveness as far as that ewe is concerned, and if the percentage of losses is great, as it can be, perhaps the difference between profit and loss. Fortunately sheep are not troubled by contagious abortion, and usually losses from this source are small.

Severe sickness due to feeds, or injury due to careless handling or to varmints, may cause abortion.

Any type of feeding that seriously sickens a ewe is likely to cause her to abort. Just a list of possibilities may be enough to call to the reader's attention the feeds or methods that should be avoided. The list is short—*foundering on grain* or poisoning on poisonous plants or moldy hay—but it encompasses many of the common operations of sheepmen. Wherever grain-stubble fields are used there is this danger. Sheep moved onto a "fresh" field and not carefully herded invariably will hunt out the heavy grain spots and gorge themselves. Such spots will be in corners or about the edges of the field where the harvester has not made a clean sweep or where heavy grain has been knocked down by wind or rain and could not be picked up by the harvester.

Don Tomlin

Fig. 35. Abortions are infrequent but costly.

Often, too, sheep find sacks of grain hidden in the stubble. The obvious prevention, of course, is never to permit the sheep to roam the field at will until it has been closely inspected or fed down so that no big deposits of grain remain that might be consumed without sufficient other consumption of leaves to lighten the grains. In other words, herd the sheep— force them to eat in confined areas, mixing leaves with grain until the field has been well covered. Wheat stubble entails greater danger than that of other grain because of the relatively hull-less character of the grain.

Although grape seeds may not be considered "grain," foundering, with subsequent abortions, may be caused by them. Ewes placed in a vineyard to clean up the residue after the first crop has been picked may find a large second crop of grapes still on the vines. If the ewes are not herded and forced to eat leaves along with the grapes, they will consume too many grapes. The next day a large percentage will be found stiffened with founder, some may die, and many will later abort.

As ewes progress toward the end of the gestation period the dangers of abortion increase, and lack of care in handling and/or feeding may cause losses. It is inadvisable to run and feed cattle and sheep together at this time since the cattle may butt or toss the ewes as they attempt to feed with them.

Severe "dogging," intentional or unintentional, should be avoided. Walk out after the ewes, keep the dog in hand, don't make the ewes run hard or for long distances, and above all don't crowd them through gateways or against corral walls.

Preparations for Lambing

In the few weeks previous to the time the first lamb should drop much can and should be done to make this most important period less troublesome, more profitable. Nothing is to be considered more important than keeping the ewes in good condition through and after lambing, so the first and obvious preparation for lambing might be to be sure of an adequate reserve of hay, grain, or supplement.

Shearing or Tagging. As to preparation of the ewes: They are either to be shorn in the fall or "tagged" a short time previous to lambing, or perhaps both. If, say, the ewes were shorn in September and are to start lambing on January first, they will then carry only a 3 1/2 months' fleece; in some breeds the wool will be short enough to make tagging unnecessary.

Tagging consists of removal of the wool from about the tail and rear, inside and along the front of the rear legs and over the udder so that the teats of the ewe will be free of locks that might interfere with the lamb's suckling or of burs that might discourage him, and of wool that would collect dung resulting from eating loosening green feeds. This tagging is done more successfully with the clippers of a shearing machine than with blades that cannot cut so close.

Fig. 36. The complete tagging job clears the eyes too.

Don Tomlin

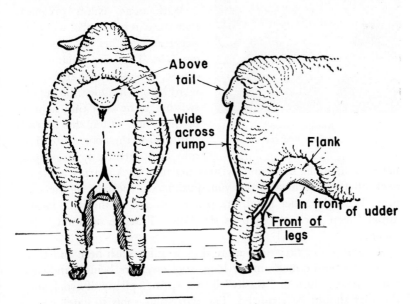

Above tail

Wide across rump

Flank

In front of udder

Front of legs

Fig. 37. Tagging ewes just before lambing saves labor later.

81

Naturally, the nearer the start of lambing this job can be done, the longer it will be effective in preventing the above-mentioned troubles. Where spring feed grows lush, cases have been known where a second tagging was necessary before the spring shearing in order to prevent the ewes being attacked by blowflies and maggots.

Further, it is essential that extreme care be exercised in handling the heavy, pregnant ewes when performing the task of tagging. If

hired tagging crews are used, the owner should insist on quiet, slow, deliberate corralling and "throwing" of the ewes, and should vigilantly exercise his right to put a man off the job who is rough. (Remember, practically the whole year's returns depend on getting that lamb born alive.)

With large, heavy pregnant ewes the careful shearer will practice throwing her in a peculiar manner. The usual manner, of course, is to pull her sharply backward by one hind leg, lifting and twisting at the same time in order to drop her. Often this severely slams her to the floor. Instead she may be floored easily by grasping

Fig. 38. "Nosing down" a heavy ewe for tagging.

her muzzle in one hand and twisting her nose back sharply along her neck on the side away from you, pushing to the rear at the same time. With the other hand, grasp her tail, and as the neck twist is applied step back one step as she falls. (Practice on some "dry" sheep.)

A good job of tagging is more than a quick slash here and there. Especially where medium- or long-wool ewes are being handled or where feed is lush or "washy" in the spring, plenty of wool about the rear should be removed. The particular spots to catch are, in order of importance: above and to the side and on the dock, down the rear of the legs, far up into the flank, and down the front of the legs.

Shear *high* above the tail and *widely* down the rear legs. If the tagging is done too narrowly, the long wool quickly picks up dung and very little help has been gained by tagging. The completed job also includes one cut across the belly in front of the udder, the removal of wool on the udder itself and down the front edge of the rear legs, and on the inside of the legs if burs are present in any numbers. Quite often a ewe carrying burs in the short wool on the inner side of her legs will wear her udder, after it has developed, so raw in walking that she will refuse suckling to her lamb. To have the wool off the udder close to the teats and on the front edge of the rear legs and up into the flank will save many a weak lamb at time of birth.

Usually these crutchings will sell for a good price because they are relatively clean in comparison to what they would be as only a part of the spring clip. They should be sacked separately from the fleeces.

Conditioning the Ewe Flock for Lambing

It has already been stated that a uniform condition of the ewes throughout the year is desirable and advisable and that the condition should be one of moderate fatness. It is natural to expect that a good-milking ewe will fall off in flesh when her lamb is suckling. Some ewes are such heavy producers of milk that no amount of feeding can keep them from getting thin. On the other hand, others milk so poorly that they stay or get overfat on good spring feed while suckling their young. This point has been suggested as one to be considered in culling the flock.

If the flock has been flushed and ewes in varying states of flesh have been brought to the start of the breeding season all at about the same degree of flesh (lean but gaining) in the manner suggested in a previous chapter, it is surely desirable and to be expected that they should and can be improved in flesh steadily through the gestation period.

Opinion varies as to how fat a ewe should get at lambing and as to the effect of her state of flesh on troubles at birth and on the size of her lamb at birth. Three ideas are often expressed: (1) that a ewe that started the gestation period very fat will produce a small lamb and have difficulty in producing it because of her fatness;

(2) that a thin ewe will grow a very large lamb; and (3) that excessive feeding of protein supplements or hay during gestation will make the foetus grow oversize and result in difficult birth.

These arguments all seem reasonable and can readily be upheld from a physiological standpoint, but they are not sustained in actual practice. Just about as often as not a very fat ewe will produce a very big lamb and a thin ewe a little one. Also, if protein supplements have been fed to a flock during gestation, just as many little lambs as big ones will be born.

It is true, however, that a flock of ewes suffering malnutrition throughout the gestation period, ewes that are really thin and undernourished, will produce a big percentage of lambs that are small and weak at birth. It is advisable, therefore, that every effort be made to get the ewes as fat as possible as they approach lambing; this practice, applied to ewes that are known to be good milkers, should result in fast-growing lambs. If the lamb born to a fat ewe does happen to be small, he will have plenty of milk to help him catch up in size with the lamb that was larger at birth, and it will be very difficult to note or unlikely that either lamb at marketing time will have an advantage.

Feed the ewes well, then, get them fat but at the same time *keep them exercised* and their flesh in good tone. This will mean more toward eliminating trouble at lambing than any other one thing. "Lambing paralysis" is one trouble that may come into the picture under certain circumstances, if exercise is neglected. This particular trouble is discussed in detail below.

What, then, should be the program of care of the ewe during gestation?

1. *Feed her liberally but carefully.* Avoid poisons, and feeds that will founder, or bloat, or in other ways sicken the ewes. Keep the ewes gaining steadily; it should not be a program of feast and famine but of steady daily allotments and, as previously stated, protein supplementation started *early*. This may be either such concentrates as cottonseed cake or perhaps even better, where possible, green pastures such as Sudan grass or, later, irrigated barley, for these supply Vitamin A abundantly.

If every sheepman could be assured of at least one month's green feed for his ewes before they lambed, lamb crops would be improved considerably. Perhaps nothing is more desirable than this, and positive returns in the elimination of births of rickety lambs or dead calcified foetuses have many times been noted.

Plant something to provide green pasture for the ewes during part of the summer. Grains especially will make an abundance in the fall or winter, the latter part of the gestation period, when most needed.

2. *Get the ewes fat but keep them exercised.* Again, the availability of green pasture during the later gestation period will be ideal for fattening *and* exercise. Of course, grain-stubble fields and

Fig. 39. It is best for ewes to be fat at lambing, if exercised.

hay-field pickings, or natural dry grass range may be, of necessity, the only feed that can be used. Supplement, then with protein early or feed hay and/or grain. Don't let the ewe slip in condition, for it will cost more to maintain her after she lambs. Remember that the wool clip suffers too when ewes get too thin.

Various methods have been suggested for keeping ewes properly exercised. Most generally this need will be felt with farm flocks run under fence. Steep hill pastures are ideal; the feeding of hay or grain or cottonseed cake at the distant end of the field from bedding grounds will help. Also, if watering places are controlled, their placement at a considerable distance from the bedding ground is in order.

If it is necessary to corral the ewes and to feed hay (especially alfalfa) nearing lambing time, daily exercise enforced by driving the ewes up and down the lane or road may be necessary to help prevent lambing paralysis.

3. *Prevent injuries and possible abortions* by driving sheep carefully through gateways, using dogs less as lambing approaches, corralling as little as possible, and feeding away from cattle.

4. *Prevent lambing paralysis* (preparturient paralysis). When ewes are confined during the period a few weeks previous to lambing and especially when fed heavily on alfalfa hay, some of them, carrying twins, will be subject to this disorder. The exact cause of this paralyzing and killing disease is not too clear from a physiological standpoint, but the results of improper and of proper handling are quite striking and clear. Generally only a small percentage of ewes are affected, but the contrary has been experienced where no preventive measures were taken.

The first symptoms of the trouble are quite apparent and should give fair warning so that losses can be minimized. If the ewes are being watched carefully in the corrals, it may be noted that one ewe seems to be going blind, refuses to move, or moves very slowly and hesitantly or with a staggering gait. She needs immediate attention if she is to be saved. If the disease has not progressed too far and she still has a desire to eat, putting her into a green pasture such as barley will often effect a cure. The exercise that she will take as she finds herself separated from the other sheep may be effective.

About a day after these first symptoms are noted the ewe will absolutely refuse to walk but stands gritting her teeth and frequently violently flickering her eyelids. From then on the usual picture is that she will finally drop to the ground in a coma and death will occur in a few days.

Invariably the ewe, upon autopsy, will be found to be carrying twins. The generally accepted explanation of the disease is that the added weight of the foetuses and their demands upon the dam, coupled with lack of exercise, causes sluggish circulation of the blood and results in some type of poisoning. The natural processes, when a ewe carries but one lamb, seem to be able to dispel this poison. Other investigation seems to bear out the contention that a sys-

Courtesy I. E. Newsom, Sheep Diseases

Fig. 40. Pregnancy disease (Lambing paralysis). Ewe in coma. Resultant mottled, fatty liver.

temic poisoning is the result of breakdown of the liver, overworked in itself in transforming body fats into food. This idea seems likely because few cases of lambing paralysis occur in flocks fed grain close to lambing time or in those for which molasses (in tubs) is made available. Further, it seems unlikely that a ewe carrying twins could eat a quantity of hay sufficient to meet her needs, whereas the ewe carrying only a single would be able to do so.

It is therefore recommended that ewes confined close to lambing time be fed concentrates and be regularly exercised by driving them out of the corrals at some time in the day for a brisk walk.

The particular value of molasses (fed free choice) is that it is a very readily digested concentrate. When a ewe carries such a heavy load in lambs she is not able to consume enough food nutri-

Leslie Crane

Fig. 41. A covered trough supplies molasses as a supplement to range.

ents from coarse feeds to supply her needs. Therefore the liver is overworked transforming body fats to her uses.

Treatment of a ewe in coma is of little or no avail. It has been noted on occasion that when a ewe gives birth (or aborts) her lambs while she is very sick with this affliction, she recovers almost miraculously. Feeding of sugar dissolved in water and injection of glucose into the armpit and into the jugular vein have been used as treatments with varying degrees of success. The latter method, of course, would most quickly get energy food into the sheep's system, but it is virtually impossible for the average sheepman to administer the injection. The jugular vein is very difficult to locate and to puncture with the hypodermic needle.

When sugar is fed it is dissolved a cupful to a cup of water and given by bottle or syringe. Molasses too would suffice. This treatment is effective, however, only when the ewe is caught in early stages of this trouble, before coma slows down all her functions.

The injection of 60 cc of a 50% glucose solution into the armpit or intravenously in the early stages of the trouble may be expected to save some ewes. (A somewhat similar affliction of sheep called ketosis or milk fever is treated in Chapter 12.)

Separation of Ewes before Lambing

Much less trouble at lambing time will result if the "heavy" ewes are placed in separate drop bands a week or two previous to lambing. This will be found to have many advantages. First, it will be possible to watch the heavy ewes much more closely and to prevent the loss of many lambs at birth. A good lambing man checks his drop band very frequently and is much more likely to discover a "stuck" lamb or a ewe in trouble if the numbers are smaller. Then too, more of the ewes (the less heavy ones) can be kept away from the corrals for a longer period, which is desirable from the standpoint of exercise, prevention of lambing paralysis, and perhaps conservation of the hay reserve (if pasture is still available for those not ready to lamb.)

Another good feature of separation appears when the band is made up of many yearlings mixed with the older ewes or with the previous year's ewe lamb replacements. Much more likelihood of a yearling giving birth to her first lamb and immediately running off and leaving the newborn will be experienced in a big bunch. Also the 12-month-old ewe replacements are often curious about the fresh lambs to the extent of bothering them, butting them, and occasionally killing them if their mothers are not well acquainted with their newborn and do not stay close to them.

So by all means separate out the heavy ewes; more lambs and much labor will be saved. Various methods of effective separation will be found, varying with the size of the band or flock. In a band of 2,000 ewes probably the largest number desirable in a drop bunch will be 300, and most of these should lamb out and be replaced by others in a week to ten days. (During the heaviest part

of the season this number might be 500.) In smaller flocks a similar
proportion might be separated.

The careful selection of these 300 so that only the heaviest ewes
are brought in demands some training and careful handling. Some
ewes will show good-sized udders for over a month before they
lamb, whereas others "bag up" in ten days, and others—especially
yearlings—hardly show a bag even when they lamb. Therefore
handling of every udder is necessary. It would be entirely wasteful
and perhaps dangerous from the standpoint of lambing paralysis
to keep a ewe in a confined drop band for a month.

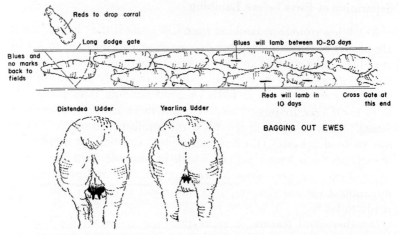

Fig. 42.   Bagging and chalking to separate a drop bunch.

A good procedure in accomplishing the separation in a large
band might be as follows:

1. Provide yourself with two colors of marking chalk or crayon
(perhaps red and blue) and construct or make available an alley,
preferably 2 1/2 to 3 ft wide, quite long and with a dodge gate at
the far end.

2. Fill the chute with ewes (the first time on a date a week
previous to that when the first lambs should drop) and then, with
the ewes fairly closely packed, start at the rear end of the alley
and feel each udder.

3. Mark with *red chalk* all ewes with udders in which there is
some distension. If the teats are filling or are somewhat taut, these

ewes will lamb soon. The *size* of the udder is not the correct sign; an aged ewe with an enormous bag may not lamb as soon as a young ewe with an udder that can hardly be seen. (If the ewes have been tagged, this job will be much easier.)

4. Mark with *blue chalk* any other ewes showing bags, but whose teats are not tight. To distinguish between the two degrees of "springiness" of the udder requires considerable practice if much accuracy is to result.

5. Leave *unmarked* those showing no udder.

6. Run the ewes on through the chute and separate out by the dodge gate all those with red marks.

7. The blues will go back to the fields with the unmarked ewes, and when they are brought in again 10 days later they may all be separated through the dodge gate without "bagging" the band. Another 10 days later, however, the remainder of the bunch will have to be bagged again, the same marking procedure being used.

If very few ewes are involved, separation will generally consist merely in bringing them to a small corral where they can be looked over and the tight-bagged ewes caught and slipped into the next corral. To make sure that none are missed, a little trick that will be helpful is as follows: Walk backwards into the group of sheep, then as they move to the other side of the pen—or out through a gate into another pen, their rear quarters can be observed and other possibilities caught.

Another even more accurate means of making up the drop bunches was discussed in Chapter 2. It consists of branding groups that are harness-marked by the rams at breeding time. These differently branded groups are then separated out at lambing.

Chapter 4

Equipment for Lambing

Anything special in the way of equipment to make the lambing season easier (other than natural or artificial means of protection from storms) is not even considered by the owner of a small flock, or by many range men. However, to other range operators, owners of large farm flocks, and purebred producers this topic is all-important for it means the saving of labor when it is most needed and the saving of lambs, which is so necessary to profitable production.

Barn Lambing. Many sheepmen are forced to lamb in barns. Others, because of their location or the season they make use of, lamb on the open range. This would generally be considered ideal but not to be enjoyed by all.

If several hundreds or thousands of ewes of necessity must be lambed about a barn, it behooves the owner to put that barn and surrounding corrals into shape so that feeding, penning, and care of the drop band will require the least labor and time. Although many barn and corral arrangements in use are seemingly satisfactory, their owners would be most willing to know of things they could do to improve conditions. It is with this thought in mind that the accompanying plans (in the next chapter) and suggestions are made. Variations will be required according to the need for grain feeding, the type of hay to be used, the length of time necessary to keep the band protected, the proximity of pasture, etc.

Basically, in planning the barn and corrals the needs to be considered are as follows:

1. Storage space for hay—loose, chopped, or baled—and for grain (whole)
2. Feeding facilities for the drop bunch
3. Feeding facilities for ewes that have lambed
4. Pens of various sizes to keep fresh lambs and their dams separate for varying lengths of time (individual and group pens)
5. Fencing and paneling making it easy to move fresh lambs and their mothers into the barn from corrals

Fig. 43. A lambing barn is often a necessity.

6. Separating chutes
7. Shearing and wool-storage facilities (unless a separate barn or shed is thought preferable)
8. Protection in the corrals for the drop band

Only when a man has been confronted with a night's drop of a hundred or more lambs, perhaps, will he appreciate how valuable a little careful planning can be.

Previous to a discussion in Chapter 5 of how the barn is used for lambing, it is thought desirable to describe and discuss the features of the various parts of the barn. Also, because it is true that many ideas are held in relation to these sections, the good and poor points of some of them will be discussed.

Use and Construction of Jails

Jails, as shown in the barn described in the following chapter, have several important uses. If their construction and placement are carefully considered, their use will help to greatly increase the crop of lambs for marketing. In fact, the writer knows of one case where, to the use of jails could be largely attributed a 120% crop marketed from approximately 1,800 ewes (and practically all the lambing and feeding was handled by one man).

These small pens are used for the following reasons:

1. To confine ewes with newborn twins until they and their dams are well acquainted. This is helpful in two ways. By immediately placing the ewe in the jail after the birth of her lambs, the drop corral can be cleared more quickly after a heavy night's lambing and one of the pair will not be continually straying from the other or its mother with consequent danger of being finally disowned by its dam. Secondly, the owner can be surer in turning out a ewe with twins so handled that they will not stray and become "bummers." This corral-clearing feature of jails is very vital.

It is usually desirably to keep the ewe and twins jailed for 2 or 3 days; 5 or 6 days is even better if the weather is bad or jail use is not pressing—until the lambs "fill out," get a little fat under their hides. Occasionally a ewe will lie on a twin and smother it, but these losses are more than compensated by the savings in time and effort upon the part of the lamber in attempting to keep lambs together and in having fewer "bummers" to contend with.

2. Possibly the greatest usefulness of the jail is for ewes that refuse to take their own lamb or whose lamb dies and to whom another must be "grafted." Here too the jail is very helpful in clearing the drop corral as a ewe and her dead lamb may be jailed quickly and later, when all others have been attended to, a second lamb may be put with her and suitably handled (as described in Chapter 6) so that she will take it quickly.

3. Rather than place a ewe with her newborn, but very weak (or injured) lamb, in a large pen with several other ewes, it is safer

to pen her individually where the lamb may be regularly helped to suckle or carefully handled.

4. Ewes that have lost their lambs at birth but for whom no twin is immediately available are conveniently jailed so that they can be regularly milked out twice a day to keep their flow coming until a lamb is available.

Construction ideas vary but essentially the jail unit is as follows: The individual pen has over-all dimensions of 4 ft by 4 ft and is

Calif. Woolgrowers Assn.

Fig. 44. Lambs with ewes in jails fitted with brooders, for cold-country lambing (Front gate opened).

32 to 36 in. high. It is fitted with a door that is the full 4 ft in width so that it may be swung out across the lead-in alley to block it completely. Spacing of the horizontal rails of the entire pen is designed to prevent small lambs from going through the openings. These rails are of 1-in. by 4-in. material with spaces ranging from 2 to 3 in. near the bottom to 4 to 6 in. above.

Because water and feed are so essential in maintaining the milk flow of a jailed ewe, they must be provided by the jail in such a way as to keep them both fresh, clean, and unlimited in quantity. A bucket of water placed in the confined space of the jail is very unsatisfactory. It is either tipped over, leaving the ewe without water when she needs it and wetting the pen; or it becomes filled with hay or droppings from the ewe and so is not usable. Tying the bucket to the rails off the ground in a corner will help.

To overcome these undesirable features, our line of jails is shown in the next chapter with a *water trough* placed outside the jail so as to serve several pens. Holes about 8 in. by 8 in. in size are cut through jail walls (or the outer wall of the barn) through which the ewe may water. These troughs are filled by hoses and may readily be cleaned from the outside, though this is not a frequent necessity.

Hayracks in the jails are shown (in diagrams in the next chapter) built between pairs of pens so that ewes in adjoining pens eat from one rack. Hay thrown into the corner of a jail does not provide sufficient feed, for it is soon soiled and wasted and creates a cleaning problem that is very difficult in such small areas. The racks may make it impossible to provide quite as many jails down one length of the barn as where simple panel jails are used, but where a permanent setup is desired, this construction is advisable.

Grain boxes, too, may be built into the jails. These need be nothing more than about a 6-in. by 6-in. box built into a corner about 2 ft from the ground level.

Cleaning out the jails must be considered in locating them. After several weeks of use the wastage of long hay pulled into the pen will build up and it must be cleaned out. To be able to fork out the accumulation directly into a wagon or truck or manure spreader is desirable as it is heavy and handling it a second time is troublesome. Therefore, roof clearance over the jails should be ample.

The gate to each pen should be hinged in like manner and from such corner of the jail as will make it easiest to fill the jail. That is, if the ewe comes into the barn from the north end, say, and is to be driven down an alley and into the jail, the gate should be capable of being swung across the alley so that she can be directed back into the jail after passing it and returning toward the north. (Hinging gates in this way will also be found very convenient for holding pens for shearing.) When a ewe finds herself at the end of an alleyway down which she has been driven, her natural instinct is to wheel quickly and bolt back up the alley. If the jail gate (or holding-pen gate) is so hinged that she can then be directed into the pen, she will not have to be pushed in. Her lamb may be dropped into the jail as she is driven past it, and she will stay with it after running back.

Other ideas for jails might be mentioned. The writer has seen successfully used jails that were only about 2 ft wide and 5 or 6 ft long, allowing plenty of space for the ewe and the lamb to lie down. These had a hayrack at one end, but the watering problem was not as well handled as in the previous case.

In forcing a ewe to take an unwanted lamb it is sometimes necessary to tie her securely to a wall of the jail or in some manner make it possible for the lamb to suckle and impossible for her to fight it. This is rather more easily accomplished in this narrow jail by the simple expedient of stretching ropes or wires across the jail under her breast behind the forelegs and ahead of her udder. The jail being narrow, she cannot turn around.

An often suggested but less useful type of jail is a "demountable" sort made only of hinged panels, each part 4 ft long. These panels are set up as needed, starting in a corner of the barn, and are hooked to each other. These obviously cannot provide the feeding and watering advantages of the stationary type.

Probably the most useful type of jail is one made in sections of two portable pens, set upon a slatted platform. If, then, chopped hay is fed, most of the difficulties concerning cleaning are avoided. This double set will have a foot-wide box 6 in. or more deep set between the two pens so that its upper edge is 14 to 16 in. off the platform. At this height no baby lamb will jump into it, and it can be kept reasonably clean as far as the ewe is concerned. The box is the full 4 ft long (the entire jail width) and will hold plenty of chopped hay for two ewes for a day's feed. This is the type of jail diagrammed for use in the barn discussed in the next chapter. Because it is set on the slatted platform and chopped rather than long hay is used, there is no accumulation of manure within the small enclosure, and the mean cleaning problem of the other type of jail is obviated.

Feeding Equipment in Barn

Other equipment for the sheep barn will include, certainly, adequate and handily placed *hayracks* for feeding both the drop band and the lambed ewes.

The simplest and most satisfactory hayrack from many stand-points is the panel type shown in Fig. 45. It is easily made, allows the ewes to eat readily, and requires the least attention to ensure

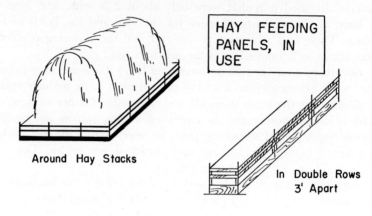

Around Hay Stacks

HAY FEEDING PANELS, IN USE

In Double Rows 3' Apart

As a Permanent Feeding Fence Next to Hay Mow

The Individual Panel, 10'-12' in Length

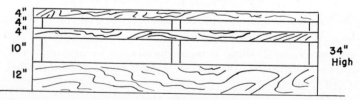

4"
4"
4"
10"
12"

34" High

Fig. 45.   The hay feeding panel has use at several different locations.

that hay can be reached. Such racks may be built in solidly at the barn. A supply of separate hay-feeding *panels* of this sort, however, may become quite valuable for use in feeding sheep hay on the range, instead of simply throwing the hay onto the ground. Very little time is needed for driving posts (steel preferably) and lining up two rows of these panels two to three feet apart on some piece of hard ground, and much hay will be saved.

The other type of rack often used and supposed to have advantages in terms of keeping leaves and stickers out of the sheeps' head

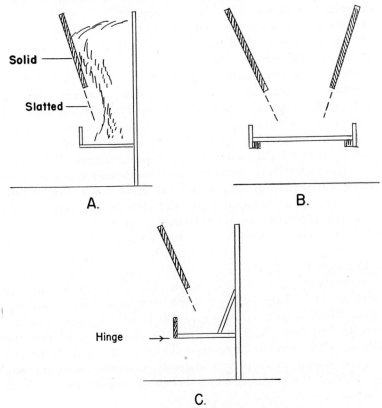

Fig. 46. Hay-wasting, slatted-panel, feeder designs.

and eyes generally are very troublesome to keep feeding, to say nothing of their added cost. Such racks are panels with upright (or vertical) slats spaced about 3-in. apart, the whole panel being slanted outward at the top or the back of the rack, away from the feeding side as shown in diagrams A, B, and C of Fig. 46.

Diagram A shows the rack slanted out toward the sheep, so that a solid board, high up, is necessary if leaves are to be saved or kept from falling into the fleece. If chopped hay is fed in such a rack, it will need constant attention to keep the hay in reach of the sheep, for they will eat it as shown. Also, long hay cannot adequately be fed in this rack as the narrow space between the slats prevents the ewes from getting their heads in far enough to reach more than a small amount of the hay supplied.

Similar slatted panels are used often in hayracks like that shown in B, where the sheep feed from two sides. All of these waste hay and are very difficult for sheep to use.

In the cross section shown in C it will be noted that *both* surfaces supporting chopped hay slant toward the 8-in. opening through which the sheep eat. The slanted side toward the sheep is solid and is supported at intervals of 6 ft by bracing not shown in the cross section. The forward side of the feeding trough is hinged so that it can be dropped and easily cleaned of accumulations of dirt and chaff. This rack is more usable but again too expensive. It is claimed that the edged floor of such a rack (as shown) will make it possible to use it as a combination hay *and grain* feeding rack but this is not true, generally. Successful feeding of grain demands a *clean* trough, and when combined with a heavy hayrack the grain trough is very difficult to clean. It must either be swept out, or the entire rack must be turned over.

As shown in our barn cross section (Fig. 58 Chap. 5) our *hay panels* are built along the edges of the haymow and are simply and quickly filled. If plenty of space (a full 12 in.) is allowed for the sheep to feed through, the panel may be 18 in. or more from the wall and all the hay can be reached. These panels should be braced by posts spaced at about 6-ft intervals. Concrete under the hay will prevent urine from soaking below it, causing the sheep to refuse it.

Salt troughs in the barn are very desirable. They will generally be built in solidly and permanently, but these items should be kept in mind in so doing: Half-ground salt is the type to use, and salt must be kept *fresh* and *clean* if it is to be consumed in sufficient quantities. Therefore protect the trough from rain and from being fouled by sheep jumping over it or lambs into it. It is advisable to construct the trough so that it can be lifted out of its supports and dumped. Diagrams are shown in Fig. 47.

Even these troughs are not foolproof. That is, they may become easily dirtied by sheep standing up in them on their fore feet or backing around to them and defecating into them. A very desirable trough that largely prevents this, also shown in Fig. 47, has a roof

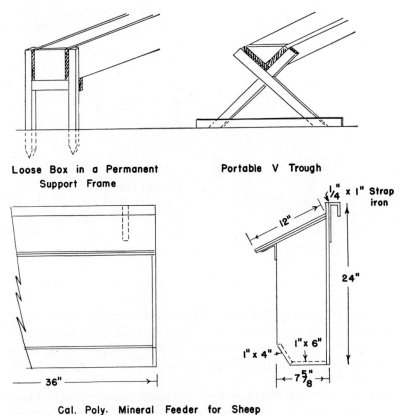

Loose Box in a Permanent Support Frame

Portable V Trough

Cal. Poly. Mineral Feeder for Sheep

Fig. 47. Salt troughs of varying design find use in different places.

and dimensions such that sheep can neither stand in it or back up to it.

A portable salt trough for use in the field is also shown in Fig. 47.

Grain feeding troughs may be needed at times for the ewe band and for rams and of course are essential for creep feeding lambs.

Various designs are suggested in about every bulletin or book published on sheep. Years of experience with nearly every kind imaginable has led the writer to one type as being most satisfactory. It is illustrated in Fig. 48. The advantages of this type of trough are that it can be dumped without tipping it all the way to the ground, it is relatively light and easily handled, it is of very sturdy

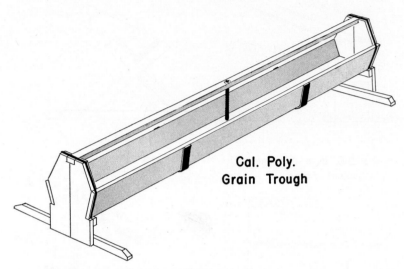

Cal. Poly.
Grain Trough

Fig. 48.   A sturdy grain trough such as this lasts a long time.

construction, not as likely to collapse as many other forms do, and the legs do not interfere with movement of the sheep in the manner that the "A" type of legs do. When lambs or sheeps are anxious to get to the grain they are often tripped by the A legs or suffer shoulder injuries.

A demountable trough is desirable when considerable numbers are needed and they are to be hauled frequently, as when a creep setup must be moved. The trough discussed above, with crossbar and solid legs, loads very poorly, a large truck being able to handle only a few, so the demountable type is preferable. In this trough the legs are removable and the crossbar can be set down into the trough; then the trough parts can be stacked solidly in a truck. See Fig. 49. In building such a trough the pattern *must be unvaried* for each trough so that any pair of legs can be used on any trough. Also, the small cleats on the trough sides between which the legs slip should be spaced a little wide for the legs as dirt or swelling due to dampness may cause the legs to stick or be difficult to fit.

Medical and Miscellaneous Equipment

A medicine chest in the lambing barn is an essential item, for certain remedies and implements are necessary if all the exigencies

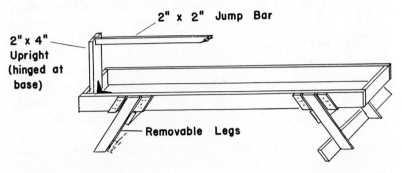

Fig. 49. A demountable grain trough simplifies the problem of hauling numbers of them.

of lambing are to be properly cared for. A list of items it should contain, and some discussion of their uses, follow.

Shears
Knife
Docking irons
Castrating and docking instruments (All-in-One, Elastrator, or Burdizzo)
Docking stove
Tweezers
Sheep dip
Iodine
"Cu-Nic" mixture (concentrate)
Phenothiazine
Needle and rawhide threads
Penicillin -G in oil
Mineral oil, light weight
Raw linseed oil

Branding irons
Scissors, straight edge, small
Hypodermic syringe
Dose syringe or dosing bottle
Nipples (goose bill)
Fly-repellent (turpentine-lard)
Argyrol
Sulfa pills (5-7 1/2 gr. tablets)
Shepherd's crook
Butter of antimony
Bluestone crystals
Ovine mixed bacterin
Dextrose
Bloat medicine
Scarletol

Sharp sheep shears head the list, to be used in clearing away wool wherever it causes trouble; for instance, about the ewe's udder when loaded with burs, about her tail or the lamb's rear quarters when soiled from feed and presenting a danger spot for fly maggot infestation, etc.

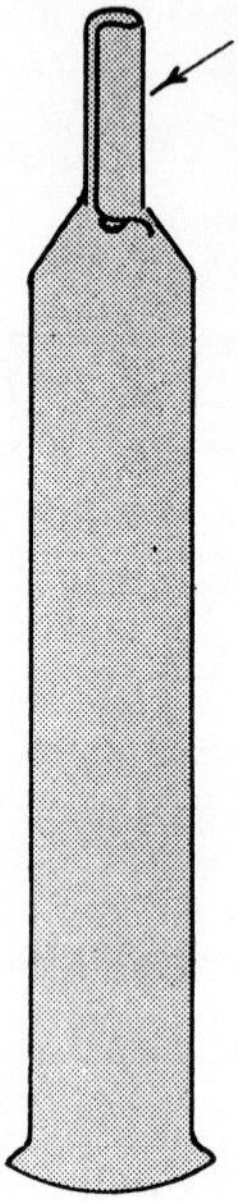

Excess length of spring can be cut off and a short portion rolled in.

Fig. 50. A docking iron made from a truck spring leaf holds the heat well. (Note shape of cutting edge.)

A sharp knife to skin dead lambs, to remove hides from dead ewes, to clip eyelids when they turn in and blind lambs.

Docking irons for "hot" removal of tails. (These are discussed in more detail in Chapter 8.

Castrating instruments such as the "Burdizzo," "All-in-One," or "Elastrator" may be considered desirable, though other methods are quicker (as discussed in Chapter 8).

Sheep dip is always usable and is needed for disinfecting purposes—mostly for killing maggots infesting wounds. Other materials are considered less injurious to tissues, but sheep dip, if used as directed, is satisfactory and cheap.

Iodine is considered desirable for use on a newborn lamb's umbilicus. However, this point must be kept in mind: Unless the iodine is applied rather soon after birth it does little good. Germs responsible for navel ill may enter the body through the cord very quickly, and about as many cases of navel ill have been seen where the cords were iodined as where not. It is of use on docking and castrating wounds too, especially where stiffness has caused trouble.

Fly-repellent. The writer's choice of many ointments he has used is a very simple one; namely, lard with enough turpentine stirred into it to give it an odor yet not to make it too thin. Again, here is a remedy easily made up and cheap. It is effective for several days and usable on screwworm and blowfly wounds or wounds likely to become so infested. When docking *late* in the spring when blowflies are about, a daub of this material on the tail stub and scrotum will effectively keep off flies until the wound is healed. BHC dip is also very effective.

Worm treatment or preventatives. These will be "Cu-Nic" mixture or its components (bluestone and "Black Leaf 40") or phenothiazine. These are discussed in more detail in Chapter 8.

Sacking needles and rawhide threads, the former obviously of use in sewing up wool sacks, the latter used with the needle in cases of eversion of the uterus. (Details of the operation are discussed in Chapter 6.)

Nipples of the "goose bill" variety will be needed to suckle "bummer" lambs or those whose dams for a time are not producing enough milk. Usually the holes in such nipples will need to be enlarged, either by cutting a slight piece out with a sharp penknife or by burning it out with a heated needle or nail.

A hypodermic syringe may find occasional use by a sheepman. Injections of ovine mixed bacterin have been found useful in combating certain cases of lamb stiffness, and occasion may arise for using hemorrhagic septicemia bacterin to prevent shipping fever, but these needs are not common. Disposable syringes are now provided with Penicillin G in oil and are frequently used in many infection cases.

A dose syringe or *long-necked dosing bottle* will come in handy when sheep need treatment for founder or bloat troubles, which happen all too often, especially among farm-flock animals.

Medicines (not all listed above) may include butter of antimony and bluestone crystals used in the treatment of contagious foot rot (as described later) and dextrose solution, calcium gluconate, and molasses—all valuable in the treatment or prevention of lambing paralysis.

"Scarletol" or red-colored mixtures of oils having similar trade names are very effective in hastening the healing of wounds such as dog bites.

A shepherd's crook is extremely useful, and once the art of handling it is mastered, it will save much crowding and effort in the handling of ewes and lambs. A word of caution at this point is in order: Be careful in catching a sheep by the hind leg to catch and pull directly from the rear; many ewes have been ruined by having their stifle joint displaced when they were caught with a hook and the leg was pulled out sideways. Also the hock joint is frequently badly injured by catching a sheep when it is running too fast.

Branding irons for sheep are often not made of iron and of course never use heat, but rather a branding fluid. Numbers or letters may be formed from metal, and the surface that stamps the sheep should generally be less than 1/4 in. in diamenter.

Very useful branding irons can be made from a section of a cedar post when an owner wishes to combine a letter and a circle or some similar form. The proposed combination is drawn at the butt end of

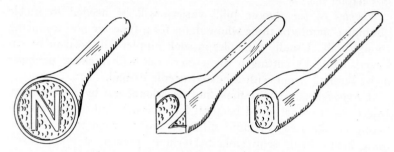

Fig. 51.   Wooden branding irons made at home.

the post (or a section thereof) and then, through the use of a brace and bit and a knife to cut away the portions not wanted for the brand, the form may be carved out. No letters, etc., should be narrower than 1/4 in. nor should they be drilled or carved out to stand up over 3/4 in.; otherwise they are too easily broken through rough handling. Back of the "brand" face, the wood will be carved (by draw shave and knife) into a handle as indicated in Fig. 51.

A blade grinding jig (commonly called a "hoot-nanny") is a useful piece of equipment that can easily be made and that will enable a sheepman to keep his blades properly ground and therefore sharp and usable.

This is a contrivance to which the blade is clamped to hold it on a grindstone so that an unvarying bevel grind will result. It is supplied with an arm having a metal prong at its tip which may be driven into a solid post or wall behind the grindstone, ensuring the unaltered bevel angle of the grind. (Blades should not be ground on a dry, fast-moving emery wheel as the high-carbon steel of the shears will not stand overheating.)

Figure 52 illustrates the features of the "hoot-nanny." It can be made fairly easily at home and will save many times its cost in lengthening the serviceable life of sheep shears.

Will creeps be needed? This question cannot be definitely answered in the affirmative, but it may be said that every type of sheep operator—farm flock, purebred, or range man—can use creeps to advantage. The degree of advantage will vary with years (grass growth) and may mean hundreds to thousands of dollars of dif-

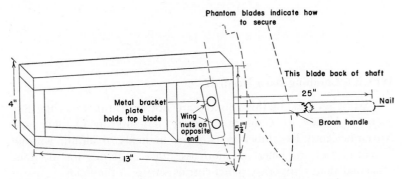

Fig. 52. The "hoot-nanny" helps to grind blades evenly.

ference one year and little or none another. However, their use is insurance and is in the some category as an extra tonnage of hay in the barn "just in case."

Creep panels need be nothing fancy or expensive and may be located inside a barn or shed if much precipitation is experienced during most of the lamb-growing months, or out in the fields if such is not so much the case.

Various designs of creeps and the technique in using them are discussed in Chapter 7 on Growing the Lamb.

Chapter 5

The Lambing Barn and Its Use

Why is a Lambing Barn Needed?

Most sections of this country are not as fortunate as the San Joaquin Valley of California, where lambing in October and November and December takes place in fields of alfalfa without benefit of roof and where no more assistance in getting the job done is needed than temporary panel corrals set up in the fields.

Because lambs must be dropped, at most locations, when weather is cold and wet (to make proper use of the native green feed which follows) barns, or protection of some sort, must be resorted to by most sheep owners.

In the previous chapter several of the parts of the barn were discussed. This chapter will consider them as a whole, in use, and suggest their proper utilization.

How Large Should the Barn be?

This question must be answered, with qualifications, for every different setup. The number of ewes owned, of course, the rate or speed with which they lamb, the variations in weather at different locations, etc., will affect the answer.

In order not to be too vague, the author has attempted to picture in the following pages a barn of a size suitable to the lambing of 500 ewes, a fair-sized farm flock. If more or fewer ewes are owned, increases or decreases in dimensions and facilities may be read into the descriptions that follow.

Feed storage, floor space, hay feeding space, etc., have been figured on the basis of 500 ewes that would lamb over a 2-month span of time.

What Special Facilities Might Be Included?

Shearing sheds (separate from the barn) are notoriously little-used structures, so in the interests of economy the author has placed this facility in the barn proper and used its space through the lamb-

Fig. 53. A separate shearing shed finds few days of use in the year.

ing time as extra jail space and through the summer months as storage space.

In order further to picture maximum use of the barn, a feeder-lamb feeding setup, making use of the lambing barn through the summer or fall months when otherwise it would be out of use, will be discussed.

While dry-lot feeding of lambs may not fit into the picture of every sheep owner, it would certainly seem judicious to make complete use of every facility an owner possesses, and often extra hay and grain is grown on sheep farms above the needs of the lambing ewe band. As labor, too, is often available in the summer and fall months which is not needed in tending the then "dry" ewes, it would seem advantageous to feed lambs.

What About Hay Storage?

The main item as far as labor is concerned in the barn will have to do with the placing and design of the hay storage area. Careful planning here before a barn is constructed will save many hours of heavy work in coming years.

Our barn plan (see accompanying diagrams) shows hay storage centrally located and surrounded closely by all the feeding racks needed. The drop bunch feeds on one side, the singles group on the opposite, and the jailed ewes at one (or both) ends of the hay storage. Thus no difficult or heavy carrying of hay is required and one man can do much more than feed.

How much hay will be needed may be figured roughly on the following bases:

1. If a ewe receives nothing but alfalfa hay, she will eat (and waste) about 6 lb of loose (long) hay daily. (Should she receive some grain or molasses, this amount would be reduced.)

2. In the drop band lambing system not over 150 ewes (of the total 500) will be confined at the barn, eating 6 lb daily, at one time. Some of these will have lambed but will be kept at the barn for a few days before being turned out to field. In other words, only about 150 ewes will likely be requiring 6 lb daily for the 2-month lambing period.

3. The other 350 ewes, during the 2-month lambing time, will either be awaiting their turn to spend about ten days in the drop corrals or will have been turned out from them with lambs. Since this season is a slow-growing time for grass, some field feeding of hay, which may be stored at the lambing barn, is usually required. An average-to-good figure for the hay that may have to be fed to these ewes as a supplement to grass intake would be 2 lb per head daily.

4. *An emergency or reserve supply of hay* of 200 lb per ewe is considered good insurance and should be kept in reserve for years when weather conditions are extreme when the sheep may have to be fed for longer than the 2-month lambing time. This reserve may not need to be stored in the lambing barn.

How much hay storage space is needed?

5. The hay needed for the dry-lot lamb feeding mentioned above need not necessarily be stored in the barn as it will be used (in our setup) during dry months. Although hay will be fed those lambs in the barn facilities, space for the total amount they require need not be provided for in the haymow. They will be fed from the hay stored in the mow but the amount they consume will be replenished

Fig. 54. Emergency hay supply is good insurance.

from hay stacked outside and put into it following sale of the fed lambs and before the barn is put into use for the lambing ewes. The hay storage space needed can readily be figured according to the needs of the ewes and the space per ton required for hay.

If chopped hay is to be used, a ton (settled) will require less than one-half the cubic space needed for a ton of loose hay. Roughly, a 6 ft cube of chopped hay and an 8 ft cube of loose hay each weigh a ton. These cubes, respectively, contain 216 and 512 cu ft. If baled hay is to be stored, it will require space somewhat between these two amounts.

Using the hay consumption figures given above, we can estimate that the 150 ewes at the barn, using 6 lb daily for 60 days, would consume 27 tons, and the 350 ewes (in the fields), using 2 lb daily, would eat 21 tons in 60 days. This would total 48 tons. The reserve supply of 200 lb per ewe is another 50 tons (for 500 ewes). If the reserve is to be kept in the lambing barn (which is perhaps proper, considering the feeding facilities there), the barn must be large enough to hold approximately 98 tons. On the other hand, it may be

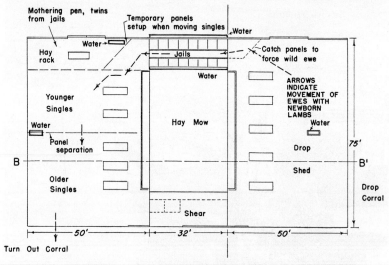

Fig. 55. Plan of complete combination barn.

more desirable to store the reserve in a separate hay shelter or stack in the open. In the event that the reserve had to be used, it certainly would be used in late season and would probably be fed to the ewes (with their lambs) out in the fields rather than at the barn.

In the particular barn diagrammed here, the author considers that *the reserve will not be stored in the lambing barn*, so that the capacity need will be for only 48 tons of hay (for a 2-month period). This amount would increase to 72 tons in another month.

The *width* of the hay storage space should not be more than 30 to 40 ft (the former preferable) if the job of feeding the hay is to be reasonably easy. Hay will be stacked from the ground level in the central portion (see Fig. 58) and will be stacked overhead at each end of the barn (above the jails at one end and above the shearing section and emergency jail section at the other).

If the central portion is 30 ft wide and 50 ft long and the hay is stacked (settled) 20 ft deep this portion will have a capacity of 30,000 cu ft and will hold about 140 tons of settled chopped hay or 70 tons of settled loose hay. If the sections over the jails and shearing areas could be stacked 10 ft deep, their combined capacity would be 35 tons of chopped or 17 tons of loose hay. Thus a barn having a central hay area such as diagrammed would hold 175 tons of

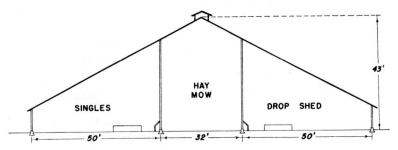

Fig. 56. Cross section of barn through BB'.

chopped hay or 87 tons of loose hay. These dimensions, then, would allow ample storage, in terms of loose hay, and almost double the hay normally required in terms of chopped hay.

Incidentally, although chopped hay has many advantages for sheep feeding and is certainly economical, it has the disadvantage of being difficult to move, so that the reserve should probably be thought of in terms of loose or of baled hay.

Though the dimensions given above would perhaps indicate a barn larger than necessary (to take care of hay needs), they are perhaps necessary in terms of sheep space required.

How Much Feeding Space Will Be Needed?

If 150 ewes (of the 500) is the maximum number in the drop bunch, they will all need to be fed on one side of the barn for only a *few days*, as the lambing program will be to remove ewes with

newborn singles from the drop group to the opposite side of the barn
as they are dropped. Twins will be put into the jails.

Hay feeding panels set up 3 ft out from the 50 ft of haymow will
not provide sufficient lineal footage for every one of the 150 ewes
to feed at one time, and *extra bunks* may need to be provided. Each
"heavy" ewe requires a minimum of 12 in. of space and probably,

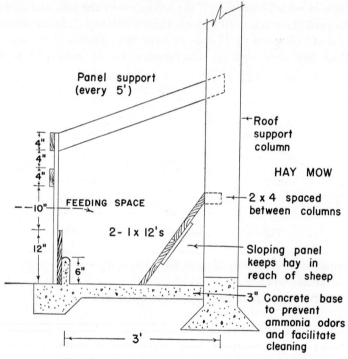

Panel support
(every 5')

4"
4"
4"

Roof
support
column

HAY MOW

10"
FEEDING SPACE

2 x 4 spaced
between columns

2- I x I2's

12"

6"

Sloping panel
keeps hay in
reach of sheep

3" Concrete base
to prevent
ammonia odors
and facilitate
cleaning

3'

Fig. 57.   Cross section of hay feeding bunk.

for larger ewes, 16 in. or more. However, if reasonable care is taken
to keep the bunks full and turned over occasionally so that the feeding becomes pretty much "self-feeding," the 150 ewes could do well
with perhaps less than 1 ft of space for each. The extra 100-ft space
can be provided cheaply by placing *lightweight 10-ft racks* at right
angles to the haymow (as shown in Fig. 55). These racks should be
simple in design like that indicated for the panels along the mow.
If these bunks are set out 4 ft from the mow feeding panels and are

10 ft long and 3 ft wide, five of them may be spaced far enough apart to allow the ewes to move easily around them and will provide about 120 ft more space. This, in combination with the mow panels, should be sufficient to meet any needs of the drop bunch.

These hay bunks should be built solidly and provided with a wooden floor. If not over panel-height, they may easily be pulled aside when the time comes to clean out the manure from the barn floor areas.

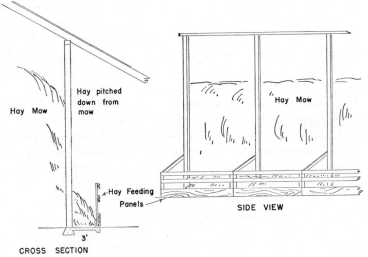

Fig. 58. Views of hay feeding at the mow.

A desirable feature of any permanent hay feeding bunk such as the setup along the length of the mow would be a concrete base to prevent urine from soaking in under the hay. This feature is indicated in the detail diagram for the haymow feeding racks. The base should be built with a 3-in. thick curb at the front extending about 6 in. above the level of the floor. A cross section of this feature is shown in Figs. 57 and 58.

Feeding hay to the jails is made easy because the jails are located close to the mow. However, the hay must be dropped through a chute to the 3-ft alley that runs between the two rows of jails and then must be distributed to the hayracks located between alternate jails (each feeding two ewes). The hay chutes extend 10 ft above the level of the jail area ceiling and, when the haymow level is at top height, receive hay through the open upper end. As the hay level drops, a door at the 5-ft level can be opened to receive the hay. The chute is 3 ft square.

What Spaces Will Be Needed for Lambing?

As stated previously, three or four separate areas in the barn will be used for different purposes in the lambing operation.

After the "heavy" ewes have been bagged out to make up the drop bunch, they will be kept on one side of the barn (the drop area) until they lamb. There they will receive hay. Usually such ewes are not fed grain, but if any history of lambing paralysis has been experienced in past years it should be fed or a vat of molasses should be made available to the ewes.

The *"drop shed"*, for most regions, will not be a closed structure, but will simply be roofed and perhaps solidly boarded only on the side of prevailing winds or rain. The roofed area may be paneled off or be entirely open to the drop corral. This corral should preferably be sloped away from the barn proper and have some natural protection in terms of trees or large rocks. Figure 55 indicates the entire plan for barn and corrals. Figures 59 and 61 are views of the jail end and the shearing end, respectively.

The *drop shed* dimensions are 50 by 75 ft, or 3750 sq ft of floor space. This, in terms of space per ewe, amounts to 25 sq ft, more than doubly ample. However, in the event of extreme weather for a short period, extra space may become extremely important and a minimum of 10 sq ft per ewe and lamb is probably desirable. With this contingency in mind, the drop area and the singles area will total 7,500 sq ft and provide 15 sq ft for each ewe in the band of 500.

How Will the Newborn Lambs Be Handled?

Much of the work attending lambing has been discussed in the previous chapter. However, the movement of sheep in the lambing barn may be of interest and value, and a few instructions can save much labor.

The ewe with a strong single lamb is to be moved from the dro**p**

side to the opposite side of the barn and into a part of it set aside
for the younger lambs. She will go across (under control) through
the alleyway between the jails. This is under roof and should present
no problem except in the case of a pretty wild ewe. For her, temporary panels should be in place at the *entry to the alleyway* to *hold*

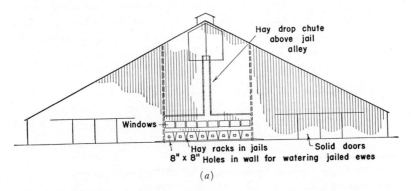

(*a*)

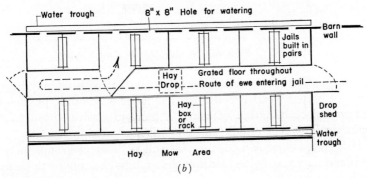

(*b*)

Fig. 59. (*a*) Jail end of barn.
(*b*) Jail section detail indicates how to handle entering ewes easily.

her and force her into this narrow passage. These panels are indicated in Fig. 55.

The ewe with twins or a ewe whose single is dead or one that
shows any sort of trouble or uncertainty about the mothering of her
lamb should be taken into the jails.

Jail gates should be the full 4 ft in width so that when they are
swung across the alley they will block it and cause the entrance of
the ewe to the jail. Also, as stated in Chapter 4, they should be

hinged from a corner of the jail so that the ewe, advancing up the alley, will go to the end of it, turn around, and run back into the jail. This works much better than to have to push the ewe into the jail from the entry end. Once in the jail, the ewe with twins must be fed and watered well to keep up her flow of milk. The best watering setup is as described in the previous chapter—outside the jails. Eight-inch square holes in the barn wall through which the ewe can get water from open troughs will help keep it clean and fresh. Hay for the jails is dropped from the loft through the chute above the alley and then distributed to the hayracks (or boxes, if chopped) located between alternate jails.

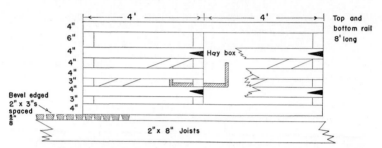

Fig. 60.   Details of a double jail on slatted floor.

The flooring of the jail either is simply the earth or may be an elevated grated wooden platform. The latter is certainly preferable in terms of cleaning but of course is more expensive to build and maintain. This type of jail (and floor) is illustrated in Fig. 60.

If a grated floor is used, the jails will be built in groups of two and then may readily be lifted off the grating and moved to permit raising the sections of grating for cleaning beneath them.

Also, as stated previously, this type of jail lends itself best to the using of chopped hay, which will readily drop through the slats if any is spilled or thrown out, whereas long hay may bring about a buildup of manure, even on the slats.

One other item (if a slatted floor area is used) is that a rise of about one foot will be necessary, and a ramp must be built up from the drop area to that height, or a pit a foot deep must be excavated to receive the droppings.

The sections indicated in Fig. 55 as being for "younger singles" and "older singles" are separated only by panels, but these should be constructed so that small lambs cannot go through them. A trough should be placed in this dividing fence to provide water for each group and should have a board across its length and above it to prevent ewes from jumping across the trough.

Lambs will remain in the "older singles" pen until they have smoothed up (fattened). This may require a week, but heavy lambing and too much congestion resulting therefrom in the "younger singles" pen may force them out sooner.

The section indicated in Fig. 55 for "mothering up" the twins is an essential and valuable area. Lambs that have been confined in the jails with only their own mother need a day or so of contact with a few other ewes (and their lambs) before being turned into a large group or out into the fields.

Should more jail space be needed than is indicated (16 jails), the shearing end of the barn can pretty readily be fitted with extra jails (especially if they are of the portable type, in pairs, as illustrated in Fig. 60.)

If a larger band of sheep than the 500 used to ilustrate this barn is being lambed, it is still undesirable to widen the central (haymow) section simply to have more space at the end of the mow to provide more jails. Extra jails may be built in the same line, but out into the drop and singles areas along the back wall of the barn.

In the author's experience where 2,000 ewes were lambed at one location, 80 jails were used and were usually filled through the lambing period, mostly with ewes with twins. It was the practice to keep such ewes and lambs in the jails 6 to 7 days. This particular band of sheep were heavy twinners.

Of What Should the Shearing Setup Consist?

The shearing section of this barn is designed for the use of only two men, about the right-sized crew for as few as 500 ewes or for shearing the 1,000 head of feeder lambs in the summer or fall.

It is not provided with the counting pens that are customary with larger shearing outfits, but these could readily be arranged by means of panels if they were deemed necessary.

The plan of the shearing end of the barn is indicated in Fig. 55 and in more detail in Fig. 65.

Previous to running the wooly sheep into the shearing pens, they must be separated, in the spring, from their lambs, so *a dodge chute and accompanying corrals* must be provided. The shearing process is described in Chapter 10, and plans showing essential parts of the shearing setup are diagrammed there as for a separate shearing shed setup.

The *placing of the dodge chute* in relation to the shearing setup for this barn should be such that the control into which *the wooly*

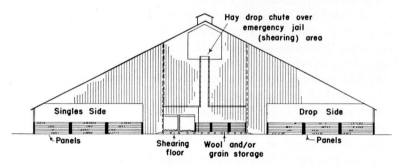

Fig. 61. Shearing end of the barn.

sheep are sorted will lead immediately therefrom into the alley to the holding pens for shearing, and the corral or area into which *the lambs* are separated will lead easily to the point where the ewes are turned loose by the shearer. There, ewes and lambs will be reunited. No dodge chute should lead *immediately* into the lead-in alley but rather to a good-sized corral or pen.

More than one location for the chute could be used. Figure 65 illustrates one with the chute inside the barn, under the roof but at the edge where there would be sufficient light. This location affords a movement through the chute *from dark to light,* which is desirable, and also is shaded to overcome dust glare in sunlight that might cause sheep to stop moving. The *roof edge* should be 8 to 10 ft off the ground.

A dodge chute through which sheep will move easily is the result of building into it many clever features. Some of these are indicated in the diagram of the shearing section of this barn. Others are listed and discussed below.

1. The chuteway itself should be the *right width.* If it is over 18

Don Tomlin

Fig. 62. Carrying newborn lambs by the front legs is usual.

Don Tomlin

Fig. 63. "Mothering up" a small bunch in the fields.

in. wide, small sheep will have more of a tendency to stop and attempt to turn around. If too narrow, of course large, wooly ewes may have trouble pushing through. If it becomes necessary to separate a group of lambs, the 18-in. width of the permanent chuteway can be narrowed down toward the gate temporarily by the insertion of a 10-ft panel inside it. At the gate end a 4-in.-square block may be placed between the chute side and the panel to hold it out and narrow the passageway.

2. The chuteway and the forcing area for 10 to 20 ft ahead of the chute should be *solidly boarded* so that sheep moving through cannot see other sheep, already through, moving in an opposite direction. Everything should be planned to focus the attention of

the sheep on the exit at the far end of the chute. Naturally all posts should be on the outside of the chute.

3. *A cleated board floor* made of 1-in. lumber (which will re-sound the clatter of moving feet better than heavier lumber) will help draw the attention of following sheep to the escapeway up the chute. The boards will also prevent dust that might be stirred up otherwise.

4. A particular point at the chute that causes stops in movement of sheep is at the entrance where the flared guide panel meets the chute proper. Often two sheep attempt to enter the chute at the

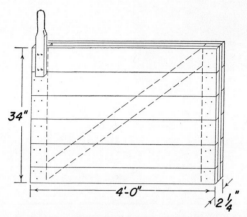

Fig. 64.   The dodge gate should be long, smooth-sided (braced inside).

same time and become jammed. A sharp-edged, small, short post, with its upper end 14 in. above the ground level, placed at this juncture will cause one of the two jammed sheep to jump up (to prevent the post from gouging into her breast) and break the jam.

5. *The chute should not be too high.* Not over 30 to 34 in. is correct because, if the chute is higher, a man tending the movement of sheep down the chute has difficulty in reaching in to "tail" a stopped sheep.

6. *The chute should be sufficiently long.* Twenty feet is about right as this allows six to eight sheep in the chute at one time, so that it is quite difficult for a sheep to back out quickly if startled to a stop. Also the man at the gate often needs to see back some distance

to spot ear marks or lambs of varying condition which he will dodge out.

7. *The dodge gate should be placed in line with one side of the chute.* This will allow a clear view ahead for sheep as they move up the chute.

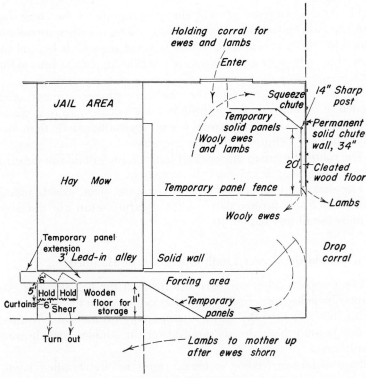

Fig. 65. Portion of barn showing position of dodge chute and means of entry to shearing section.

8. *The gate should be lightweight, solid, and long.* Too short a gate is likely to cause injuries to sheep traveling at a fast rate down the chute and turning too quickly at the gate as a result. Especially is this true if the *brace* on the gate is on the *outside* rather than *inside* of two smooth surfaces. The gate should be 4 ft long (see Fig. 64).

9. The gate should be hinged strongly and should ride clear of

the ground as it must be moved quickly if movement of the sheep is not to be impeded.

10. If the dodge chute is out in the open, it should face north and south so that when it is used in early morning or late afternoon there will not be sunlight directly down the chute into the eyes of the sheep.

11. Any corral fence at right angles to the line of the chute and past the gate end of the chute, forming a part of either corral into which the sheep are dodged, should be more than 10 ft beyond the gate. This will help give the sheep a feeling of escape into a free area.

12. *Extra gates put into the chuteway proper* are not often needed in a commercial enterprise but are suited more to commission yards and such enclosures where separating more than two ways with one "chuting" may be desirable.

The route of a group of ewes and lambs brought into the shearing area in the spring is indicated by arrows in Fig. 65.

The shearing floor, holding pens, count-out pens, and branding chute which are further parts of the shearin setup are discussed in more detail in Chapter 10.

How Should the Feeder Lamb Operation Be Handled?

The complete all-in-one barn described at the beginning of this chapter includes the necessary items for feeding grain to 1,000 lambs. Figure 66 indicates the further temporary, or movable, features needed beyond those already supplied for the lambing and shearing operations.

Because farmer feeding is usually most profitable when home-grown grains and hays can be used and when the owner's labor can be utilized more fully, this feeding setup is designed for feeding whole grains by hand twice daily rather than feeding an all-in-one mix of chopped hay, grain, and molasses, which is common in larger sheep feeding layouts and requires considerable expensive mixing equipment.

No attempt will be made here to discuss the economies of dry-lot lamb feeding, but the barn arrangements for this operation are included for the sheep farmer who may wish to engage in the practice.

One thousand lambs can be fed pretty easily by one person if hay and grain feeding facilities are at all adequate. It is generally considered proper not to require more than 250 head in one group to line up at grain troughs twice a day for concentrates. Therefore the barn areas on each side of the haymow are divided equally by paneling, providing four pens each holding 250 lambs. The floor

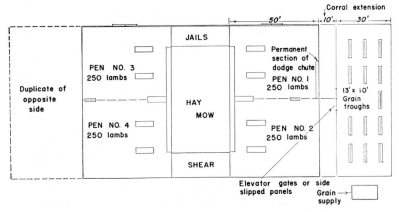

Fig. 66. Additional grain feeding corral for lamb fattening project.

Fig. 66A. Farmer feeding of thin lambs in the fall can add to income.

space *under roof* in this barn is therefore about 7 1/2 sq ft per lamb, which is ample.

Each group of 250 lambs will have a length of 37 ft along the haymow rack plus about 60 ft of space at two and a half of the 10-ft hay bunks. This amounts to only about 100 lineal feet of hay-rack space for 250 lambs, therefore the racks must be filled frequently and turned so that the hay becomes practically self-feeding.

The grain feeding area is shown as an added corral enclosure outside of the barn, one corral being used to feed two groups of 250 at each side of the barn. If the grain is stacked (in sacks) close to this enclosure, a fairly simple operation of graining can result. The procedure would be to put out the grain, turn in pen No. 1, and while they eat go to the other side of the barn and feed pen No. 3. By the time the latter had been fed, pen No. 1 would be ready to be returned to their shed, and pen No. 2 could then be grained and turned in. Then Pen 3 would have finished eating, and Pen 4 could be fed.

The arrangement of the grain troughs and of entry gates to the grain feeding enclosure should be carefully planned so that all the lambs can get quickly to the troughs and so that each one can get his share of grain.

Figure 66 shows a large clear space just inside the enclosure from the entry gates and plenty of space between the rows of grain troughs so that lambs will be able to pass others already starting to eat at the nearest troughs.

Another important item in the grain feeding corral is the design of the grain troughs themselves. A good grain trough has the following attributes:

1. It is sturdily built to withstand tipping (for cleaning) and pushing by the sheep.
2. It can be tipped over easily for cleaning.
3. It has no protruding parts that would injure lambs crowding up for feed.

Such a trough is shown in Fig. 48 in Chapter 4 and has been very successfully used.

Chapter 6

Lambing Time

If adequate facilities and preparations have been made, the job of lambing, important as it is, becomes no drudgery but a busy, pleasant task. It will demand 24-hr attention to the drop band in the heaviest time, but the satisfaction of saving lambs, sending every ewe into the fields with a strong lamb, and doing so without undue trouble and worry is very gratifying.

Regardless of whether lambing is done with the help of a barn as adequate as that described in Chapter 5 or is done out in the open, the herder will find that he has much the same tasks to perform. Ewes will have troubles giving birth to their young, lambs will stray and need to be brought back to their dams, some will suffer from exposure and need to be protected, others will lose their mothers by death and need to be forced onto another ewe or raised on a bottle.

How Should the "Drop" be Handled?

The "drop band" of heavy ewes, gathered as described in Chapter 3, is the immediate concern of the lamber or shepherd. Proper handling and preparation for lambing will facilitate operations and cut down the drudgery greatly.

The drop band is handled in various ways. It may be corralled in the open at night and turned out into a lambing pasture during the day. It may be corralled around a barn, fed hay and perhaps grain and not turned out to any pasture until it has lambed; Or it may never be corralled, but simply lamb on pasture (or more

127

properly "range" in this case) and move to new bed ground each
night, leaving the "drop" behind to be grouped up later.

The first case (where the drop bunch is corralled in the open at
night without benefit of barn shelter) is more or less confined to
lambing in fair weather if high percentages of lambs are to be
saved. Ewes that lamb during the daytime will be brought to sheds

Fig. 67.   Lambing in the open is ideal, weather permitting.

or barns if protection seems needed, or simply slipped over into the
next field. The heavy ewes are corralled at night, and preferably
such a corral should be located in a naturally protected area that
is well drained. Large rocks, brush, or trees in the corral will provide some protection and save lambs if a storm should come up.

Most of these corrals are not tended at night as they are usually
located away from the herders' quarters or the owner's home. However, many lambs may be saved by "fitting up" such a corral so that,
at least when the ewes are lambing most heavily, some night atten-

tion may be given them. If such a corral may be looked over as late as ten o'clock at night and be reached at daylight, many lambs may be saved. Lights flooding the corral all night are helpful. If electricity is not available, bright-burning gas lanterns are very effective. A row of jails set up in the corrals, preferably with a shed roof over them, will save many lambs and make it possible for the lamber greatly to cut down the mixups on a night of heavy drop. If such pens cannot be provided, the drop must in some way be segregated in the morning *before* the ewes that have not lambed are turned out. The tendency for *all* the ewes corralled overnight is to head for the gate, lambs or no, when it is opened in the morning, and often a ewe that has lambed will slip out, leaving her lamb behind (perhaps returning to hunt it up later), or a lamb will follow a ewe out that is not its mother. If such a lamb is a twin and it is not discovered for some time, its own mother may not claim it when it is returned to her, and therefore it will die or become a bummer.

Another common occurrence in the drop corral is for a ewe approaching lambing to attempt to steal away a fresh lamb from another ewe, and often she succeeds, especially if it is a twin. Thus if she gives birth to twins, she may end up with three.

These are common trials the lambers experience, and often, especially when they have not arrived at the corral until late in the morning, the mixups are such that a good part of the day is consumed in straightening them out, and the likelihood of having to jail ewes to make them claim lambs and of ending up with several "bummers" is greatly increased.

The procedure upon arrival at the corral in the morning to clear the drop will be about as follows. The ewes should be looked over for any in immediate need of help: a "stuck" lamb, a ewe on her back, one just producing her lamb. After these are helped, twins should be gathered. If jails or small pens are not available, each pair of twins should be tied together while the remainder of the band is looked after and until the ewes are turned out. Some lambers carry several lengths of sisal twine about 4 ft long, knotted about their waists, with which to tie up the twins as they sort out each pair. (It is often true that a ewe, seeming to have only a single, is really the mother of another lamb that has strayed from her or has been stolen by another ewe. Such lambs are the hard ones to mother up and the ones that cause most of the difficulty in clearing the drop corral.) Division of the corral into sections will help cut down mixups.

Perhaps a better type of tie is a shorter piece of sisal twine or 1/4-in. rope (about 14 in. long), knotted at each end after a piece of leather to be used as a clamp about each of the lamb's legs has been fitted to it. This tie is diagrammed in Fig. 68. The shorter

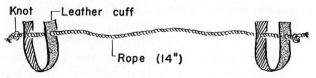

Fig. 68. Twin ties may be fancier than a simple cord.

length makes it less possible for a pair of twins tied together to get on opposite sides of their mother when she lies down and to be injured as she gets up with the rope over her back. This tie is more suitable for use for twins lambed on bed grounds on the range

Fig. 69. Tying twins together temporarily helps to clear the drop corral quickly.

where it may be desirable to leave them tied all day for one or more days. Twins so coupled are tied just above the hoof on the left front leg of one and the right front leg of the other. After the twins are tied and abnormal births have been attended to, the gate is opened and the ewes that have not lambed are allowed to move out. The herder must stand inside the gate and turn back any lamb that attempts to follow the ewes (they are easily attracted by any moving object) or any ewe that has newly lambed. This is sometimes a difficult task.

After the drop bunch is well away from the corral, the lambed ewes may be moved out to other close-by pastures—the singles and the twins being put in separate pastures. Of course there will be many lambs not well enough "mothered" to turn out with the others, and they will have to be taken to sheds, barns, or jails located centrally (if none are available at the corral).

Many real young lambs must be carried short distances by hand and at the same time their mothers must be attracted along with them. Most ewes cause no trouble during this move, but "wild" ewes and some yearlings or first-lambers will need to be handled expertly. The easiest way to carry the lamb is by its front legs, grasping them just above the ankles. Then the lamb will hang rather close to the ground as the shepherd moves along, and if he

Fig. 70. Moving a newborn lamb. The natural position helps reassure its mother.

makes small "bleating" noises like those of a baby lamb, usually the ewe will follow easily. It is good practice to keep one eye *very closely* on the ewe. If she shows any inclination to turn back, the lamb should *immediately* be placed on the ground on its four feet and the ewe be allowed to smell and nuzzle it before it is moved a short distance again.

Some ewes are so wild that further measures must be taken to entice them to move. One means is not to pick the lamb up, but to grasp it at its loin and drag it along backward, so that it will face the ewe at all times. Sometimes this nearness of the shepherd to the lamb is disturbing to the ewe, and the lamb must be pulled along supported by the crook of a shepherd's hook caught under its breast.

When Does a Ewe Need Help with Lambing?

Realization of what is happening and knowing what to do when a ewe shows signs of giving birth to her lamb may mean the saving of a considerable percentage of the ewes in the band or of their lambs.

Most herders or lambers do not believe in letting a ewe strain for hours before investigating her to determine the position of the lamb. If she has passed the first "water bag" and does not within a half hour or less give birth to her young, she should be caught, thrown, and examined.

The normal position of a lamb at birth is right side up (that is, its backbone toward the back of the ewe), and the nose should be presented first, with the toes of both front feet alongside. Many lambs will be presented differently and demand various modes of handling to be born successfully. The more common variations are discussed under the six paragraphs following:

1. Often a *big-headed and big-shouldered lamb* presented properly (front feet alongside his nose) cannot be ejected easily by the ewe, even by a strong, fat one. Thin, old, or weak ewes many times will need help. In this case, one leg at a time should be stretched out and then both pulled together by one hand, while the first two fingers of the other hand are slipped up the lamb's forehead and in back of its ears, stretching the lips of the vulva. This method may require considerable strength but usually will slip the lamb out. It is a good practice to let the ewe expel the lamb once its shoulders are out, or at least to pull it out *slowly* and then place it immediately at her head where she can clean it. If she is not inclined immediately to clean and recognize it, forcing her muzzle into the warm lamb will start her.

In pulling a big-shouldered lamb it will be found much easier to pull to the left or right of a straight pull. A straight pull places the two shoulder blades exactly opposite each other and at their widest, so that they must be squeezed severely to allow them to enter and pass through the pelvic girdle. By bending and twisting the lamb, as the pull is made, the shoulder-blade positions will be altered so that they can pass through more easily.

2. The next most common cause of trouble is when *one front leg is turned backward*, the other presented properly alongside the lamb's nose. If the lamb can be pulled with the one leg back without too much force being put upon the other leg and the neck, it should come in that manner. If a tentative pull indicates that the pull required to remove the lamb will be too strong, place a soft

string noose about the ankle of the foot presented and push the lamb back only as far as is necessary to slide the hand down the lamb's neck, hook a finger under the other leg, and straighten it out. Then usually the lamb can be born.

It often happens that as the lamb is pushed back into the ewe in order to catch the other leg, the head drops out of the pelvic girdle and getting it started right again becomes very difficult. Getting the head started into the pelvis again is very difficult (see paragraph 4, below).

3. *Both legs back and head alone presented* is a common case. Often when this occurs and the ewe is not discovered immediately, the head is badly swollen by the time the lamber arrives and it seems impossible to push the swollen head back into the womb. However, it can be done with a little strength and patience. Raw linseed or light mineral oil worked in onto the wall of the vagina will assist. If help is available, the ewe's rear should be elevated. Then by pushing steadily for perhaps a minute or more against the ewe's straining, the head can be made to go in. Next, letting the ewe rest on her side, the hand can be slipped down the lamb's neck to bring the front legs into proper presentation to allow birth. Usually the pelvis has been well dilated by what has previously occurred and the lamb comes easily.

4. Perhaps the most difficult operation of all occurs when the *legs are presented but the head is twisted back* along the lamb's ribs or down between its legs. With the legs extended through the pelvic girdle, it is next to impossible many times to straighten out the neck and get the head to pass through. If it starts through and a pull is made on the legs, the usual occurrence is that the head slips back into its original position (or down toward the ewe's udder), and persistent but unsuccessful attempts get more and more irksome. In this case string nooses should be slipped over each ankle and the legs should be folded back into the womb—of course making sure enough string protrudes. Then, with the lamb's shoulders no longer in the way at the inner mouth of the pelvic girdle, it is possible to draw the head up into the pelvis within the palm of the hand and to bring the front legs along by pulling on the strings.

To assist in drawing the head out, if it cannot be guided in the palm of the hand, a piece of baling wire will be very useful. This wire should preferably be rather heavy and of course unrusted. Bend a length of wire at its middle and form a noose a little bigger than will slip over the head of the foetus, twisting the wire to form such a loop. This noose may then be carried into the uterus (in the palm) and fitted over the lamb's head with the twisted part under the lamb's chin and the loop in back of the lamb's ears. Then, when the front legs are pulled by the strings, the head will be guided, chin up, into the pelvis by pulling on the wire. Care should be exercised in fitting the noose over the lamb's head. Be sure, before pull-

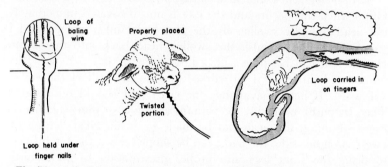

Fig. 71. A baling wire noose can often be used to assist the birth of a lamb.

ing, that it has not caught a fold of the uterine wall, for this might cause rupture of the uterus and loss of the ewe. The wire should be resorted to immediately if it is found at all difficult to guide the head into the pelvis.

Some lambs are so large in relation to the pelvic passageway that even this method of guiding the forepart of the lamb cannot effect a birth. The combination of the large chest, the large head, and the straightened-out front legs of the lamb is too much. It is then necessary to turn the lamb around inside the uterus and to remove it, tail first (or hind legs first). This is usually quite possible although it is sometimes difficult to turn the lamb. Assistants may raise the rear end of the ewe to allow the operator to find and secure the hind legs.

The removal of a lamb by such an operation should be followed by an injection of penicillin for the ewe unless the operator is sure that no serious abrasion or tearing of the uterine wall has occurred.

It is most important that an early decision be made about the probable eventual manner of removal of the lamb, and that entering of the vaginal tract, which destroys natural lubrication and tears the uterine wall, be held to a minimum.

5. Sometimes *only the tail is presented.* In this case, it is often advised that the lamb should not be pulled hind-legs-first but that an attempt should be made to turn the lamb around and get its front legs and head presented. This sounds easier than it is, so it is

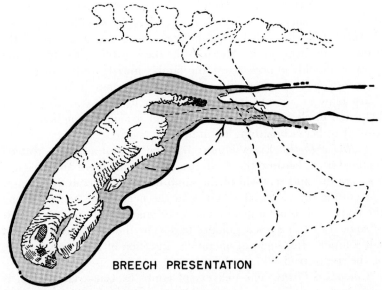

BREECH PRESENTATION

Fig. 72. Breech birth is generally preferred to turning the foetus.

generally agreed that pulling the lamb hind-legs-first is safer. Usually the attempt to turn the lamb involves running the arm into the ewe above the elbow, causing considerable danger of badly scratching or even puncturing the uterus and consequent death of the ewe from blood poisoning.

6. Other presentations sometimes encountered are *ribs first*, the lamb just twisted sideways. The experienced lamber can generally spot such a trouble, but the inexperienced, because there is *no external indication* of the imminence of lambing (such as a foot or tail protruding, or any fluids) may allow the ewe to go so long that

the lamb dies inside her and her own life may be jeopardized. The only indication of the need for help will be that the ewe is uneasy or has been attempting to produce the lamb over a long period. It is true that sometimes a ewe may have strained so long that she simply gives up and stands around in a listless manner. The unobserving shepherd may miss her trouble entirely. As mentioned previously, any ewe seen straining for half an hour should be caught and examined as to the position of the lamb.

Start of Breathing. Often a lamb pulled rather than born naturally (and sometimes even then) will not start breathing. The lamber then should shock the process into a start by slapping the lamb sharply on its ribs as it lies on its side or by lifting it a foot off the ground and dropping it. Also to assist the breathing, the fluids and mucous should be pressed off the lamb's muzzle and nostrils, and its mouth should be opened and the mucous removed. Sometimes a sharp blow of air into its mouth to clear its throat is effective. It helps too to elevate the lamb's head and straighten out its neck to assist it to begin breathing naturally.

Stillborn Births. Every lamber has had to pull a dead, "rotten" foetus. Often, because the fluids are missing, the lamb and passageway are dry and removal of the lamb demands forcibly pulling off (or cutting off) a leg at a time and the head, and then removing the body. This is not a pleasant task and may require pliers or hooks or some sort. It is a good practice to douche the uterus with a warm salt solution after such an operation. Insertion of a uterine capsule, or the use of penicillin, is also advisable.

Caesarian Births. The delivery of lambs by Caesarian section is possible, but owners of commercial ewes are very unlikely to resort to this method because of the cost of hiring the job done by a veterinarian. In the author's experience Caesarian operations on valuable purebred ewes saved the ewes but required a long period of sulfa-drug or penicillin medication to prevent death from possible infection. The use of the *loop of wire* around the head of a big lamb, or a forced-breech birth, should generally obviate the need for a Caesarian operation.

In several instances, when extreme difficulty was being experienced in extracting lambs from aged ewes, they have been killed and immediately opened through the belly wall—a crude Caesarian process that has saved the lamb. It is certainly better to save at least the lamb than to let a ewe die with the lamb in a position preventing birth.

Always feel inside the womb for other lambs after a single lamb has been manually extracted (there may be triplets).

Abnormal lambs, such as dwarfs or those having extremely bowed front legs, stiff necks, very low backs, or bad jaws, are frequently born normally. It is certainly better to destroy such lambs, put their hides onto normal ones, and "graft" them to the ewe (as will be described later in this chapter).

Yearling ewes or other first lambers often appear to like their lambs but don't clean them or allow them to suckle. Such ewes should be penned closely and the lambs put to the teat until their mothers get used to the suckling. Then they are generally extremely anxious to "mother" their lambs, especially if they are fat and have plenty of feed.

It is a good practice to lamb any considerable number of yearling ewes separately from the main band and under conditions where they may be watched closely and where jails are close by.

A ewe cleans her lamb by licking it vigorously as soon as it is born. Usually there are no serious consequences from this process, but an occasional ewe may be so anxious that she bites the lamb's tail off and also chews the naval cord close to its belly.

What Can Be Done to Ensure that the Newborn Lamb Will Live?

First, check the condition of each lamb, and its mother, as it is born. In addition to being on hand to see that the lamb does not become smothered by the "veil" or placental tissue, which often does not break upon birth of the lamb, there are several things a good shepherd can do that will give the lamb a better start than it otherwise might have.

If the lamb is chilled badly, not having filled up on milk for some reason, or having been exposed to a driving rain, it should be warmed in some manner. If warm water is available, the quickest method is to immerse the lamb in a bucketful. Keep it in the water long enough to get it really warm, then dry it. Another method is to roll it in one or more burlap sacks, preferably along with another lamb that is not cold. Be wary of placing the lamb in the stove oven!

Ewes teats are often plugged tightly, or the milk is extremely thick and waxy for some time, so that the lamb starves. As soon as the lamb is born, squirt milk from each of the ewe's teats so that this will not happen. Seldom, but sometimes, it will be found that one teat has been "ticked" by the shearing machine and skin has grown

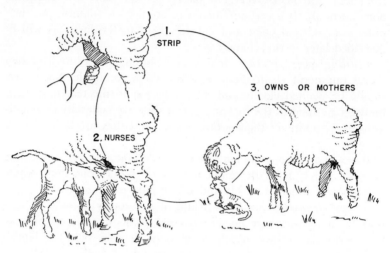

Fig. 37.   A good shepherd ensures the life of each lamb by stripping the teats, making sure the lamb suckles and the dam claims her lamb.

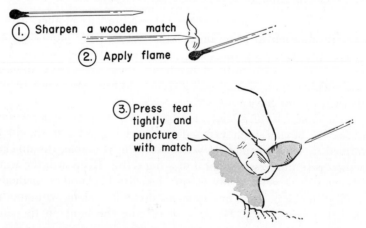

Fig. 74.   Plugged teats may be opened safely by this crude means.

over the end of the milk duct. The duct can generally be easily opened. The usual herder's method sounds crude but works: Sharpen a match, apply the flame of another match to the sharpened point, and use it to puncture the skin at the tip of the teat. The proper spot can most easily be determined by distending the teat by pressing milk up into it. Do not run the match into the duct any deeper than necessary.

Inspection of the udder should include removal of burs near the teats and especially also on the side of the udder and the inside of the flank that rubs against it. Painful abrasions often result from this rubbing, and the ewe will not allow the lamb to suck.

When the first milk (colostrum) is so thick that it will not flow at all, or when the ewe is actually dry at lambing, until such time as the lamb can get the flow started (often several days) the lamb must be fed on a bottle or suckled on other ewes. This would certainly be a case that should be jailed. The lamb should get colostrum from some other ewe or have mineral oil in its first bottle milk.

In cold, stormy weather, if the ewe has lambed in the open, don't take a chance that newborn lambs will be all right. Make sure that they suckle and if possible get them into pens or jails at the barn.

To encourage a lamb to suckle its dam, or another ewe, a trick that really works is to copy the actions of the ewe. She licks the lamb under the tail. The same result can be effected by tickling the lamb, by finger, just under the base of the tail on the fleshy part. Once its mouth is on the teat, this will be all that is needed to make the lamb begin to suckle, provided milk is "on tap."

To prevent mixups of lambs and to find their mothers easily should they seem to be lost, many sheep owners now brand a number on the back of each lamb and a corresponding one on the dam's rump. Numbers are purchasable or can be made of heavy wire (1/8 to 3/16 in.) and fitted with handles. They may also be carved from wood. This practice is quite feasible in barn lambing. As the ewe and her lamb are picked up from the drop corral and brought into the barn they are delayed just a minute inside the door to be branded. It may be more convenient to brand twins as they are turned out of the jails.

Night lights in the drop corral and barn have saved many lambs.

When the drop is especially heavy, the expense of a night man is many times repaid, and if the breeding job has been properly handled (that is, if the span of the drop period has been restricted), the job need not drag on indefinitely. Looking at the ewes as late as 10 p.m. and as early as 4 a.m. can accomplish about as good results as full night care.

"Hard" bags, pendulous udders, and extra large teats will cause the death of some lambs unless such ewes are penned and the lambs helped until the situation is mastered.

Of course if the "hard" bag is simply a meaty, nonproducing udder, very little if anything can be done to improve the milk flow. Some such udders may produce enough milk to keep a single lamb in feeder flesh but certainly not to make him fat or to support twins

at all. Such udders are usually very large and may appear to be heavy milk producers. They are not, and only actual feeling of the udder can establish the fact for the owner that the ewe is incapable of supporting a lamb. She should be marked for sale to the butcher in the spring.

Pendulous udders may be soft and good milk producers, but the teats hang so low that some young, weak lambs will not find the teats and so will starve to death unless helped for a few feedings. Ewes with such udders

Fig. 75. Oversize teats or pendulous udders and spoiled bags cause newborn lambs trouble.

should be penned with their lambs so that the lambs may frequently be helped.

Extra large teats will often cause similar trouble. To some extent milking out the udder on the side that has the large teat will induce the lamb to suckle that side, but usually it will want to suck only the side with the normal-sized teat and must be forced to take the other side. Sometimes this can be accomplished by tying the ewe tightly to a panel or to a side of the jail, with the large-teat side out toward the lamb. Fairly constant watching and care must be given to cause some lambs ever to use the big teat.

Should Twins Be Separated from Single Lambs?

The answer to this question, where the numbers of sheep are at all large and lambing is at a fast rate, is a definite affirmative. Twins had best be put into jails until the mother recognizes both lambs and until they fill out, which will take 5 or 6 days. Fast lambing may force quicker turnout.

If it is the custom not to use a night man, and if a large drop greets the herder in the morning, he will find it very helpful in clearing the corrals to tie the twins together as described earlier in this chapter. If this is not done, one of the twins may have strayed again by the time the shepherd returns to pen them up.

Small fields should be reserved for ewes with twins, and they should be kept in small groups for several weeks. Often, as lambs grow, one of a pair outstrips the other or one gets into a habit of staying close to its mother while the other goes astray. Soon, especially if mixed in a large bunch, one lamb may be disowned and become a "bummer." Many serious cases of a large percentage of bummer lambs have been observed where twins were run with singles or were inadvertently mixed with them in large bunches.

It has been proved extremely profitable to creep feed twins especially, and of course this practice would be quite simple only if the twins were held separate from the first. Then too, better pasture or range can be reserved for the twin bands, often making it possible to make very nearly as good lambs out of twins as singles. The writer knows of one case where a twin band of some 300 ewes (600 lambs) shipped all but two crippled lambs, and the twins averaged 96 lb per head. This was on a California mountain range setup. Twin bands should probably never be allowed to exceed 300 ewes—a band of 900 sheep—and if possible a band as large as this should not be collected until the lambs average 6 to 8 weeks in age.

In some springtimes, an owner may not think creep feeding justifiable for his single lambs but may wish to practice it for the twins. If they are separate, the job is easily accomplished. Results of such treatment are discussed in the next chapter.

What Troubles due to Lambing May Afflict the Ewes?

Occasionally the lamber will be confronted with afflictions to the ewes brought on by lambing. Aside from treating diseases and infections (discussed in detail in Chapter 8), the herder may be called upon to replace an everted or prolapsed uterus and may have to handle a ewe whose "afterbirth" or placenta has been retained.

Prolapse of the uterus most often is the result of an extremely difficult birth due to an overside lamb. It seems sometimes, however, that it must be due to an inherent weakness. On occasion a partial prolapse has been observed before the lamb was born, and the replaced uterus later allowed a normal birth. Whatever the cause, the occurrence is more or less startling when seen for the first time, but it need not cause the ewe too much distress if rather simple directions for restoring the uterus are followed.

The uterus, as it appears everted, is about 10 to 12 in. in length, averages 4 to 5 in. in diameter, and is covered with knobs (the cotyledons) about 3/4 in. in diameter. All is a bright red color, the tissues inflamed—an altogether startling picture. Of course the uterus is also often covered with dirt and filth if the ewe has lain down and also if it bleeds to some extent.

The difficulty encountered in replacing the uterus is not so much in reverting it, though this is difficult enough, but in causing the ewe to retain it once it is back in place. In its inflamed, cold, and enlarged condition, when it is immediately returned to place it gives the ewe a sensation evidently much like another foetus, and she often attempts to cast it again. To avoid this possibility the following directions should be followed:

1. Clean the everted uterus of the major portion, at least, of dirt. It is not absolutely necessary to wash it perfectly or to disinfect it, and in so doing it may be caused to bleed excessively.

2. With the assistance of a helper, if available, raise the rear end of the ewe and allow her to rest on her shoulder while the uterus is forced into place.

3. The protruded uterus should be forced into place by a constant pressure while being held in the palm of the hand (avoiding gouging with the fingertips). This will often require considerable sustained pressure against the exertions of the ewe, but eventually her efforts will be overcome and the uterus should then be completely reverted by following its full length back into the ewe.

4. As the vent of the bladder into the uterus is relieved, when the uterus is partly reverted, a heavy flow of urine is to be expected.

5. When this has occurred and the uterus is entirely back in

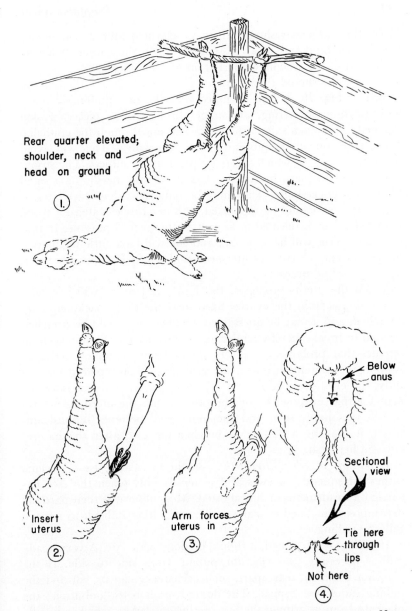

Rear quarter elevated;
shoulder, neck and
head on ground

1.

Insert
uterus

2.

Arm forces
uterus in

3.

Below
anus

Sectional
view

Tie here
through
lips

Not here

4.

Fig. 76.   Replacement procedure in a case of prolapse of the uterus. Note
that ties across the vulva should be made through skin pinched up
outside the vulva lips.

place, the ewe's rear should again be elevated and she should be tied by her hind legs to a crossbar set up in the corner of a pen, with most of her weight supported on her shoulder.

6. Two ties should then be made across the vulva in the manner shown in Fig. 76. It will be noted that the ties, preferably made with rawhide shoestring, are made through thick pieces of skin pinched up on each side of the vulva and not through the epithelial tissue (the mucous membrane) *inside* the vulva. This will avoid blood poisoning, to which sheep are particularly subject. The strings may be put in place by means of large sacking needle or a small blade of a pocketknife. They may be removed a few days later.

7. The ewe should be supported with her rear elevated for a full hour before she is released in as gentle a manner as possible. In that time the uterus will have shrunk and she will have little inclination to cast it. The insertion of uterine capsules may be advisable but is not an absolute necessity.

When the uterus prolapses, the Fallopian tubes (which extend to the uterus from the ovaries fixed near the ewe's backbone) are stretched, and it may be questioned whether they could be stretched enough to break, thereby rendering the ewe barren. Should then all females that prolapse be sent to the butcher? Evidence seems to support the contention that if the prolapse is soon replaced successfully, the ewe is not injured as a future breeder and can safely be kept for that purpose. If, on the other hand, the uterus is not replaced reasonably soon and the inner wall becomes seriously injured, it may be advisable to butcher the ewe after she has recovered her flesh.

Retention of the "afterbirth," or the placental tissues, occurs rather infrequently in ewes and generally only when the ewe has carried a dead foetus or has aborted. Most often it is then partially decomposed, inclined to tear readily, and rather difficult to remove fully by pulling.

If pulling is attempted, it should be done with care. A very steady pull is necessary, the operator pulling from side to side. If the placenta begins to tear apart, such occurrence can be felt and the pulling should be stopped. The desired result is to "unbutton" the placenta from its grip on the few uterine cotyledons which generally are holding it. It is not generally possible or desirable to attempt to enter the uterus by hand and "unbutton" the afterbirth. In the first place, the passageway is small, generally closed somewhat because of the death of the foetus, and its walls are dry, making it subject to abrasion.

Uterine capsules should be inserted into the womb. If the os uteri (opening of the uterus into the vagina) is very constricted, the capsules may be powdered, dissolved in water, and put into the sheep by syringe. If it is not so much constricted, the capsules may be placed by oiled hand or by a capsule forceps dipped in oil, while the rear of the ewe is elevated.

A good uterine capsule should include ingredients of three types to be most effective: a foaming agent, a neutralizer, and a disinfectant. Most biological houses can supply effective capsules.

Dry births, generally of dead foetuses as mentioned above, are very dangerous to the uterine wall. Also many times when considerable trouble is experienced pulling a live lamb, the tissues through the pelvic girdle lose their natural lubrication, therefore it is *very* desirable to keep the hand and arm well oiled with a light white oil or with raw linseed oil. A narrow-handed man (or woman) has a distinct advantage, too, in manipulating the foetus through the small passageway.

How Should Ewes and Young Lambs Be Handled and Moved?

Young lambs up to three weeks of age are difficult to move with their mothers and can be injured or made "bums" if improperly handled. The good lamber saves much time by making arrangements about the barn, corrals, and fields that assist in handling these babies.

If a group of *single lambs* up to 40 or 50 in number are to be moved from the lambing barn to surrounding fields with their mothers, they may be 3 days to 10 days old when turned from the barn, and the older ones, especially, will be well acquainted with their mothers and know them by call. The ewes, too, may mostly recognize their lambs, perhaps by sight and surely by smell. The lambs have been used to being *in a group* in the barn, and the singles are not very likely to run into trouble when turned out. Twins, however, and singles turned out directly from a jail where they have been isolated from a group, may become "bummers" if moved far or grouped up too fast.

Any small group of very young lambs should be moved very carefully and slowly. As the group is about to be turned out of a barn, *before the gate is opened* the lambs should be stirred up and then allowed to find their mothers and suckle. Then, with the gate open (and preferably it should be a wide gate, 10 to 14 ft), they should be allowed to take their own time about getting out. Don't shout, don't confuse the setup with dogs, simply let them drift out, each ewe with lamb at side. The transfer doesn't generally work out that smoothly, but at least the major portion of the ewes know their lambs are with them, and the others may soon pick up theirs.

As the group is directly toward the corral gate out into the fields or down a roadway, they should not be pressed too hard. Better time will be made if the ewes drift along or "eat their way" along. Should the group become mixed up and confused, it may be necessary to take means to startle the young lambs along to the point where they can be rested and mother up again. *Do not use dogs.* No dog should ever be in sight of a group of ewes and very young lambs as a ewe will bolt and rush a dog, lose her lamb, bolt back to the group, confuse others, and incite the dog into lunging, thereby causing a further mixup.

A "rattler" is useful in frightening small lambs into moving. It consists of ten or a dozen tin cans, such as condensed-milk cans strung on a circle, about 2 ft in diameter, of stiff, heavy wire threaded through holes punched in each end of the cans.

How Can "Bummers" Be Raised Successfully?

Many a sheepman has had his start raising "bottle lambs," and many a sheep owner's wife or children earn a good deal of spending money raising bummers. The lambs are fairly easily raised, and if a few precautions are observed, the results are very gratifying.

A bummer lamb is usually a twin born to an old ewe whose owner feels she is unable to carry two lambs through to good market condition. In most cases the bummer has had 2 or 3 days of suckling on colostrum milk and so has the needed start. Sometimes, however, the lamb must go directly onto a bottle. If the lamb can be suckled even only two or three times on a fresh ewe to enable it to get some colostrum before going on the bottle, it will have a much better chance to get a fast start. Colostrum, aside from being laxative, is extremely high in vitamin content in relation to normal milk and very effective in starting the lamb strongly. If the lamb has not had colostrum, a teaspoonful of *raw* linseed oil, light mineral oil, or castor oil should be added to the first milk feed (perhaps the first 3 or 4 feedings). The nipples used should be of the "goose bill" variety.

Very young lambs will need frequent feeding. For the first 2 or 3 days the minimum should be every 4 hours, and it is generally necessary to feed a newborn lamb in the night of its first and perhaps second day of life. The amount of milk needed will vary with the lamb. A good indicator of when the lamb has had enough is how it fills out in the flanks. Never let a real young lamb take more than enough to bring its flanks out even with its hips. Such a lamb will die quickly from colic if overstuffed on milk. Older lambs can take more.

The milk fed to lambs is generally undiluted cow's milk. Some feel that if the milk is of high butterfat content, as from Jersey cows, it should be diluted to some extent, but not if from other breeds. It must always be fed warm—warm enough for a drop of it on the wrist to feel warm. Milk inadvertently overheated or boiled should not be used. If just a few lambs are being fed, out of nippled bottles instead of a trough, the milk is probably best warmed by placing the bottles in a water bath. Larger quantities of milk must be heated over a flame and need watching to prevent overheating.

Of extreme importance is careful cleaning and sanitation of bottles, nipples, and any other milk-holding equipment used. The best procedure is to rinse first in cold water to "cut" the milk, then to follow with warm and hot water, and finally to place the utensils out in the direct sunlight, if possible, to dry. Any sour or souring milk is fatal to young lambs.

Of most importance, then, concerning feeding is not to overfeed, to feed only warm milk, at regular intervals, and to keep utensils clean.

The lambs will prosper further in direct relation to how much care is given to keeping them dry, clean, and comfortable and to how soon they can get started eating grain and fresh, palatable forage. As early as two weeks after birth the lambs should be given access to grain in a trough situated in a dry place and protected from being soiled by the lambs climbing into it. Whole milo, oats, or barley are very acceptable.

The most thriving bummers observed in the writer's experience were some that were never confined in pens but "had the run of the ranch" and helped themselves to a great variety of fresh grasses and browse. They were very nearly like ewe-raised lambs.

If grain and good grazing can be provided, milk feeding can quickly be cut down. A lamb 2 or 3 weeks old needs only three feedings daily and only two when 5 or 6 weeks old. It is better to cut down on milk feeding to force grazing rather than to feed milk too heavily and too long. Such heavily milk-fed lambs are the ones most likely to become "pests." If some of the bummers are ewe lambs and good enough to go into the flock as breeding ewes, they should learn to graze early and be weaned away from the bottle by 2 months of age. It is thought undesirable to leave any ram lamb fed on a bottle, a ram. He should be castrated, as if left a ram he will be a pest and a fighter as a yearling.

Many ideas for milk feeding have been developed, but in the writer's experience, when as many as 100 lambs were to be fed, the simplest and most foolproof equipment was a metal V-shaped trough constructed so that six nipples could be attached to it as shown in Fig. 77. It was attached to one wall of one of the holding pens in the shearing shed. The lambs were brought into the adjoining holding pen by way of the regular lead-in alley used at shearing time, or left in the alley if there were too many to enclose in the one pen. Enough lambs were lifted over the low fence between the adjoining small pens to use all the nipples on the trough. Then as each lamb got full enough it was pulled off the nipple and set outside that pen and another lamb was procured from the waiting group. Thus a continuous process of feeding with time out only to refill the trough with warm milk made for a very quick job of feeding.

"Grafting" Lambs

One of the primary aids in getting a large-percentage lamb crop is the "grafting" of lambs to ewes that for one reason or another have lost their own. A man who is good at this job can keep many ewes producing that might get too fat if they were not made to raise a lamb; and besides, he will end up with many more pounds of lambs that are better lambs, too.

A few basic directions concerning the job may be stated. If a ewe's lamb is stillborn:

a) Replace the dead lamb as soon as possible.

b) Do the job at the spot where the ewe lost her own (if she is not too wild).

c) Make sure that she mothers the new lamb well before turning her out with other ewes.

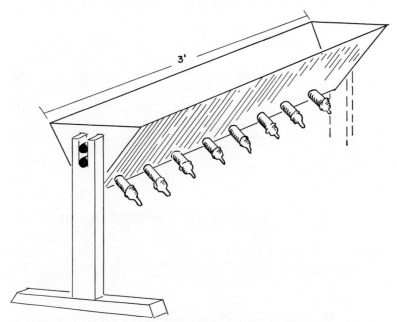

Fig. 77. A metal V-shaped trough fitted with nipples speeds the nursing of large numbers of bummers.

Several ideas for transplanting the new lamb are suggested. In the author's experience, removing the hide of the dead lamb and placing it on the new live lamb has been most satisfactory. Some ewes, caught quickly enough, will take a lamb if it is "odorized" with kerosene and similar material is rubbed on her nostrils. Too, ewes can be made to take lambs simply by being tied up in a jail with a lamb in such a manner that they cannot butt it away. (This is necessary where the ewe's own dead lamb cannot be found (perhaps carried away by varmints, so that no hide is available.)

With a little experience the hide of a dead lamb can be removed and placed on a bummer or a twin in five minutes or less. The hide is removed much in the manner that a rabbit is skinned and is put on the live lamb without tying it. It imparts an odor to the

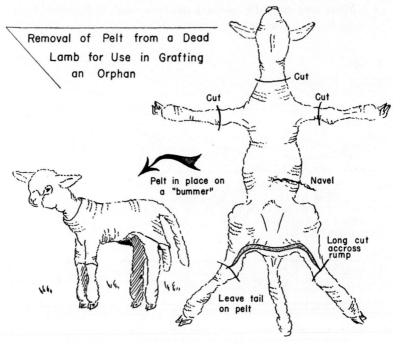

Removal of Pelt from a Dead Lamb for Use in Grafting an Orphan

Cut

Cut   Cut

Pelt in place on a "bummer"

Navel

Long cut accross rump

Leave tail on pelt

Fig. 78.   Steps in removing the hide of a dead lamb.

new lamb (due to putrefaction of the hide) which makes possible its removal in 2 or 3 days (or less if the weather is warm). The first effect of course is due to the fact that it is the hide of the ewe's own, but dead, lamb, and if she has licked it immediately after birth, she recognizes whatever lamb carries that hide.

The process of removing the hide correctly requires four quick cuts with a pocketknife, as follows (see Fig. 78):

1. Front legs are cut off at the knees. (Do this first as it will make the job easier.)

2. A slit is made from hock to hock on the underside of the carcass. (The hide is later *pulled* off the hocks.)

3. A slit around the neck is made after the hide has been pulled off up to the ears.

4. *The bone only of the tail* is cut after the hide is pulled loose around its base, and the tail then stays with the hide.

5. Usually the tender hide pulls apart below the hocks and no actual cut needs to be made there.

No cut is made down the belly as the hide is to be pulled over the new lamb like a pull-over sweater, and with the lambs head through the neck-hole of the hide and its front legs through the two front leg holes, the hide need not be tied to the live lamb in any way.

It should be kept in mind that a ewe lamb might be preferable to a ram lamb as a substitute because the latter will urinate inside the hide. However, this is not usually an important factor.

A hide too large for the foster lamb may be trimmed so that the excessive length will not trip up the lamb. A hide too small may be stretched somewhat by slitting the neck-hole and two front leg-holes of the hide to allow it to be pulled back well over the rump.

In presenting the new lamb to the ewe a few directions, if heeded, may save a great deal of time and make the transfer easy. Some ewes are quite wary of the change, and a careful job is needed.

1. Present the lamb to the ewe butt first so that she smells the hide first at a place where it cannot be mixed with the odor of the new lamb. In other words, the *head and neck* of the new lamb are not covered by the hide, and if smelled first may be enough to cause an occasional ewe to refuse it.

2. To help prevent the above-mentioned refusal, the head and neck of the new lamb may be smeared with the afterbirth, if available, or with fluids from the dead lamb, slit open.

3. As has been said before, if the presentation can be made *at the spot* where the ewe has lambed, she will generally accept the change better. The process of skinning the dead lamb in sight of the ewe will not be recognized as out of the ordinary by her.

4. *If the ewe is wild,* it is perhaps best to get her to a jail with her own dead lamb before making the hide change. The dead lamb should be left with her for some time so that she recognizes it and feels that she has not been parted from her own lamb.

In warm weather, after the blowfly has become prevalent, rotting of the hide on the warm body of the lamb may attract them to lay eggs, and maggot infestation soon develops. Remove the hide or at least the rear portion of it after it has been on the lamb 24 to 36 hours.

A large, lively foster lamb substituted for a newborn lamb sometimes will startle a ewe by its activity to such an extent that she will refuse it immediately upon presentation to her. It is wise in such a case to tie the legs of the lamb after the hide is placed on it so that it will be forced to lie inactive until the ewe gets used to it.

If a ewe for any reason does not have the opportunity to smell her newborn dead lamb, she will take another live lamb without a hide's being placed on it. This so-called "slime" grafting of lambs (the new lamb smeared in the birth fluids) is possible many times when a ewe is down and cannot rise or when down and a dead lamb is pulled by the shepherd. It would be most desirable in this case to get a fresh twin from close by to replace the dead lamb. If an older lamb must be used, it should be smeared and tied down before the ewe is allowed to rise and smell it.

Twin lambs may be grafted onto ewes that give birth to singles only if they are immediately at hand and the ewe has not gotten up after giving birth to her own single lamb. It is preferable to have a ewe that is fat, strong, and a good milker raise a "bummer" than to have to raise it on cow's milk.

If a ewe is slow to accept the new lamb—and this will happen especially when no hide is available and the ewe has been tied up to break her—a small dog that barks often will bring about the active acceptance by arousing the protective mother instinct in some way.

If one of twins dies, it is useless to try to make the ewe take another lamb. In the author's experience, at least when the two lambs had lived for several days prior to the death of one, it has been impossible to fool the ewe into taking a hided lamb in place of her dead one. Evidently there is some recognition by sight as well as by smell.

If a ewe has lost an older single lamb and its hide is not available she can still, most of the time, be forced to take a lamb, and every effort should be made to bring this about. Usually a lamb lost after 3 weeks from birth cannot be replaced as the ewe knows her own too well by that time. Even the extra hide will not always work in this case.

However an attempt should be made to get all ewes losing their lambs to take others. It not only is poor business not to have the use of the ewe's milk, but often, unless put on poorer feed, the ewe will get too fat running with the ewes with lambs and will be in danger of not breeding in the future.

Such a ewe must be "broken" to accept a lamb, and a strong, vigorous twin will be needed to help do the job. The ewe should be tied tightly to the panel side of a jail section with broad "ropes" of burlap around her chest and in front of her udder. Sometimes a third tie will be needed around her neck to prevent her reaching around to butt the lamb away as it attempts to suckle. Usually the ewe is tied tightly, faced one way for 6 hours or so and in the opposite direction

Fig. 79. Ewes must sometimes be tied up in jails to force them to accept a lamb.

for a similar time so that the lamb can suckle from each teat. The ewe is usually released at night (in the jail), to rest. Three to six days of such treatment is necessary to break down the ewe's resistance, and rigorous attention to tying her will help.

Such ewes, as they approach the time when they will accept the lamb, let it suckle without struggling at one time only to butt it away the next. The barking dog brought into the picture then will help. Also it seems to help if the lamb is removed from the jail and allowed to call for its mother. If she answers, the "breaking" is about completed.

No such pair should immediately be turned out with a large group of ewes and lambs. It will take several days of association in a small enclosure with a few other ewes fully to complete the "mothering."

Chapter 7

Growing the Lambs

How May Adequate Grazing for Lambs be Attained?

It must always be kept in mind that if profit is to result, *grass must be* the main food and must therefore be fostered and supplied abundantly and in palatable condition. Surely lambs can be grown well by supplying much supplement to little or poor grass or browse and often this may be desirable, but primarily, cheap grass must be relied upon, so it is extremely pertinent to discuss in detail grass as suited to *lamb* growth.

It was mentioned in Chapter 1, and will bear repeating here, that lambs naturally desire and do best on *short, tender, fresh, green* varieties that are *palatable*. They will nibble at longer, coarser stuff if forced to it, but not with relish. It behooves the owner to keep this fact in mind and to maintain his fields or ranges in this condition. There are tender, sweet "lamb feed" areas and coarser "ewe feeds."

There are obvious pitfalls that must be avoided in attempting to maintain this state, however. Too early and too heavy grazing (overgrazing) mean that the ewes will not get enough grass to produce sufficient milk and also that grass growth is slowed down to such an extent that the total seasonal production is drastically lowered. Of course overgrazing may also be disastrous to the following year's growth, and no discussion of livestock production should fail to emphasize the need for *careful range management*.

How then can we maintain *tender, green* grasses of the *better varieties* in a short form and *not endanger* the productivity of the range as a whole?

In the first place, what do we mean by "short" grasses for lambs? Decidedly, not grasses only half an inch long. Decidedly not just a "fuzz" on the earth's surface. The lamb and the ewe must be able to get a mouthful at a time, and a "belly full" without having to

Fig. 80. Lambing jails and separation pens for use when spring feed is not immediately available.

pick all day to do it, but the grass does not need to be six inches to a foot tall, and from the standpoint of tenderness and the lamb's desires this height would be out of the question. Grasses maintained at about two to four inches in length should provide about the correct pasture.

The answer to the question of how short, tender, green grass of the right variety can be maintained is given in the words: *rotation of grazing.*

In this system sheep will be held away from some parts of the range—eating other parts closely meanwhile—until the grasses on those parts have a chance to freshen up and harden. On farms, large or small, this separation is accomplished generally by cross-fencing the range or pasture, dividing it into at least four parts for the maintenance of a group of sheep. This will allow perhaps 3 to 4 or 5 days of feeding on one section before the ewes and lambs are turned into the next and 10 to 15 days of growth on the first area before sheep will be returned to it.

If any proof is needed of the desire of small lambs for fresh feed, it may be had by watching such a bunch turned into a fresh field. They will fan out ahead of the ewes and feed aggressively until

Fig. 80A.   Ewes with lambs feeding on short, fresh, sweet native pasture.

filled. After the area becomes soiled, the lambs eat much less vigorously, but turning them into a new field serves immediately to enliven their appetites.

To be most satisfactory, this system requires, that each field be *just large enough* to provide plenty of feed for, say, the limit of 3 to 5 days for the band. If too large, the field becomes soiled and trampled, demanding that the sheep be moved before the *poorer grass varieties* are fed sufficiently. By the next time the sheep are turned into that section, these spots of less palatable varieties will have gotten too tall and coarse and tough, and will not be touched. And finally the poorer varieties gain the ascendancy in the pasture, driving out the better.

Two further items of range management should be mentioned at this point. Don't feed *any* area so early in the spring that the grass is excessively tender and "washy," and don't feed all areas to the ground late in the growing period, so that a seed crop cannot be matured. These two precautions are among the prime requisites of good range management, and just another word or two will serve to emphasize their importance.

As to too early grazing: In order for a plant to grow and to produce feed it must have leaf surface. The only way it can grow beyond its initial growth from food stored in the seed or in the root system is from food manufactured in the leaf itself by the process of photosynthesis, in which the green coloring matter chlorophyll takes an active part. If there is little leaf surface, there will be little growth. Therefore grazing too early not only provides poor feed (mostly water) but also retards greatly the date when nutritious pasture will be available. Stay off the range, then, until the grasses harden and darken in color.

As to grazing closely late in the growing season: Although most annuals will not require the production of a seed crop *every* year to maintain a stand, it is necessary to allow them such production once every 3 or 4 years. In a rotation system such as that outlined above, then, each year one of the four fenced areas should not be fed closely or at all as the growing season approaches the time when seed should be forming. If the seeds are to be numerous and fertile, the plants should get a good growth—not be stunted by too much feeding.

After the seed has matured and dropped to the ground, sheep may and should pasture the area, but *not too closely*. This will serve two purposes: to drive the seed into the dry ground and to provide feed. Do not leave stock too long on such areas, especially where such palatable and large seed as that from bur clover is found. The writer has seen pasture areas transformed in one year from luxuriant producers almost to barrenness by holding stock on them until, literally, the seed was licked from the ground.

Rotation in grazing an area where sheep are herded is simple and does not require cross-fencing. The herder simply confines his band to different portions each day, just allowing the lambs to nip off the best and freshest feed, and not returning to the same area until it freshens again. The general practice is to be *extravagant* in providing quality pasturage for growing lambs. After the lambs are marketed, the dry ewes are held on the ranges to the extent necessary to use the feed fully.

It is a fact that farm-flock lambs generally will not have as good pasture or grow as fast as well-managed herded bands unless the farm is subdivided and the flock is rotated to the separate sections. If the sheep have the run of the entire farm, rather than just a portion at a time, the whole place will always be soiled, only the better grasses will be fed, and little or no real range management can be practiced.

All of the above discussion presupposes, of course, that the grass growth is being used to its fullest. Where inefficient undergrazing is practiced, sheep or any stock naturally will do well unless, or until, less palatable varieties crowd out those they prefer.

How Fast Should a Lamb Grow?

In areas such as the interior valleys of California, where it is essential that lambs grow fast in order to reach maximum size and be marketed before the green feed dries and "stickers" head out, it is mandatory that the lambs be pushed in every conceivable manner. These "spring" lambs are marketed milk fat off their mothers at less than 5 months of age and weigh 80 to 90 lb. This figure is exceeded, many times, by those more fortunately situated as to range, and often lambs marketed from good mountain ranges reach 100 lb or more at 6 months of age or less.

The author has known of an individual lamb that weighed 82 lb at 60 days of age, others 105 lb at 105 days, and a particular ram lamb 132 lb at 112 days. Such figures are unusual but serve to illustrate the fact that essentially, if you give a lamb of the right breeding a chance, he can grow fast.

Of course, there is much variation according to breed. Southdown-sired lambs from Merino ewes certainly would not be expected to grow at any such rates as those given above. There are breeds suited to every set of conditions, and the Southdown-Merino cross just cited has a place; it would *not* be in the interior valleys of California. Where Hampshire- or Suffolk-sired lambs out of large Rambouillet or crossbred-wool ewes weigh 75 to 90 lb at 90 to 100 days of age the Southdown-Merino cross might be just as fat—but 15 to 20 lb lighter.

Conversely, where the Southdown-Merino would be fat and weigh 65 lb at 100 days, the other cross might never get fat enough to market off the same particular range.

These illustrations serve to emphasize the fact that conditions outside the realm of good sheep or range management may alter

Fig. 81.   Really fat spring lambs show short, dense fleeces.

the rate of growth to be expected from a band of lambs. It is desirable to use many types of range for sheep feed and to fit breeds with inherently different growth rates to them, because the range that might be right for one breed would not be suitable for another.

Some breeds can gain nearly 1 lb per day, others cannot make more than 1/3 lb. Somewhere within this range will be the figure at which healthy lambs should gain while suckling their dams.

A good indicator of the gaining condition of lambs is *wool growth*. It is a well-known fact that when a lamb is receiving plenty of milk from its dam, its wool is short and dense (for the breed), whereas it opens up and gets long and frowsy when the lamb is suffering from a deficient ration.

These facts seem contradictory, considering that wool is a highly protein material. It would seem that plenty of milk for the lamb would grow its fleece at a fast rate and produce a long fleece on a very fat lamb, rather than the opposite. The only possible explanation seems to lie in the assumption that the fleece grows at a steady rate (if nutrition is not too deficient) and that if food is insufficient for fattening, wool growth is the last to suffer. Or it may be simply that less dense wool seems longer.

A 4-month-old, very fat lamb weighing 80 lb would not be expected to have a long fleece, because of its age. Another lamb that had suffered from low food intake might weigh only 75 lb but be 7 months old and have a longer fleece, a bigger frame, and less fat.

As discussed above, the provision of grazing of the right type is of paramount importance. This will include plenty for the ewes so that their *milk flow* will be at a maximum amount for a long period. (A conscientious effort on the part of sheep owners to improve the milking ability of their ewes, principally through culling, would greatly influence the rate of lamb growth.)

How Should Creep Feeding Be Used to Push Spring Lamb Fattening?

The use of creeps certainly will further push the rate of lamb fattening, and besides, it is a potent insurance factor. It has been proved conclusively to the satisfaction of many users that the benefits are not limited to faster fattening of the lambs. Primarily, however, the purpose of the creep is to provide more, and more concentrated, fattening feed for the lambs.

The seeming difficulties of creep feeding have deterred many a sheepman from ever trying it. Those who have mastered the difficulties once, however, seldom would be willing to relinquish the practice. Using a creep in a shed or barn to which the flock comes regularly and daily is quite simple, but big operators, carrying their bands entirely on the open range, have also found means of doing the job successfully.

Creep feeding in the barn consists of nothing more than establishing the creep panels and grain troughs at a *central location,* feeding palatable grains, beginning to feed the lambs at the right age, and being careful about regularity and cleanliness.

If a suitable, palatable grain is placed in clean troughs regularly and the panel openings are right (that is, all the lambs can get into the enclosure but *all* the ewes are excluded), the difficulties will be entirely eliminated.

It may be, however, that if creep panel openings are not adjustable, they may need to be so wide to accommodate the larger wooly lambs that, especially after the ewes have been shorn, some of the smaller ewes can enter the creep. This problem can be overcome by

Fig. 82. Lambs make good use of creeps where native grass is in short supply.

using a panel with a rail placed horizontally at such a height that the ewes cannot go under it. This type of panel is illustrated in Fig. 82. When, for instance, large Hampshire and small framed Southdown ewes are run together, this condition may be somewhat of an aggravation. The Hampshire lambs may be actually as large as some of the Southdown ewes.

Once lambs are accustomed to the creep, they will force themselves through rather small openings so that, at most, it should not be necessary to widen the gaps more than once. It is advisable to build the panels originally with wide gaps (10 in.) and then to add 2-in. strips to narrow the gap. The added strips may not need to be removed in a given season, and the 8-in. space will be sufficient to keep out all ewes. If lambs are creeped longer in some other season, removal of the 2-in. strips may be desirable, and still most of the

trouble caused by ewes getting into the enclosure will be eliminated
—especially if the horizontal rail is added. A desirable height for
the rail is 18 in. above the bottom board.

Regular grain feeding troughs can be used in the creep. At first
they should be set down into the ground so that the small lambs
can easily reach over the edge. A height of 10 in. to the lip of the

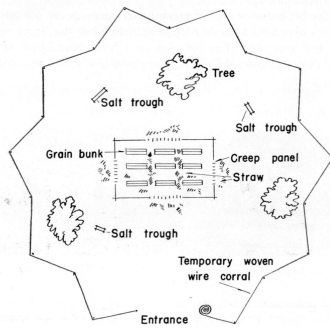

Fig. 83.   The creep, located at a natural bedding spot, is surrounded by a
temporary corral to hold the ewes while the lambs learn to use it.

grain box is about right. Be careful to select troughs with bars across
them (see Figs 48 and 49) that are pretty close to the grain. This
will better prevent the lambs from jumping into the trough and
soiling the feed.

In the barn, it will often be possible to place the creep where the
lambs can also get at hay, which will give them an added boost.

Grains to use in the creep can be varied and may be selected from
many. If a single grain is to be used, the preference seems to be
about in this order: milo, wheat or corn, barley, oats. None of these

will need to be ground; in fact, it will be far better not to grind or crush any of them except to crack corn coarsely. In the whole form grain is more palatable to the lambs, more easily handled, and less likely to absorb moisture. Mixtures of grains with beet pulp and mill feeds such as bran or alfalfa meal are quite palatable, but they are not necessary and are justified only when the lamb is fed under cover. After all, the lamb is generally getting plenty of protein from the dam's milk and requires the addition, rather, of the starchy type of food. No high-protein supplement needs to be added.

Creep feeding, then, becomes simple: no grinding, nothing to do but establish the setup and tend it regularly. The lambs will do the rest. They will consume during the creeping period an average of only about 1/4 lb of grain daily or a total of about 20 to 30 lb. This amount will be more than paid for by additional gains in the lambs.

The method found most satisfactory in feeding the grain is as follows: Start use of the creep when the average age of the lambs is about 3 weeks. At this age the lambs will have a desire for dry or hard feed, but that craving will not be so strongly developed that they will overeat and founder. If the feeding is started later, when the lambs are considerably larger, say 2 months old, it may become difficult to prevent some from eating too heavily when the program is first started. This would result in foundering and perhaps the loss of some lambs. It has also been found that many lambs older than 3 weeks when started on grain, will not eat it at all, having discovered the taste of grass.

Careful management of the creep, then, demands close watch of the amounts of grain first put out. If the lambs are all reasonably close as far as age goes and are quite young, a little sprinkle of grain in each trough will be taken slowly and be well distributed among the lambs. Never put out more than will be consumed in one day; in fact, until the grain troughs are completely emptied by the lambs themselves at each feeding, it is well to remove the amount refused, feed it to the ewes or make some other use of it, and feed a fresh batch to the lambs the next day. It will be found that if the grain troughs are kept clean and the grain is fresh, after only a few days most of the lambs will be very anxious for their share. Don't give up because the lambs take so little grain that "it seems not worth feeding."

As to the time of day to feed the grain, this will depend upon the particular setup. If the sheep come to a central bedding point in the middle of the day, a late morning or noon feeding will be in order. If, however, the sheep range out some distance from the barn or night bed ground, an evening feeding is preferable. This time would be more suitable for sheep that are herded. Once a time of day has been established, it should be rigidly adhered to. Also it is good practice to force the lambs to the habit of staying away from

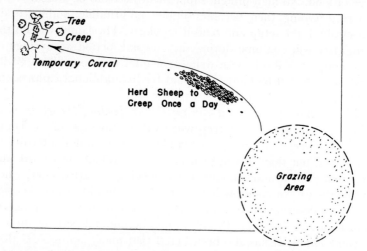

Fig. 84. The proper creep feeding program makes the creep only complementary to free grazing.

the creep until the predetermined feeding hour, otherwise some will leave their mothers, head for the enclosure too early, overeat (if the grain has already been put out), or fret about the corrals waiting to be let into the barn and creep.

Creep feeding on the open range presents a few more problems than those encountered under cover. These will be problems brought about by stormy weather, the necessity of moving frequently, and the fact that it may be difficult to hold the band at a fixed spot as readily as when corraled. The extra returns that can result from creep feeding a range band should be sufficient inducement for every effort to be made to overcome these difficulties.

Before discussing means of overcoming the difficulties and doing a satisfactory job of creep feeding a range band, it will be of interest to see some evidence of the advantages to be had. Three sets of figures determined for three different operators in California are given for this purpose.

Creep feeding twin lambs naturally would be expected to be even more beneficial than for single lambs. Evidence of what such handling can accomplish is furnished by figures acquired from the Frank J. Arburua sheep ranch in California, and covering a test made in the season of 1937–1938 in cooperation with the County Agent. On January 1, 1938, the ewes lambed up to that date were divided into three bands, namely: twins, early December singles, and late December singles.

For a period of 44 days the twin band *ewes* were fed 1/2 lb yellow corn and about 2 1/4 lb alfalfa hay per head daily while the singles band got no supplemental feed. All the lambs were creeped from January 1 for 115 days and ate an average of 0.2 lb milo grain, fed once daily. Wet weather through February and March was unfavorable for creep feeding, but the practice was not relinquished, although the pens had to be moved often and extreme care had to be taken to keep the troughs clean and dry.

Note particularly that the percentage of lambs going as "fat" was equal in the twin band to that in the earlier singles band and considerably more than in the later singles band, although this is explained by the occurrence of stiffness in Band No. 2. Although the average weight of the twins sold was 5 lb less than that of the singles, this difference and more would be expected because of the simple fact that twins are born smaller. Note that the extra cost per lamb was only $0.24 plus $0.42 for the supplemental ewe feed. If half the extra ewe feed were charged to each twin the extra cost per lamb would total $0.45, which would have been paid for by 6 lb per lamb added weight. It is rather certain that the creep feeding put on more than this amount, but no data are available for a band not creep fed.

The pertinent feature of the above figures is that the twin lambs, even though only an average of 4 1/2 months old when marketed, sold as well as the single lambs not creeped. When creeping is not practiced, the twins usually must be marketed much later or at much lighter weights.

Other evidence, reported by R. F. Miller of the College of Agri-

Table 3

1938 RECORD OF THREE BANDS OF LAMBS PRODUCED ON FRANK ARBURUA RANCH, LOS BANOS, CALIF.

	Band No. 1 earlier single lambs	Band No. 2 later single lambs	Band No. 3 twin lambs from Bands 1 and 2 (Ewes and lambs fed)
Number of ewes..........	921	843	460
Number of lambs raised........	909	837	883
Percentage lambs raised.......	98.7	99.3	192.0
Average birth date of lambs....	Dec. 10	Dec. 20	Dec. 15
Supplemental feeds fed........	None	None	Lambs fed milo in creep for 115 days. Av. total milo per lamb, 23 lb. Ewes fed yellow corn and alfalfa hay for 44 days. Av. total feed per ewe: corn, 22 lb, alfalfa, 52 lb

Marketing record of lambs	Dates	No. head	Av. wt.	Price	Dates	No. head	Av. wt.	Price	Dates	No. head	Av. wt.	Price
Fat lamb sales...............	4/20	827	82.5	$7.50	4/28	459	81.7	$7.50	4/20	397	77.5	$7.50
									4/28	103	79.1	7.50
									5/3	304	76.3	7.00
	5/7	78	78.0	6.00	5/7	317	78.0	6.00	5/7	73	74.0	6.00
Percentage fat and feeder lambs sold..........	Fat, 91; Feeder, 8.9				Fat, 54.8; feeder, 37.9				Fat, 91.0; feeder, 8.3			
Av. wt. all lambs sold..........	82.11 lb				80.1 lb				76.9 lb			
Av. wt. of lambs sold, per ewe..	80.6 lb				78.2 lb				146.7 lb			
Income per ewe from lambs sold	$5.96				$5.30				$10.57			
Av. cost of supplemental feed..	None fed				None fed				Per ewe, $.42; per lamb, $.24			
Income per ewe, after charging Band No. 3 with extra feed..	$5.96				$5.30				$9.91			

4 cripple and bummer lambs in this band not sold and not counted in above figures except in showing percentage lambs marketed.

61 bummer and cripple lambs held back and not sold but are figured in av. wt. of lambs produced and return per ewe. Av. wt. of these lambs 60 lb. Value figured at $5 per cwt. This band had trouble twice with stiff lambs so did not show finish and bloom of the other 2 lots of lambs.

6 bummer lambs in this band not sold and not counted in above figures except in showing percentage lambs raised and percentage lambs marketed.

culture, University of California, Davis, California, is quoted in full:

"One sheepman operating extensively in the Sacramento Valley, creepfed about 4,400 lambs in 1939. He grazes his sheep on a rather inferior type of range covered mainly with filaree, foxtail grass, brome grass, and weeds—not, of course, rated as good feed for spring lambs. His ewes are mainly of the crossbred type, and he often begins feeding a small amount of shelled corn about a month before lambing time or sometimes sooner if the fall feed is short. He begins lambing about December 1 and gradually makes up bands of 700 ewes and their lambs. Instead of attempting to segregate the twins, he makes a practice of creep-feeding all the lambs. The creeps are set up, and feeding begins when the lambs are 2 to 3 weeks old. He observes every detail, such as proper location of creeps, sufficient room, cleanliness of troughs, regular hours of feeding, and rotation of range. This year he began selling lambs on March 23 at the age of about 3 1/2 months. The following table gives the account sales and emphasizes the effect of creep-feeding on early finish and weight of lambs.

ONE GROWER'S SALES ACCOUNT OF CREEP-FED LAMBS (1939)

Date sold	No. of lambs	Av. wt. per lamb, lb	Total wt., lb	Price per cwt	Total amount
Mar. 23......	633	88.4	55,976	$8.50	$ 4,757.96
Mar. 31......	719	85.7	61,615	8.50	5,237.27
Apr. 6.......	790	89.3	70,520	8.85	6,241.02
Apr. 7.......	1,302	87.7	114,130	8.85	10,100.50
Apr. 28......	260	91.0	23,660	8.50	2,011.10
May 10......	617	88.5	54,576	8.50	4,638.96
Totals	4,321		380,477		$32,986.81

"On May 10 there were only 62 lambs left as feeders and culls of all lambs dropped prior to February 1. This is an exceptional record and shows the importance of creep-feeding particularly during seasons of low rainfall when the lambs respond so well to supplemental feed.

"Calculations made from the table show an average weight of 88.04 pounds with a gross return of $7.63 per lamb. Allowing an average charge of 50 cents per lamb for feed and 10 cents per head for equipment and labor, this leaves a return of $7.03, which is very favorable considering the shortage of rainfall. Many growers of spring lambs who did not creep-feed did not realize over $5.00 to $5.50 per lamb during 1939."

Further opinions of sheep owners on creep feeding have been expressed and bring out the additional advantages that accrue. Two opinions are recorded here.

E. V. Wing of Tehama, Calif., in the northern part of the Sacramento Valley, has creep fed his lambs for several years. His sheep are moved to the mountains in the summertime, but previous to that move he operates on what would be classified as poor range land. The predominant feed is alfilaria or "filaree," plus a weakly growing foxtail, plus wild oats and wild brome grasses.

The grass grows slowly and the ewes must do considerable traveling to fill up. However, the herded bands are returned to a creep feeding center every evening and the lambs do well.

Mr. Wing states that creep feeding has alleviated many of the trials that previously beset his operations. His mountain ranges have deteriorated, owing to growth of brush and timber, so that it has become more difficult to finish the lambs in the mountains. Since creeping was started, he finds it possible to ship a large percentage of the lambs to the butcher before going to the mountains, thereby making it unnecessary to take as many ewes to these ranges and allowing more feed for those that do go. He also states that the lambs ship (and many go to the East) in much better shape and with less shrinkage. This would be natural, as they are used to eating grain and would fill better en route. The lambs also were easier to handle and when killed exhibited a harder fat than that of strictly milk fat lambs. (This fact should make such lambs worth more per pound.)

Aside from these advantages, Mr. Wing believes that creeping the lambs allows the ewes to stay in better condition, thereby producing a milk flow that holds for a longer period; also that he has fewer ewes that "dry up" as a result of falling off in flesh, and he has less loss due to varmints and to poison because the ewes do not stray so much hunting for feed. And of course the fact that the ewes go to the mountains in better condition allows greater carrying capacity for that range.

Mr. Wing quotes a recent year's figures: 3,459 lambs creep fed ate 257,160 lb of milo grain at a cost per head of approximately $0.87 for about 60 lb of grain.

Mr. Wing also states that most of his twins are saved, fewer become feeder lambs, and even the feeders are better than such were previous to his practice of creep feeding. Naturally, these

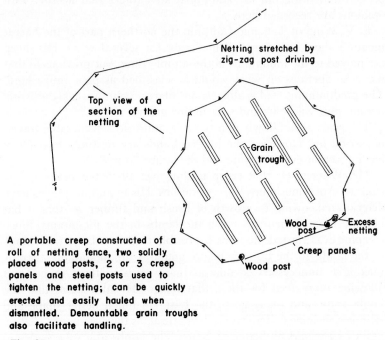

Fig. 85. An easily moved creep setup includes demountable grain troughs, few creep panels and a netting enclosure.

feeders also sell better. He finds also that the trouble of hunting up pastures to which to move has been decidedly diminished.

One additional idea is contributed by Mr. Wing. Perhaps the one item that has discouraged more sheepmen from creep feeding than any other is the bother of breaking in the lambs to using the creep. Mr. Wing overcomes this trouble by constructing a temporary netting corral around the creep enclosure for the first week. This holds the ewes close by until the lambs get acquainted with the setup. The creep is always situated on a knoll.

Another California operator, Gatzmer Wagoner, of Livermore, used a unique idea for a creep enclosure with success. Finding it necessary to move the creep several times during the season and wishing to avoid hauling too many wooden panels, he decided to construct the enclosure of wire netting and a minimum of creep panels. This was accomplished quickly and easily in the manner illustrated in Fig. 85. First the panels were set up, then the ends of the lengths of netting were attached to sunken posts and stretched simply by pushing outwardly when each steel post was driven. Mr. Wagoner's opinion was that the netting gave the lambs less of a feeling that they were "fenced in" than did a complete corral of panels and that they would stay and eat more quietly. It would seem that the only objection to using such an enclosure, rather than one completely surrounded by creep panels, would be in the original troubles experienced in training the lambs to enter the enclosure. However, once this was overcome, it would certainly be an easier combination to move. Undoubtedly it would be advisable to *start* the creep feeding process on an enclosure made entirely of creep panels.

The grain troughs used in a setup that requires moving often would preferably be of the demountable type shown in Fig. 49.

How Can Lambs Be Kept Healthy and Comfortable?

If lambs are to grow fast, they must be healthy and comfortable. These conditions will be ensured only by observing the following precautions:

1. Allowing freedom of grazing accompanied by a minimum of bother through herding
2. Protecting from wetness, excessive cold, heat, and poor ventilation
3. Keeping free of internal parasites
4. Avoiding conditions that would make the fleece uncomfortable

These four items are discussed in the ensuing pages of the chapter.

1. *The principle of free grazing* is one that cannot be overemphasized if lambs are to do their best. Of course, under fence, it would seem that this ideal would automatically become a fact. But such is not always the case. Even though the sheep are not

herded, oftentimes they are "bothered" too frequently, resulting in what could be expressed as a state of mind for the sheep that keeps them perpetually uneasy and does not induce best gains. Many times, sheep owners have remarked that a certain herder was able to make his lambs do much better than any other man had done. The answer could most always be traced to the fact that this herder had "bothered" his band less.

Under fence, flocks are "bothered" by being forced to do some of the things that have been suggested as good practices, such as creep feeding and rotation of pasturage. These practices would *not* be considered good if precipitation, for instance, was never short, or grass growth never stunted, or soils never depleted—ideal conditions which of course never exist. The ideal setup for sheep would be an understocked range under fence where the animals would only occasionally see a man.

It is necessary, therefore, to "bother" even fenced sheep to the extent that they are assured plenty of feed, but to go much farther than that is to court the possibility that the animals will not do well. Therefore: Don't corral the sheep just as a matter of habit. Don't send the dog out, when they are peacefully grazing, to "round 'em up" so that you can "look at them." Don't wait until the middle of the morning to open a gate into the pasture when they have been used to passing through that gate at the break of dawn.

In other words, suckling lambs and their mothers and the dry ewes, too, will prosper most when man makes it possible for them to keep regular habits and to experience very infrequent change.

A herded band likewise should be allowed freedom of grazing to the extent of practicability.

It is a well-established fact that a ewe band or a herded band of feeder lambs will not do its best until it has been "broken" into strict habits. To prevent the band from straying it will be necessary, at first, to "dog" it frequently. For a time the band will not do well because the excitement caused by the dog will be excessive, but soon the sheep will not react so violently to the dog or the herder's whistle, and will begin to prosper. From then on the good herder does more walking in order to be at the right spot to "tuck in" a few straying sheep quietly rather than to punch them in violently from a distance through use of the dog.

If creep feeding is the program, the band will be habituated to staying away from the creep until the appointed hour is reached. Once the habit is established, the band will graze quietly toward the creep area, and the lambs will take their grain at a regular time.

2. *Protecting the lambs from excesses* of wetness, cold, and heat (still keeping in mind the principle of "free grazing") is essential if you would have them do well. In the winter and spring, in the West at least, sheep will frequently have to be subjected to driving, cold rains, to damp bed grounds and accompanying sloppy conditions. Sheep instinctively dislike mud and soft, wet conditions, and every effort should be made to keep them, if not absolutely dry, at least bedded on high, well-drained ground.

Lambing grounds particularly should be so located. If it is impossible to barn the entire drop band, the surrounding corrals should be sandy or sloping. The best ground for lambing will not have mud that will pack between the sheep's hooves, and it will have rock piles or trees or solid board fences that will cut driving wind and rain. In very flat areas, mounds can be scraped up and even bedded frequently and deeply to keep the sheep from soaking up water. River gravel or rock hauled into lambing corrals that would otherwise be muddy is very helpful.

Should sheep be moved in the rain? Generally not. It may often be desirable to bring a small bunch of young lambs and their mothers into a barn or shed for protection from a protracted, cold, driving rain. Really cold rains are fully capable of killing fairly large lambs. In some of the flat country where sheep are pastured in winter and early spring, these rains are quite frequent, and thought must be given to protection of the sheep.

Any driving of sheep should preferably be halted until the storm abates. When the sheep move, their fleeces open, and especially over the loin they can get really soaked to the hide. This is especially hard on old ewes and young lambs. It is far better to let the sheep alone where they can turn their rumps to the storm and occasionally shake the water out of their fleeces than to attempt to drive them to a barn.

Sheep accustomed to certain pastures will naturally drift to the lee side of hills or wooded areas that will afford protection. In flat country, of course, there is no such haven and three-sided sheds, open away from prevailing storm winds, should be built at intervals in such areas. They will save many lambs.

In regard to the last point a further statement should be made. A three-sided, open shed that will just break the wind is suggested. Sheep prefer to be in the open if they are happy otherwise, that is, cool, dry, and out of the wind. Especially when *wet* sheep are brought into a *poorly ventilated barn,* subsequently to be turned out into more or less stormy conditions, they suffer about the worst trial humans impose. And even in dry weather, in such confinement they are subjected to conditions that are not good for them. Moreover, when they are turned out from a warm, ammonia-heavy atmosphere in which they have been very uncomfortable and over-warm, they are subject to colds and pneumonia, both difficult to treat. Sheep should never be confined to quarters not having very excellent ventilation. The author recalls one barn, provided with no ventilation in the roof or even under the eaves, in which it was almost impossible to breathe because of fumes, even though the doors and small windows along the barn sides were open.

How should sheep be handled in heat? For the larger part of a market lamb's life heat is no problem. Rather, mature ewes, through the summer, and feeder lambs, bear the brunt of the effects of heat. Only occasionally do suckling lambs get into trouble caused by heat, but their troubles are no less serious.

Sheepmen dislike to move or work sheep when the temperatures are up. Man and beast both suffer, and the work is much harder and less can be accomplished than at times of the day when it is fairly cool.

If sheep are to be moved on the road in the hot time of the year, the camp tender or owner and herder should be ready to go at daylight (or sometimes a little before). A band of ewes and lambs will travel on a well-fenced road at the rate of two miles an hour early in the morning, but when the temperature rises to the point that some of the ewes travel with their mouths open, it is better to stop and wait until late in the afternoon unless the remaining distance to go is only a mile or so. Sheep will often stand in the shade in the middle of a hot day after too much driving and pant, their mouths open, until the temperature falls. Excessive driving in heat cannot but reduce the life of a ewe band.

3. *Will suckling lambs need protection from internal parasites?* In general, no. If the ewes are in good condition and milking well so that the lambs keep fat, that amount of milk affords pretty good protection to suckling lambs from internal parasites. Later in the suckling period—when milk flow slows, pastures are plucked more closely, and temperatures have risen—even a suckling lamb may suffer from worms.

Will C. Minor, Fruita, Colo.

Fig. 86.   On the road in summer heat.

This threat of stomach and intestinal worm infestation is much more serious to "farm-raised" lambs, especially those that have been grown on irrigated pasture, even part-time, than to range lambs. Too, it is the weaned (ewe or ram) lamb, on its own after being taken from its mother, that is hurt most severely. Without the protection of milk, and eating grass exclusively on a confined field, it may become heavily infested within a month and start fading away rapidly unless protected by anthelmintics (worm medicines).

Tapeworms do not seriously affect sheep. They seem to be able to harbor a rather heavy infestation without very much injury. Usually the only apparent loss occurs in the "tanking" of lamb's livers at slaughter time upon condemnation by the inspecting veterinarian. Purebred lambs kept for replacements or as rams to be

Courtesy Swift and Co.

Fig. 87. Carcasses damaged by "stickers" must be drastically trimmed.

grown out for breeding purposes certainly could well be protected, however, to assure maximum growth and well being.

As these troubles afflict lambs more severely *after weaning,* their control more properly fits the discussion in the following chapter and is treated there.

4. *What conditions affecting the fleece* slow the growth of the lamb?

Many thousands of lambs marketed each year are infested with spear-pointed seeds of a number of troublesome weeds, mostly of the wild bromes. Pelts and carcasses suffer in value as a result of the sticker invasion, and of course lambs will not make normal gains.

In areas where the awns of various weeds start to dry and shed before lambs are fully grown (or have reached a desirable weight for marketing), the extent to which they exist and shed is the direct determinant of a choice of several actions sheep owners must take: shear the lambs, sell them, or move them. Often in the arid West failure of late rains has caused awn-bearing grasses to mature and to start shedding barbs before lambs have attained weight and finish. This has caused sheep owners to shear their lambs, and if some strong feed could still be used (even though awns were present), continued milk production and further gains in the lambs have been possible. (This subject is discussed further in the following chapter under the title of Weaning.)

What should be done if lambs are not sold by awn-scattering time? Usually the farmer sheep-raiser has no alternate pasture to move to, or dislikes the idea of moving off a range that still has considerable nutritious feed, even if some grasses are casting their barbed awns; certainly, if it is possible, the feed should not be wasted. The only recourse is to shear all the lambs and to watch eyes and ears that may act as receptacles for the flying barbs, even after the sheep are shorn. Clipping of the fields, where topography makes it feasible, also is helpful, but this is practical only under limited conditions. Such clipping had best be done *before* the seed heads actually dry (in, or before, the fully-formed green stage). The clipping will cause the plant to remain green longer, thereby producing more feed as well as less danger from the stickers.

Shearing of every lamb (no matter how young) is advised once stickers begin to fly. Most of the barb invasion is around the mouth, and in the breast, legs, and bellies of lambs, and often the barbs completely penetrate the hide and move into the flesh. This results in much trimming of carcasses (a Government inspection requirement) and in a consequent lowering in the value of a carcass by a third to a half.

If the lamb is close shorn, very few if any stickers can work into the flesh, and generally by the time the fleece does get a half-inch long (long enough to retain the stickers), the scattering period of the grasses has passed.

In small enclosures singeing of the drying heads with a weed burner may be resorted to. Perhaps more complete protection than would result from simple mowing would be achieved by raking the mowed stickers into windrows for later burning. However, if a few days are allowed for the stickers to settle to the ground (or if they have been cut green), burning will not be so necessary.

Chapter 8

Health Control for Growing Lambs. Marking. Pest Control. Weaning

The troubles and diseases that plague sheep are almost numberless, and many texts and veterinary publications go into great detail concerning their symptoms and treatments. It is not the purpose of this text to cover all these items because, as the range man or flock owner well knows, sheep in general are extremely healthy animals and, although the list of afflictions may be long, the actual incidence of disease is low.

It will be only an individual animal or a very minute percentage of the flock that will ever be diseased. In the experience of many range sheep operators, not over half a dozen diseases or afflictions are ever encountered. It is these troubles that need to be emphasized, and this text will deal only with those that afflict, first, lambs and secondly the more mature animals.

THE LAMB MARKING OPERATIONS

The jobs of castrating, docking, and ear-marking are commonly grouped under the title of "marking" and demand attention at this point in the story of the sheep year. Marking time is a busy time, and in the operations of range sheepmen is concentrated into perhaps only 2 or 3 days of work.

Under strict range setups the job is not regarded as offering any serious problem as far as the health of the lambs is concerned but it is vitally true that as concentration of operations increases, more and more exposure to disease and injury of the lamb crop is possible, especially at this time. Some of the dire consequences of marking are outbreaks of "stiffness" that cripple the lambs in various ways, lockjaw (tetanus), blowfly infestation, and diseases of the joints.

The precautions that should be taken to avoid these troubles are not complex or hard to provide but do need attention if regrets, losses, and extra labor are not to ensue.

When a lamb is marked it is first castrated (if a male), then docked, and then ear-marked, and the details of each job will be considered in that order. First, however, a discussion of where the marking should be done.

Where Should Marking Be Done?

The position of the marking corral is important. Whenever open wounds are caused, the possibility of infection arises, so it would seem only sensible to avoid situations that increase this danger.

The typical working area of many sheep setups is a permanent arrangement of corrals, usually in conjunction with the shearing shed, where a dodge chute and various holding pens are available. It may also be, and often is, a corral in which ewes bed down night after night for year after year, and although it is true that much of such a corral is exposed to sunshine, it is also true that bacteria are very small and are persistent, too. The marking corral does not belong in or near manure-laden lots.

Mark the lambs out in the pastures on a fresh piece of grass. When a freshly castrated wether lamb is turned loose he doesn't want to travel far, in fact not over a few feet. He should have the opportunity to lie down on a clean, dirt-free, filth-free spot if he is to be given the best chance to heal without trouble.

Oftentimes large operators mark 500 lambs in a day. The lambs must be separated if young (as they should be) by dodge chutes from their mothers to avoid trampling and consequent injuries. The problem of doing this job without using the permanent corrals is a real one. There are two or three means by which the lambs, alone, can be moved to marking pens away from the permanent corrals.

Temporary netting guide fences or perhaps permanent lanes can be used to drive them to or near such pens. (They could be trucked in small groups a short distance to the temporary pens set up out in the field.) Such guide fences or lanes should be "leak proof," and the lambs should not be overheated by running too much. This happens when help is insufficient, gates are insecure, or fences are not well put up. At any rate *it is possible* to move the lambs from a

Courtesy Oregon Wool Growers Assn.

Fig. 88.   The small, temporary, marking pen set up on clean ground, helps save lambs.

permanent dodge chute to a clean marking spot. The only need, at that spot, is a corral (better made of panels) and a smaller pen not over 15 ft square in which to concentrate the lambs to be picked up to be marked. It should be possible to place the lambs, immediately after the job is done, onto a green sod where their mothers wait to "mother up."

When only a handful (20 to 30) are to be marked, it is probably not desirable to run them through a chute to separate dam and lamb. Such a small bunch of ewes and their lambs may be driven into the small corral and pen set up in the corner of a field and the lambs segregated by hand. Little if any injury to the lambs need result from this process if reasonable care is taken to avoid piling up and the lambs are quickly placed in the small pen by themselves. See Fig. 89.

What Is Needed at the Marking Locations?

First, as has been stated, a small pen 12 to 15 ft square is desirable. If it is larger, the lambs are too difficult to catch, and especially if few "catchers" are employed in relation to the "markers," the job may be slowed down. A *marking shelf* should be constructed on the upper edge of one of the panels on which to hold the lambs

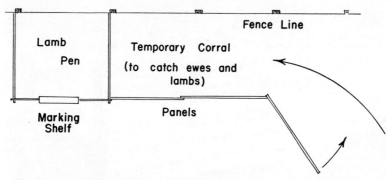

Fig. 89. For lamb marking, a pen set up this way allows the lambs to be placed onto clean ground after the operations.

as they are marked. This shelf preferably should be a plank 2×10 in. in cross section and long enough to provide a space of 3 ft for each "holder." Of great importance is the height of the shelf from the ground surface. It should be about 3 1/2 to 4 ft, as this best fits the needs of the average-sized holder, who must get a lamb into position quickly and hold it adequately for the man who does the marking. This plank should be set level and secured firmly.

Depending upon the manner in which the job is to be done, the other requirements at the pen are a fire and docking irons, a knife, disinfectant, blades (sheep shears), ear-notching devices, fly repellent, and perhaps a hypodermic syringe and needle and thread to be used should a rupture of the castration wound occur (this happens infrequently).

Because some blood, from tails and ears, is certain to spurt on the operators, a simple disposable "shirt" is often fashioned out of a burlap grainsack. By cutting out the corner and a head-hole in the bottom of the sack it can be made into an effective pullover protection.

When Should Lambs Be Castrated?

Castration by any method is easiest on the lamb the younger he is. Newborn lambs may be castrated the day born if the pulling is done slowly and carefully, realizing that such a lamb is tender and specially subject to rupture. (Oftentimes this is done for the last few lambs born so that they will not have to be caught up, causing great disturbance to the band, two or three weeks later.)

Courtesy Oregon Wool Growers Assn.

Fig. 90.   Lambs this size suffer little setback at marking.

The preferable *age for castration* is 1 to 2 weeks. At such age the lambs have toughened up a bit, are well-acquainted with their mothers and therefore mother up well, and are still young enough for the shock not to be too severe. Such lambs will generally be playing and jumping the next day. It is when lambs are allowed to get 4 to 6 or more weeks old or are not marked until into the fly season that complications can arise and serious setbacks result.

How Should Lambs Be Castrated?

The time-honored method of castration, drawing the testes by the teeth, probably will never be replaced. Several instruments are on the market and are usable and offer some advantages. All, however, are open to objections from some sheepmen and should not be used at some times. However, the "Elastrator," especially, has a definite advantage under certain circumstances which will be discussed later.

Castration by drawing the testes begins by the holder placing the lamb on the marking shelf (opposite the marker) on its rump, in a sitting position, with the four legs properly held and spread apart. Each hind leg is *inside* the front leg of the corresponding side, and the holder's four fingers circle the hind leg (all *above* the hock)

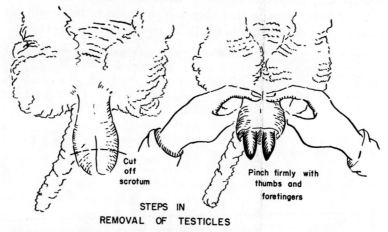

Cut
off
scrotum

Pinch firmly with
thumbs and
forefingers

STEPS IN
REMOVAL OF TESTICLES

Fig. 91. With the lower one third of the scrotum removed, rupture is prevented by pinching with thumbs and forefingers at its base as pull is made.

while the thumb circles the front leg at the knee. When so held it is only a *too large* lamb that may have strength enough to kick out of the holder's grasp and possibly scratch the face of the lamb marker as he draws the testes.

As the lamb sits on the shelf it should be slightly tilted back on its tail and be drawn against the body of the holder. This will force the lamb's back to straighten and make it easier to get at the testes once the scrotum is opened.

The marker's job is to cut the lower one-third of the scrotum completely off. The cut should not take off more than this as often a "short cut" lamb will not heal quickly because fat hangs below the edge of the cut. A long-bladed, sharp pocketknife is used, and the blade edge, if laid on the scrotum and drawn, full length, across it as it is stretched out with the other hand, will make the cut in one slice. The knife is then placed on the shelf, and the thumb and first finger of each hand are used to pinch the testes out (to be grasped by the operator's teeth) by pressing at the base of the testes where the cord can be felt as it enters the lamb's abdomen at the inguinal groove. To prevent rupture, it is desirable to pinch tightly as the testes are drawn and as the "cord" pulls apart.

In grasping the testes with the teeth, a tight grip should be taken about 3/8 to 1/2 in. above the tip of the testicle. If gripped too close to the tip, the outer tissues only may be pulled and a second pull will have to be made to get the testicle proper.

In very young lambs speed can be attained by pulling both testes at once. Often, however, the practice is to pull one at a time, which is perhaps easier on the lamb.

In defense of this method of castration—if such be needed—it can be said that there is much less danger of infection when the teeth are used than when dirty fingers grasp the testes. (Also as the testes pull with some difficulty and often slip out of a finger grasp, the lamb is subjected to more shock.) This method is "clean" as far as the operator is concerned. A freshly exposed wound such as the opened scrotum presents is practically aseptic. Further, this method cannot be approached for speed, and where time is an item, such as when a large group of lambs must be marked in a day or before a weather change, speed is important.

The Use of Castrating Instruments

Several instruments are available to be used instead of the teeth, but they are generally awkward to use and less septic too. The "Elastrator" and the "Burdizzo" or similar bloodless castration instruments offer advantages under certain circumstances. Both are used for docking, too. The latter was quite popular at one time but because of careless application resulted in such a percentage of partly castrated lambs that feeder lamb buyers objected to its use and it has dropped from acceptance for castrating. This instrument also was very slow in relation to the conventional marking method used on lambs of small size.

The "Elastrator" principle is one of stopping circulation in the scrotum (or into the tail) by the use of rubber bands applied by a tool that stretches the band as it is placed in position. Its popularity stems from the fact that no blood is lost, the job can be done safely in any weather and under more or less "dirty" conditions without much danger of infection, and the shock is relatively little. These are important matters to the sheep owner.

The chief reasons why some lambs are not marked until they are too old are that the owner fears the possibility of rain or that conditions are too bad for the job to be done with physical comfort. The "Elastrator" permits castration at almost any time.

Fig. 92.   Elastrated lambs feel the pinch for a short time.

One of the objectionable features of this instrument is that it also, in the hands of inexperienced operators, will cause a percentage of half-castrated lambs. The normal tendency of a ram lamb when set on his rump is to draw his testes up. Unless the operator takes time to make sure that each testicle (and the *whole* testicle) is outside the rubber ring before (and after) the spreading tool is removed, there is considerable chance that this will happen. The practiced operator has found that this tendency can be overcome by pressing the fingertips of his free hand between the lamb's belly and the scrotum as the tool allows the rubber ring to take hold.

Further difficulties or objections relating to the use of this instrument for docking are discussed in later paragraphs.

Too quick closure of the castration wound sometimes occurs, and the day after the operation an occasional wether lamb will be discovered "humped up" and sick, with the cod swollen. Usually the trouble will not persist if the lips of the wound are pulled apart and the serum that has accumulated in the cod is allowed to drain.

How Should Docking Be Accomplished?

Removal of the tail is the next step in the marking process and is often done by the same man who castrated, though on a big job the lamb may be moved down the shelf to another person for the operation.

Three types of docking are practiced: by knife alone, by hot irons, and by the "bloodless" instruments. When a tail is removed by the knife there may be enough bleeding to cause death. However, possibly more lambs are still docked by this means than by any other and it, again, has certain advantages.

When a tail is docked by knife, loss of blood is minor in any lamb whose tail has not gotten fat. This, then, limits its use to very young lambs and generally to whiteface lambs. Also, the lamb must not be overheated, causing its blood to be "thin." To prevent some bleeding, the man who does the docking generally will twist the tail a quarter turn before using the knife. This allows an oblique cut across blood vessels and a chance for blood to clot more quickly than if a cut straight across them is made.

The one good feature of particular value is that a knife-cut dock heals quickest, and this is very important in late season when the blowfly threatens maggot infestation. It is also faster than any other mode of docking. However, it *is not* aseptic and therefore is particularly undesirable when lambs are docked in much-used corrals. Also, with profuse bleeding, it is difficult to apply any disinfectant or fly repellent so that it will be effective. Iodine has some effect in quenching the flow of blood and is perhaps the most effective disinfectant. Water-dilute sheep dip is quite useless.

If a blackface, older lamb with a fat tail is docked by knife, it may bleed seriously enough to cause death or at least some setback. In such a case the flow of blood must be stopped (as will be discussed shortly).

Docking by hot iron is far safer for most lambs. Actually there is only *one blood vessel* that bleeds severely when a tail is severed, and if this one alone is stopped, there is no danger of death from bleeding. (This might indicate that an unsurpassable docking method would be to cut the tail off by knife and quench the one large blood vessel with a hot iron. It is true that such a method is safe and results in fast healing, but it is also slow. However, where time is not a particular element this is the best docking method.)

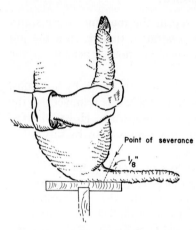

The point of severance of the tail for a ewe lamb, no matter what the method, is rather well agreed upon by sheepmen of all classifications. It is at a point that cuts about 1/8 in. of the flap of skin extending from the tail base to the tail proper on the sides of the tail, seen as it is pulled taut to be docked and as illustrated in Fig. 93. Wether tails are cut much longer (in the West), principally because, then, it is easier to distinguish wethers from ewe lambs in mixed groups when separating out the latter for replacements. (Usually ear marks differ, too.)

Fig. 93. Tails of ewe lambs are at preferred length when docked as shown.

The simplest and perhaps most effective docking iron is home-made from a truck spring leaf. Such a leaf is about 2 in. wide and heavy enough to hold heat well. A 2-ft length is about right. It should be heated in a forge and made straight, then the cutting end should be forged to shape as shown in Fig. 50. The "cutting" edge should not be too sharp; preferably the edge should be 1/32 in. thick so as to burn through the tail rather than cut it off. A handle may be formed at the opposite end by heating and pinching in a vise. Two or three or more irons should be on hand for any docking job where large numbers of lambs are to be tailed.

The *proper heat* for docking is a black heat but not so cold as to slow the cut too much. If good coals are maintained in the heating fire and the several irons are rotated in their use, there may be no time when the irons get too cold, but such would be the exception. A too-cold iron "cooks" the tail too much and causes a long-healing sore (very attractive to the blowfly, in late season). On the other hand, the iron can be so hot as to pop off the tail so quickly that the large blood vessel will not be seared. The operator should always make sure before the lamb is turned loose that this large vessel is not bleeding. If it is, the holder should set the lamb so that its dock extends out past the edge of the shelf. Then the docker can grasp the wool on the lower side of the dock, as shown in Fig. 94, pull it down to expose the severed blood vessel, and touch the spot just over the spurting artery with the flat of the corner of a hot iron. The iron should barely more than be touched to this spot, for if held there too long, it will char the flesh and bleeding will not be stopped so effectively.

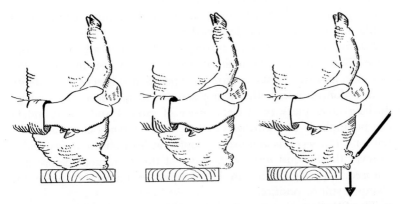

Fig. 94. When a fresh dock bleeds, move the stub over the shelf edge, pull down at the arrow and touch the artery with the hot iron.

If other blood vessels than the main one do bleed a little, it probably indicates the best sort of job, as the shallowest "burn" into the tail stub will have occurred and therefore the quickest healing will take place.

Disinfection of the hot-iron dock is possible immediately after the job is completed because it is "dry," and putting a swab of iodine on the stub (and on the lips of the castration wound, too) is good practice if "stiff lambs" (probably stiff because of erysipelas infection) have occurred in the flock. The heat of the iron itself disinfects, and there is much evidence of lessened infection when hot-iron docking has been used than when docking has been done with the knife.

The handling of the hot iron in the actual docking process demands a little attention. When a ewe lamb is docked, the heat is close to her vulva and it can easily be burned by an inadvertent slip. Care should be taken to avoid this. Usually protective iron (or wooden) slots extending up from the docking shelf through which the tail is placed for the docking operation are awkward to use and experienced sheepmen do not care for them. If a *straight iron* such as was described above is used, the handle will extend above the docking shelf about 2 ft and be at about the eye level of the operator. This enables him to throw his weight into pulling down on the iron as he sets it at the correct spot on the tail. It is often necessary to apply pressure to get through a heavy tail bone.

Hot docking pincers are slower to use and are not recommended in place of the chisel type described above.

Docking with "bloodless" instruments has some advantages and some disadvantages. The main attribute of such instruments as the Burdizzo and the Elastrator for this operation is lessened possibility of infection, although this is not serious, as has been said, where docking takes place on a clean piece of ground and where iodine can be applied. The Burdizzo is slow, as it demands clamping each tail for a few seconds and using a knife (at least on the bigger tails) to sever the tail just *outside* the jaws of the instrument before it is released. (Smaller tails can be snapped or pulled off while the clamp is still in position.)

The Elastrator is not slower than the use of a hot iron, but it is objected to because of a definite shortcoming for docking in fly time. As the circulation is cut off past the rubber ring, the tail putrefies but is still held for a long time, sometimes three weeks, by the tail bone and by wool fibers caught by the rubber ring. In such condition it is often flyblown, and many cases of maggots have been reported. They start their life on the rotting end of the tail and move up over the rubber ring to the lamb's body very readily. The Elastrator should not be used for docking late in the season.

When docking late lambs that will be in danger of fly strike before they heal, the method mentioned above, i.e., knife and hot poker to quench the large artery, is undoubtedly best. However, an application of a *fly repellent* should be made even with this method. This repellent should be such that it will soak into the wool about the stub of the tail (not seal over the wound) and should contain an ingredient that will repel flies. In the author's experience the best material is a *lard-turpentine paste*. Simply add enough turpentine to lard to produce a rather sharp aroma and still leave the paste fairly thick (in cool weather). One application will repel flies for three or four days, and generally no second application will be required.

In the author's experience, neglect of this caution concerning late lamb marking required the reworking of one lot of 500 lambs, practically every one of which required tweezer extraction of many maggots that had burrowed deep into the tail stub. After application of the lard-turpentine paste no recurrences were experienced.

What Is the Procedure for Ear-Marking?

Ear-notching or marking is the third and last operation performed at marking time (aside from that for turned-in eyelids, discussed below). Ear-marking is usually done last because of the bleeding. Marks are generally made with a sharp-pointed pocket knife, although V-shaped or U-shaped bits can be cut nicely with instruments manufactured for that purpose.

Of course, the reason for ear-marking commercial lambs is to provide another mark of identification (than branding). In case lambs belonging to one owner become mixed with those of another it then becomes possible to separate them through a dodge chute by the ear marks. Often, brands put onto baby lambs become hard to read, especially as the lambs go through a chute, but ear marks are easy to see.

Ewe lambs and wether lambs are usually ear marked differently so that the owner can readily distinguish the sexes through the dodge chute. Often the ewe lambs will be sold to one buyer and the wethers to another, or the ewe lambs are to be held by the owner for replacement of his own flock.

Ear-marking by pocket knife is more common with commercial sheepmen than is the use of a notching pincer which is limited to cutting V or U notches.

The more common forms of ear marks are as follows: crops (straight cuts across the end of the ear), half under-crops, half over-crops, slants, and underbits (V notches made by folding the ear and cutting one slice through both parts of the folded ear at its lower edge). Some spurting of blood occurs from large arteries in the ear and so this operation is the last in the series of marking jobs.

No disinfection or cauterizing of the ear wound is needed as the bleeding soon stops and dries quickly.

How Should Turned-in Eyelids be Treated?

Turned-in eyelids should be treated at marking time or earlier, if they are noted. Every lamb should be inspected before being turned loose after marking, and a very simple operation then will effectively prevent blindness in lambs so affected. The incidence of this trouble

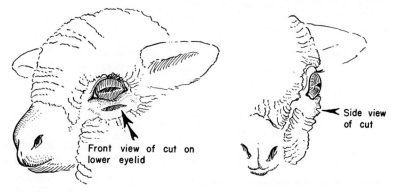

Fig. 95.   Turned-in eyelids are easily repaired by the knife, scissors, or sheep shears.

is fairly large, and if the lamb's eyes are not noted *before* marking time, the irritation resulting from the hairs in the eyes will surely be apparent then. The eye is usually very wet from tears.

Usually only the lower lid is turned in and can be corrected by cutting a small ellipse of skin out of the lid, either with a sharp knife maneuvered against the thumb pad or with a pair of shears or scissors as illustrated in Fig. 95. This bit of skin should be snipped from a point as close to the edge of the lid as possible (about 1/16 to 1/8 in.) and should be large or small depending on how much the lid curls into the eye socket. As the wound heals, scar tissue is formed and draws the lid out of the eye. Some eyes are so bad as to require two or three snips to be made, not clear through the lid but deep enough to cause a little bleeding.

Post-Operation Handling

After completion of the marking job (and the eye operation), there is a proper way to place the lamb on the ground. It should land on all fours to keep its wounds out of filth. This is most effectively accomplished if the holder releases the lamb's hind legs (holding onto its front legs), then leans across the shelf until the lamb's hind feet touch the ground and tosses the fore part of the lamb lightly ahead.

Do not move freshly marked lambs too far too soon. If they can remain in the clean field where they have been marked for several hours or overnight, this is best; they will mother up better and stop bleeding and recover quickly from shock.

What Specific Pests May Retard the Growth of Spring Lambs?

External Pests are largely limited to ticks. The sheep tick (or ked), *Melophagus ovinus,* is a member of the fly family with vestigial wings and prospers and multiplies fastest in the winter months on the bodies of the ewes. If the ewes are infested, newborn lambs quickly pick up the ticks. Lambs a few hours old will often be found infested by ticks that have dropped onto them from the ewes' udders and flanks as they suckled.

Fig. 96.   Tick-infested sheep do poorly.

If lambs and ewes are infested badly, they should be sprayed with a mixture of DDT with BHC (benzene hexachloride) Lindane, or similar materials. The old practice of dipping has nearly been discontinued since sheep scab has been practically eliminated, and spraying offers an easier means of control, both for man and beast.

Of course it would be desirable to maintain an entirely tick-free flock, and some operators who are able to keep their sheep on their own range the year round have been able to accomplish this. Such a goal has generally meant isolation of new sheep (replacement ewes and rams) brought to the place and spraying or dipping them before letting them mix with the other sheep.

Where sheep are shorn in the fall the population of ticks is very low, but small lambs, perhaps because they are more tender, soon pick up a good concentration of ticks, which cannot but deter their ability to gain.

Orchard spray rigs with regular nozzles can be used quite satisfactorily to spray for ticks (and lice). A pressure of 400 lb should be maintained from an agitated tank, and a *carrier* (of liquid soap) should be added to the DDT-BHC mixture if such materials are used. The carrier allows the liquid, sprayed in streaks on the surface of the fleece, to soak into the fibers somewhat, and ticks coming to the surface are poisoned and are generally all dead in two or three days.

The concentration of materials is as follows: 6 lb of 10% gamma isomer BHC to 100 gal of water or 1 lb of 25% wettable powder per 100 gal of water.

Calif. Wool Growers Assn.

Fig. 97.   Spraying for lice or ticks through a tunnel is fast and effective.

Lindane or BHC powder is effective in killing ticks and lice, and may be used in wet or cold weather when dipping or spraying might not be advisable. A light dusting on the backs with 6 to 10% BHC or 1% Lindane will do the job.

The animals may be sprayed while in a pen where the operator by moving about can wet each side, hitting particularly the breast and the rear end between the hind legs. Lambs should be separated from the ewes to prevent trampling. (Small lambs may be dipped in a barrel.)

The spraying of larger bands is usually accomplished by running them through the dodge chute as it leads into a *spraying tunnel.* Custom spraying outfits in the West are now doing considerable such spraying on a price-per-head basis and their work is quite effectual. The sheep are forced one at a time but closely following each other out of the dodge chute into a tunnel around the middle of which are arranged 10 nozzles, three on each side, two forcing fluid up from the floor, and two overhead. The operator stands at the chuteway, his hand on a shut-off valve so that if a sheep stops, the spray can be stopped too until she moves again and then quickly started when she comes up in line with the nozzles. A thousand ewes can be sprayed in one hour, and very little fluid is lost. The sheep are not necessarily soaked but should receive a fair wetting.

Spraying is effective for body lice, too, and on long fleeces as well as short.

Spraying for sheep scab (scabies)

Sheep scab is now most effectively controlled by BHC or Lindane spraying. While scab is practically nonexistent in America, it is always a threat, and supervisory veterinarians are now agreed that control of outbreaks is best accomplished by one thorough spraying of 0.12% Lindane (4 lb of 25% Lindane wettable powder to 100 gal of water) applied by a sprayer at a pressure of 400 to 600 lb. If dipping is resorted to, a 0.06% Lindane spray is strong enough (2 lb of 25% Lindane to 100 gal of water).

Stomach Worms

Are threats to growing lambs under some circumstances, not generally to range-raised lambs, however. These infestations were mentioned in Chapter 7 but their treatments were not given.

The "stomach worms" that affect sheep in different parts of the country are of differing kinds. Treatment and prevention, however, are not variable for the great portion of such worms, and it is not the intention of this text to present other material than that needed by the sheepman to allow him to understand the gravity of a situation and its treatment. For this reason no particular time will be spent on life cycles, etc., except as they have a direct bearing on control.

The parasitic characteristic of the stomach worms is extremely insidious. Farm flocks run on concentrated setups have practically been annihilated before the cause was discovered. Ewes are not as seriously affected as lambs (after weaning), but it is possible for them too to become parasitized to the extent that deaths occur, or that really serious lowered production results. Farm locations in areas that are subject to a great deal of foggy weather, even dry-feed areas (and of course irrigated fields) are suspect, and a regular, systematized program of control should be initiated.

Common stomach worms that cause trouble in this country are the whipworm (*Trichurisovis*), various Trichostrongyles, brown hair worms (*Ostertagia*) and Nematodirus, plus *Haemonchus contortus* in the East. Most, if not all, of these worms have simple life cycles: Eggs produced by the adults within the body of the sheep pass out with the feces in encysted form and become active and infective when conditions of moisture and temperature become ideal. Most of them then migrate as larvae up the blades of grass and may be eaten by the sheep. Many of the encased larvae can and do resist drying for long periods, and larvae have been known to migrate up through a foot of earth after being turned under by plowing. When grass is eaten short, many worms return to the system of the animal. If pasture is lightly fed, fewer worms are taken as most larvae do not move up the grass blades into sunlight.

How Should Treatment for Worms Be Administered?   Most of the stomach and intestinal worms are subject to treatment by phenothiazine. This drug has several attributes that stamp it as the one most effective for this particular type of parasite, though it is not a cure-all as far as others are concerned, and a more complete treatment would alternate it with dosages of copper sulfate and nicotine ("Cu-Nic" mixture).

Among such attributes are the following: No starving of the sheep is required previous to dosing, and the drug has great stability as it moves through the intestinal tract (about 50% of a dose may be excreted and still kill eggs and larvae as they hatch on the ground). Also, now, several convenient dosing forms of the drug are available. And a follow-up (very necessary) is simply prepared and used by mixing phenothiazine powder with salt, 1 to 10 to 1 to 15 parts by weight.

In regard to the follow-up dosage just mentioned, the necessity for it is adequately demonstrated by figures obtained from trials in Australia and quoted from Pearse's text, *Sheep: Farm and Station Management*. (Incidentally, the more complete protection afforded by phenothiazine in relation to other drugs is demonstrated, too.)

The accompanying table, from Pearse, shows the approximate daily output per ewe of *Haemonchus contortus* eggs (in millions) from each of four groups on the day of treatment and on four subsequent occasions. Treatment was as indicated at the head of each column.

Days of treatment	Group 1, pheno- thiazine	Group 2, carbon tetra- chloride	Group 3, copper- nicotine	Group 4, control
Day of Treatment	94.3	92.2	108.0	60.4
6th day.........	0.007	11.6	6.5	55.9
14th day........	0.049	20.6	8.6	51.8
24th day........	10.0	38.9	30.5	46.7
23th day........	52.6	80.4	60.8	61.3

Some sheep in Groups 2 and 3 received supplementary treatments on the fourteenth day and these undoubtedly retarded the return of egg-output to pretreatment levels.

The relative effectiveness of phenothiazine (against *H. contortus* at least) in relation to "Cu-Nic" mixture (Group 3) and others is adequately demonstrated by the egg counts shown for the sixth day after treatment.

The other item most interesting and important is the rapidity with which the count increases when sheep continue to run under outbreak conditions without follow-up (salt mix) treatment. As may be noted, on the twenty-fourth day (three weeks, plus) after the sheep had been practically freed of worms, the egg count, even with the phenothiazine treatment, was 10 million and ten days later was over 50 million, representing a high infestation.

The Montana Experiment Station states that when *Trichostrongylus* is the infecting worm, about double the recommended doseage of phenothiazine is very effective. This would mean a 40-gram dose to adult sheep and 20 grams to lambs.

Further, the Station states that for *Nematodirus,* tetrachloroethylene seems to be the best anthelmintic remedy and states also that it is very effective against all roundworms.

It is desirable, of course, that pastures be kept as free of worm eggs as possible, and therefore the ewes should be dosed, as they may be heavily infested themselves, even though they show little if any

symptom of it. Very many flocks of ewes are treated with phenothiazine before lambing with no ill effect. Of course care must be
used in handling the ewes during the dosing to prevent injury and
abortions.

The number of worms infesting sheep of all ages rises spectacu-
larly in the early spring months, reaching a peak in April or May,
after which infestation declines. Dosing should be done with this
in mind.

Another means suggested for keeping pastures clean is to rotate
grazing where possible or to rotate and graze with another type of
animal. Both these methods are effective because, first, the larvae
in the *infective stage* die of starvation if they are not ingested, and
in the other stages, although they are extremely resistant to many
external pressures, they do thin out to a large extent if no sheep are
on the land. Secondly, few worms that affect sheep also affect
horses or cattle, so that a field heavily sheep-worm infested may be
fed by the other animals without injury to them. This is another
argument for the practice of running two types of animals together
—each eats the infective worm of the other and kills it in the process
of digestion.

Although the use of worm medicines are of paramount value in
worm control, the importance of other items should be emphasized:
(1) adequate nutrition; (2) avoidance of overgrazing and over-
crowding; (3) rotational and alternate-host grazing.

How Should the Follow-Up (Salt and Phenothiazine) Treatment
Be Administered?

To be certain that sufficient phenothiazine is taken, in the salt, to
control the worms effectively, the mixture must be kept fresh and
clean. Sheep will not eat a salt mixture that is fouled by dung, dirt,
or moisture, so that *frequent refilling of the mixture receptacle*
(every two or three days) becomes necessary. Too, if rain is likely
to dampen the salt or dissolve it, a carefully constructed and covered
trough is necessary. Such a trough is diagrammed in Fig. 47.

The use of the copper sulfate and nicotine sulfate mixture as an
alternate or complementary worm treatment was mentioned above
and demands some discussion. This material can be purchased in a
concentrated form called "Cu-Nic" mixture or may be made up by
following directions provided in various bulletins or texts on veterinary treatments. *This mixture is a poison* and must be prepared

carefully to prevent overdosing, which would kill sheep. The concentration necessary to kill worms is close to that which will kill sheep. However, carefully handled, it is a very effective anthelmintic remedy and is often used as an alternate dose with phenothiazine. It is much cheaper than the latter medicine.

A *liquid-dosing apparatus* that is on the market makes it possible to dose sheep quickly simply by pressing a "trigger" on a handpiece that correctly measures out the dosage from a rubber bag to which

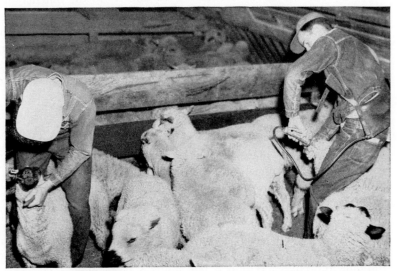

Fig. 98. Liquid dosing for internal parasites is handily done with this drenching gun.

the handpiece is attached. The rubber bag is fitted with a harness so that it may be carried over the shoulder.

Tapeworms, as has been stated, rarely if ever do damage that is discernible in the live sheep, but they divert some of the food taken by sheep to their own use. They are not bloodsuckers but live upon the partially digested food in the sheep's intestines.

A most effective remedy, recently placed on the market, is "Teniatol," a white liquid administered by a dose syringe. It causes segments that contain the tapeworm eggs to break off the ends of the worm in the intestine. These white segments will be seen in the sheep droppings very quickly after a dosage.

The treatment of tapeworms with the copper sulfate-nicotine mixture, formerly sometimes recommended, is not regarded as effective.

Other diseases and troubles of sheep and lambs are treated in Chapter 12.

WEANING LAMBS—HOW AND WHEN?

Of course most fat market lambs go directly to the butcher off their mothers, and as far as they are concerned, no attention as to weaning is needed. Their dams, however, may need watching so that their udders will not be injured. Also, ewe lambs kept for replacement purposes, as well as ram lambs kept for development, will need some particular attention when they are separated from their dams.

Early shipped lambs are sent to the butcher generally at times when spring feed is still good and the ewes are generally milking well. Lambs may be only 3 1/2 to 4 months old in many cases, and their dams' udders may and will fill tightly if these ewes are not confined away from feed for some time after the lambs are shipped.

If all the lambs are not shipped from a large flock or band, it would certainly be undesirable to "dry up" all the ewes in that band. To find the ewes off which the lambs have been shipped, so that they may be separated, it becomes necessary to allow all the ewes to return to feed near the separating corrals immediately after shipping the lambs. Within a few hours a large part of the ewes whose lambs were shipped will return to the corral, hunting their lambs, and a man on duty can confine them in a dry corral as they come in. Generally *all* such ewes will not separate themselves from the band, and too, a few ewes, mothers of lambs still on hand, may follow the others back into the corral. It therefore becomes necessary to camp (bed down) the ewe and lamb bunch outside the corral toward evening, at which time the few still owning lambs can "mother up" through the corral fence. (Observation the following morning may be necessary to find some of the pairs.) Also, distended udders will indicate ewes still in the band whose lambs were shipped, and they should be worked out of the band and confined.

It is not necessary to milk out all ewes still making considerable milk, but rather only those whose teats are very distended and red-dened should be caught and partially milked out. Confinement off feed in a dry corral for 48 hours will effectually stop the flow of milk. Such ewes should then be turned out on poorer feed and checked for a few days for any udders that may still fill dangerously.

Generally, ewes whose lambs are shipped late (and off dry feed), especially if the lambs are quite old, will need little if any attention in regard to milking out.

Weaning, as far as the lambs is concerned, is a different matter. It is generally desirable to let ewe lambs kept for replacement pur-poses suckle the ewes as long as possible, or rather as long as the ewes still make an appreciable amount of milk. This will generally be, at least with young- to medium-aged ewes, about six months if the ewes are on good feed and in fair condition. The final weaning date will be determined by the owner's plans for breeding and the amount of time he considers necessary to get the ewes properly prepared for breeding as described in Chapter 2.

Ram lambs should be weaned young. Depending somewhat on the breed, ram lambs should be no older than 5 months at weaning. This is because the little that might be gained by the extra milk is overcome by the restlessness created in ram lambs as they approach breeding maturity. It is observed that a ram lamb weaned at 5 months (especially if creep fed) and gotten immediately onto strong pasture and grain will outweigh and outgrow one kept on his mother another month. A ram lamb not weaned at 5 months may actually lose flesh and take an additional month or two to get into the condition of the earlier weaned lamb whose breeding instincts have not been excited.

Lambs weaned will forget their mothers much more quickly if removed for a time to fields a good distance from their dams. They may be run in the same fields with their mothers, if such feed is needed, after they have been separated for 10 to 14 days.

SHOULD LAMBS BE SHORN BEFORE SALE?

Generally no spring lambs going to the butcher fat off their mothers are shorn. The fleece of a typical fat milk lamb "in bloom" has a very attractive appearance. It is short, tight, and smooth-surfaced and is an indication to a lamb buyer of a good-doing fat lamb. However, in some cases shearing is a paying proposition where feed dries early, before lambs get heavy. If the lamb begins to shrink because feed conditions get poor, or if the lamb has never had enough feed, the wool has a straggly, rough appearance and the lambs are said to be "woody." In such a condition the lamb will look better if the fleece is removed by a competent shearer who does a smooth job, and the lamb will also fatten better. However, such a lamb's pelt will not have enough wool growth to be commercially valuable unless it has a minimum of 60 days' growth.

In the West, where rain is so necessary to finishing the lamb crop, there have been times (if there were no late rains) when shearing of entire crops of 60-lb lambs was necessary to keep them gaining and to keep "stickers" from interfering with the comfort necessary to gains. Rather than allowing the lambs to become infested with the weedy barbs and then selling them as "woody" feeder lambs, sheep owners have found that shearing makes it possible to take the lambs into pastures where there are some stickers but still much strong feed and finally to add 15 to 25 lb to their weight and sell fat. A lamb in short pelt will not command as high a figure per pound as a full-wooled lamb, but this difference has generally been offset by the greater weight and higher grade of the carcass, and sheepmen should not hesitate to shear to keep their lambs gaining.

The pelt credit varies of course with the market value of wool and will make a difference in the relative merit of shearing when

I. Lamb sold at light weight and wooly:
    Sells at 65 lb @ $0.28 per lb—total income $18.20

II. Shorn lamb held longer:
    a) Gains (on mother) 0.50 lb per day for 40 days
    b) Sell for less per pound because of in short fleece
    c) Costs additional for shearing, herding, and feed
    Sells at 85 lb @ $0.26 per lb $20.80
    Sale of 3 lb wool @ $0.85 per lb 2.55
                                                                        $23.35
    Less charges: shearing . . . . $ 0.40
                  feed and herding 0.60

                                                                        $ 1.00
            Net income $22.35
    Returns above sale of light lamb . . . . $ 4.15

wool values are high or are low. As an example of how this might affect a sheepman's decision, the accompanying figures (hypothetical) will illustrate what he should take into consideration.

The additional income of course depends on several items and may in one case be more, in another less, than that illustrated. Such a figure will depend upon whether the remaining feed can produce a gain of 0.5 lb per day. If the ewes dry up, this gain cannot be expected. On the other hand, if stickers and drying can be contended with because of the shearing, and sufficient strong milk-making feed is in sight, the lambs may continue to gain and at even higher rates. (Many suckling lambs on top feed gain 0.80 lb per day.)

The sheep owner will need to know about what price the shorn lambs will bring in comparison with the price obtainable for the lighter wooly lambs, and also he should have a good estimate of the weight of fleeces and the value per pound of the wool.

Chapter 9

Marketing Lambs and Surplus Stock

The job of marketing the sheepman's products is far too often too poorly handled. His products, basically only two in number (mutton and wool), go to market very infrequently, and the typical sheep owner therefore really does not have the contact experience in this phase of his production that many other producers of agricultural products have. He may well be advised, then, upon the following phases of this important operation:

1. To whom shall I sell my lambs?
2. If I ship, how should the lambs be handled?
3. What things should determine when I should sell?
4. What means are used to get most returns for each lamb sold?
5. When should aged ewes be sold to get most returns? How?

TO WHOM SHALL I SELL MY LAMBS?

As has been stated before, a poor job of selling can very easily wipe out the advantages resulting from added effort and excellent management in producing and growing the lamb crop. The successful sheep operator needs to be a businessman and needs to know the value of his product and the means at hand to realize that value.

The sheep owner has a choice of markets, some depending upon the volume of his business. These may be listed about as follows:

(a) Direct to packers (through their buyers in the field)
(b) To packers through the *central markets* (through commission agents)

(c) To local butchers or through auctions

(d) Private sales to individuals

The argument for selling direct to packer buyers rather than to them through a commission agent at a central market is difficult to uphold. Many sheep owners rebel at the idea of sending their lambs a considerable distance to a central market, only to "be at the mercy" of the market conditions of the day of arrival; they also rebel against the possibilities of shrinkage at the yards and en route and the "manipulations" of other people handling their lambs.

Calif. Wool Growers Assn.

Fig. 99. Fat lambs being sorted and loaded in one operation.

Doubtless these apprehensions, which cause the bulk of western lambs to sidetrack the central markets, are the result of ignorance of prevailing conditions in reputable markets and also of the true condition of the man's own product, his lambs.

Most packers say that they would much prefer to be able to buy all their needs from markets close to their packing plants because this would eliminate the need to maintain buying crews in the field. However, they perhaps would not have the control over the flow of lambs to market that best fits their killing (and holding) facilities.

As for the sheep owner, it would seem that central-market competition would be most likely to provide the highest price. Still, few western lambs are so sold. Instead, each spring and summer many packer buyers are out in the country, sizing up lambs and offering contracts, or waiting for owners to be ready to sell. Owners of lambs who usually sell in this manner have fairly large bands to dispose of: a thousand head and up. Groups of such size represent enough value to attract competition among buyers for several different packing firms, so that the lamb owner is in a position to do some bargaining.

One factor that attracts lamb owners to this method of selling is that when a deal is consummated and the lambs are weighed and loaded for shipment, his responsibility ends and his payment is in his pocket. If he is satisfied with the price (and he must be if he sold), his worries are at an end; and experienced sheep owners who have anually been well treated by packer buyers and who feel they know how to drive a good bargain prefer to have their responsibilities end with the shipping rather than to run some risk of losses (by shrinkage or death) en route, pay commissions and for feed in the yards, and receive a price in the determination of which they have had no direct voice.

Calif. Wool Growers Assn.

Fig. 100. A big shipment awaits slaughter at a central market.

For small-sized and frequent shipments at shorter distances from the central markets, a program of selling through commission firms located therein is more general and practical, and numbers of sheep owners employ this means with great satisfaction.

Marketing lambs through the central markets is satisfying to a lamb grower when he knows the true value and grading possibilities of his animals. This is especially true if he further follows his lambs into the market and sees them filled and sold. Keeping in close contact with his commission agent, by phone previous to shipment and at the market in person, is good practice and helps mightily in firming the relationships between the grower and the market.

Often a grower who does not know how his lambs should grade, and has had no instruction or experience in grading, feels that he has been hurt when returns indicate that all his lambs did not grade choice or prime. Growers who send their lambs into a central market from a considerable distance hoping to receive the price quoted in the papers for choice lambs, pay shipping and other charges incurred in central-market marketing, and then receive returns on quite a few lambs that graded lower, may be very disheartened. If,

U.S. Forest Service

Fig. 101. Spring lambs are the sheepman's chief payoff. Note the combination cattle and sheep chute.

instead, growers fully realize the grading probabilities of their shipments, are made aware of the market strength on the day of sale through a telephone conversation with their commission agents, and travel with the lambs to see that they are adequately handled, few if any of them can complain of this method of selling. It is seldom that shipments so handled are not sold quickly or suffer any untoward amount of shrinkage. It is true, however, that spring lambs, especially the younger sort, do not fill well and do need special attention to prevent shrinkages of over 4%, which is considered the maximum that should result for lambs weighed out of fields and off their mothers in the country.

Selling lambs to local butchers or through nearby *auction yards* is usually best for the grower of small numbers of lambs, although he may ship to a central market if freight costs are not prohibitive in relation to the numbers of lambs hauled.

Often a local slaughterhouse is willing to take small numbers of lambs whenever the grower feels they are ready to go and will pay the central-market price less only the cost of freight if the grower is reasonable about the "fill" of the lambs. This is of great advantage to a farm-flock owner, for then he does not have either to pay an excessive charge for hauling a small load a great distance or—in order to make up an economically sized load—hold his larger lambs too long while the smaller ones get some weight. If the latter practice is followed, often the too-big lambs will suffer a dock in price or affect the price paid for the load as a whole. Good relations with a local butcher are much to be prized.

IF I SHIP, HOW SHOULD THE LAMBS BE HANDLED?

The shipping of lambs or sheep to market requires some care in order to prevent loss. Losses aside from death are largely due to excessive shrinkage and in some cases to the incurrence of disease that may subsequently cause death.

What, then, are *the items in shipping lambs* that are important in helping an owner to get fullest returns for his product? Perhaps it would be well, first to itemize and then to discuss them:

1. General shipping considerations regarding space needs
2. Proper handling before and during shipment
3. Proper loading onto trucks or into cars

General Considerations (Space Requirements)

The following pages discuss in some detail many items relating to shipping, not all of which are directly pertinent to the marketing of butcher lambs. However, it seems advisable to discuss the general subject of shipping in full at this point, although some points may concern other classes of sheep.

The correct number of animals to be loaded into a car or truck is one of the first points of importance. If too many are crowded into a conveyance, there is danger of trampling and smothering, which often results in death loss. If there are too few, quick stops and sudden starts of the vehicle tend to throw them about and badly weaken them as they attempt to support themselves. If the loading is so light that many can lie down, the costs of transport become too high.

There can be no hard and fast rule concerning the number of sheep to be loaded into a given space, because the bulk varies with the size, length of fleece, and condition of the individual animals. After some years of experience in shipping, an owner should have a fair idea of the number to load, but if he has not shipped before, he may have to take the advice of the truck driver or someone else. Their advice, too, will depend for validity upon considerable experience.

It is a common and disconcerting experience to sheep owners to have filled all the trucks or car space ordered, only to find that some animals had to be turned back into the flocks. Not all truckers, even well-experienced ones, can say how many ewes or lambs their vehicles can carry. They are generally loath to state a figure (to which they will then be held responsible in the minds of the shippers) and generally it is true, too, that they have no opportunity to see the weight, condition, and fleece factors that would be needed for a close estimate.

Loading tables should show difference in shorn or long-wools. The number of lambs to be loaded in railway cars and trucks as recommended by the U. S. Bureau of Animal Industry, as well as by other organizations, are given in a publication of the California Wool Growers Association published in September, 1948. This is the "California and Western Livestock Guide," a very useful booklet which gives much more data than concerns shipping. At least in trucking, these tables indicate that less space should be allowed per individual in large trucks than in small ones—in other words, the larger truck supposedly could be loaded at a heavier rate. This is a dangerous assumption because, if partitions are not frequently spaced, the sheep have more tendency to crowd. The crowding effect of course is multiplied by the number of sheep in the compartments, and sudden stops and starts can crush the individuals badly. *It is possible to load more heavily in small trucks* or trailers because of this factor.

A more accurate guide to loading, based on a recent collection of data on the number of sheep of different weights, ages, or conditions that have been safely loaded and hauled in trucks, trailers, or railroad cars of known size, can now be presented. The data are given in terms of the *square feet of space* required by individuals of varying type. This space requirement can then be applied to any vehicle of known dimensions, and the shipper can be reasonably certain that, barring accidents, his stock will arrive at the destination unharmed. Weight seems to be the most practical, if not the most exact, measure of size of sheep, for this purpose.

Table 4 represents a range in weight for shorn and unshorn lambs and ewes and the corresponding *square feet of space* required by each if they are to be comfortably and safely loaded. These figures take into consideration that the sheep may be transported on long hauls or over mountainous roads or in warm weather. The total numbers that can be hauled in double-decked trucks and trailers of the more common sizes and in double-decked railroad cars are given. It is hoped that this information may prove useful to truckers and sheep owners alike. Neither enjoys the prospect of deaths of sheep en route and especially the owner, who feels often that he has been unjustly penalized when he is able to collect only a small portion of the value of such animals from insurance companies.

The numbers given of course can never be entirely correct as no two men will have sheep of exactly the same fill, wool length, body conformation, etc., in succeeding shipments. However, within half a dozen head for the larger shipments, the figures provide the best guide available.

Table 4 presents weights that are *net weights* rather than gross (or loading) weights. Owners get paid for their animals at market

Table 4

GUIDE TO LOADING SHEEP FOR SHIPMENT

These numbers are *maximum* for long hauls through mountains and in warm weather. For short level hauls, it is possible to load a few more animals. All numbers reckoned to the nearest whole number.

Net weights loaded off pasture or feed lot	Load for Trucks and trailers, double-decked				Load for Railroad stock cars, double-decked	
	Space per animal, sq ft	(22' truck and 24' trailer, 718 sq ft)	(22' truck and 26' trailer, 735 sq ft)	(22' truck or 29'10" trailer, rounded corners, 775 sq ft)	Space per animal, sq ft	(36'6" x 8'10", 645 sq ft)
55–60-lb wooled lambs..............	2	359	368	388	2.1	307
55–60-lb recently shorn lambs.......	1.8	399	408	431	1.9	339
70-lb wooled lambs.................	2.3	312	320	337	2.4	269
75-lb recently shorn lambs..........	2.2	326	334	352	2.3	280
90–100-lb wooled milk lambs........	2.6	276	283	298	2.7	239
100-lb fed lambs, No. 1 pelt........	2.6	276	283	298	2.7	239
110-lb fed lambs, No. 1 pelt:.......	2.8	254	263	277	2.9	222
110-lb fat ewes, No. 1 pelt.........	2.8	254	263	277	2.9	222
120-lb ewes, No. 1 pelt............	3	239	245	258	3.1	208
130-lb ewes, No. 1 pelt............	3.2	224	230	242	3.3	195
125-lb wooled ewes................	3.3	218	223	235	3.4	190
135-lb wooled ewes................	3.4	211	216	228	3.5	184
145-lb heavy wooled ewes to start lambing in 10 days...........	3.7	194	199	209	3.8	170
115–120-lb wooled ewes with 100% of 50-lb lambs (pairs).......	4.9	147	150	158	5	129

time on the net or actual sales weight, and carrying charges (by trucks and railroads) also are figured on this weight. When using the table to calculate loading numbers it should be remembered that the figures are on this basis.

In considering the factors that affect loading rates it is safe practice to ascertain the probable weather en route and to load fewer animals when the prospects are for heat. Similarly fewer should be loaded when the trip is to cover mountainous territory because on the upgrade the lambs will gravitate to the rear and tend to crush the sheep there, and then on the downgrade, those in the fore part of the compartment may be crushed. For an extremely long haul, the load should be similarly lightened, even though most of the trip is on level ground. However, lightening should not be to the extent that the sheep are so loosely packed that they can be thrown about. Most truckers are aware of the fact that the first mile or two of the trip may be the worst, as far as possibilities of loss are concerned. Until the sheep get their "traveling legs" or learn how to brace themselves, they are easily toppled, and then perhaps smothered as others fall over their heads.

To some extent other factors also influence the number that can be loaded. When animals of necessity are loaded full of food off of green pasture, they will require considerably more space than if they had been allowed to stand overnight off feed in a corral. Also, when shipments are made of animals that are noticeably weak owing to age, hunger, thirst, or disease, they should have extra space and extra attention by the carrier. These sheep have a greater tendency to lie down, and those standing may be toppled over them into positions from which they cannot rise. Very "heavy" ewes, some perhaps lambing, need to be loosely loaded, as do also lambs that have grown long, loose fleeces. The latter are particularly subject to smothering.

Referring again to the *factor of size,* it should be noted that *some types of ewes are as small as lambs.* Perhaps particularly in California there is a great variance in the "square footage" of ewes. This variation is due to the fact that areas of the state vary greatly in sheep-growing conditions and demand the carrying of different breed types to ensure profit under those conditions.

Ewes from the Coast Range to the northern part of the state are hardly over half the size of ewes that are run in the interior valleys and that have been introduced to the area from other states as replacements.

Many flocks of these small ewes weigh only 100 to 110 lbs when fat and hence can be loaded about like lambs of the same weight, as shown in the table. The table indicates figures for sheep averaging a high weight of 145 lbs. There are, of course, possibilities of shipments of ewes that would average more than this, and proper calculation must be made for these.

Likewise the *factor of condition,* i.e., *degree of finish or fleshiness,* must be considered in order to reach a near-correct conclusion. Thin animals are lighter in proportion to their bulk than fat animals, and a proper estimate of their grade will be necessary properly to interpret the weight classifications of Table 4. A 75-lb shorn lamb requires considerably more than three quarters of the space occupied by a 100-lb lamb of short pelt because a group of such lighter lambs will usually have a larger percentage of low-grading or feeder animals among it. These have bulk but not weight.

If a lamb has been stunted in his development, or at least has grown slowly in relation to others, the fleece continues to grow (and is generally also loose and open), but the lamb does not gain and perhaps even loses weight. Thus, feeder lambs often look more like small sheep than like lambs, and because of the fleece condition they require a good deal more space in proportion to their weight than larger, fatter lambs.

Shall Ewes and Lambs Be Separated? In hauling ewes with lambs that are under about six weeks of age, most owners advise separation of the pairs and the loading of the lambs on the upper deck so that they can stay clean and be more quickly claimed by their mothers on arrival. Especially is this advisable when the sheep have been on washy spring feed and are to be hauled more than a hundred miles. It is found that if a few (three or four) ewes are put into each compartment with the lambs, they will be relatively quiet and will not pile up on each other. Division of the upper deck into more than two compartments will be found helpful, too. When the lambs average over six weeks in age the general opinion is that they may as well ride with their mothers, and of course this eliminates the need for separation through a dodge chute and also allows quicker and heavier loading of carriers. When large trucks and trailers have been ordered and it appears that the load will not quite fill the last one of a truck-trailer combination, a "bobtail" truck (one without a trailer) can be ordered at little or no penalty.

Truck Bed Space. Trucks and trailers are generally described as having so many feet of bed space, this referring to the over-all length of the truck and trailer beds. Most beds measure 7 ft 8 in. inside, with an over-all width of 8 ft outside. Of course the inside width and length are the figures to use in determining the square footage of decks. Double-decked outfits naturally represent twice the floor space of the single deck, and this total, divided by the space requirements for the type of sheep to be shipped, should give the approximate number of sheep that the carrier will hold. Some trucks have rounded ends or cutoff corners, and some allowance will have to be made for these.

Minimum truck weights are confusing. The "minimum weight" requirement for large truck and trailer outfits varies considerably with areas, states, and even individual truckers within areas. This weight is the weight of stock that the given conveyor is capable of handling. The figure (usually painted in plain view on the truck rack) is the minimum weight upon which charges will be based. If less than this weight is loaded, the shipper still will be required to pay for the "minimum." This weight is supposed to be based on 90% of the aggregate of maximum carrying capacity, but the variations now found indicate that a shipper needs to check this weight with the square footage provided to make sure he obtains the proper allowance.

Shipping by rail is suited to certain classes of sheep. Many western sheepmen ship fat lambs and ewes to Kansas City, Chicago, and other eastern markets at certain times of the year, and in the past a great deal of this movement has been by rail. With decreased sheep population and increased human population on the West Coast, less of such movement now occurs, and a good many sheep from the Intermountain areas now move both west and east by truck. Still, there is much railroad movement to the West Coast from as far away as Texas and South Dakota, and some movement to Mississippi Valley markets from the West Coast. *Railroad rates are much cheaper* than truck rates, but because of speed of delivery, lessening of shrinkage possibilities, and ease of pickup from the field, trucking is generally preferred. Where breeding ewes, feeder lambs, or replacement ewe lambs are shipped for any considerable distance, rail shipment is more commonly used because shrinkage is not such an important item with these classes of sheep as with those destined for immediate slaughter. This fact, however, does not make it any less desirable that competent help accompany such shipments to prevent undue exposure or that any but the best feeding procedures be used at rest unloadings. This latter item has been generally poorly supervised by sheep owners.

Piling up in Railroad Cars. Stock cars are long and in comparison with a similar length in trucks they have no (or only one) cross panel unless more are supplied by the shipper. This is a bad feature because it is almost impossible to "stretch out" a string of railroad cars or to bring it to a complete stop without a decided jerk. This jerk invariably causes animals to pile up, and if they are not strong or are weakened by long hours in the cars, it means death loss. A conscientious attendant with such a shipment can save some of the loss.

Shipments of sheep comprising ten or more cars generally are handled more expeditiously by the railroads than shipments of one or two cars intermixed with other freight, which frequently requires sorting or switching at division points. A great deal of variation is experienced in shipping different loads over the same route at different times. Much worse consequences are suffered by sheep in a shipment that requires 8 or 9 days than in one requiring only 3 days.

Stock cars owned by different railroads *vary in measurement,* both as to length and width, so that no definite recommendation can be made concerning the carrying capacity of a 36-ft or a 40-ft car without qualifications. Table 5 shows large and small stock cars in both the 36-ft and 40-ft classes with the square footage supplied by each. Although cars of all these sizes do not belong to any one railroad company, they all may be found on any line, as cars are traded freely among the different lines. When cars are ordered by a stock shipper, any that are available may be sent to the loading corral. The eight cars indicated in Table 5 are the extremes in capacity. There are many common sizes between the extremes shown. However, the freight agent cannot definitely assure the shipper what will be the carrying capacity of the cars ultimately spotted for him. It therefore becomes the task of the careful shipper

Table 5

LARGE AND SMALL 40-FT AND 36-FT RAILROAD STOCK CARS

Space reckoned to nearest square foot

	Large 40	Diff. in space	Small 40	Large 36	Diff. in space	Small 36
			DOUBLE-DECK CARS			
Inside measurement..	40'6" × 8'6"–9'		40'4" × 8'5"	36'6" × 8'10"		35'7" × 8'1"
Space per deck......	365 sq ft per deck	23 sq ft per deck	342 sq ft per deck	324 sq ft per deck	36 sq ft per deck	288 sq ft per deck
Railroad line........	U.P.		G.N.	S.P.-W.P.-U.P.		G.N.
			SINGLE-DECK CARS			
Inside measurement..	40'5" × 9'2"		39'11" × 8'3"	36'6" × 8'10"		36' × 8'0"
Space per deck......	362 sq ft	33 sq ft	329 sq ft	322 sq ft	34 sq ft	288 sq ft
Railroad line........	T.&N.O.		Santa Fe	W.P.-U.P.-D.&G.W.		S.P.-T.&N.O.

to check car measurements and calculate his own loading rate after the cars appear.

In the table it can be seen that the difference in footage between the largest and the smallest 40-ft double-deck car is 23 sq ft per deck or 46 sq ft for both decks. This represents enough space to carry nineteen 70-lb wool lambs, and if this extra number were crowded into the smaller 40-ft car, it could mean loss. The difference between a large and a small single-deck 40-ft car is even greater—33 sq ft, enough to carry thirteen or fourteen 70-lb wooled lambs. Similar differences exist in the 36-ft cars.

Variation in car size may cause loss. Most shippers are unaware of this variation in car sizes and assume that all 36-ft or 40-ft cars are the same size. It would pay a shipper to take time to make a definite check of car measurements, to figure actual square footage, and to load individual cars differently according to his calculations.

The difference between the largest double-deck 36-ft and the smallest double-deck 40-ft car is 17 sq ft per deck or 34 sq ft for the two decks, enough space for fourteen 70-lb wooled lambs. A comparison of the largest single-deck 36-ft car with the smallest single-deck 40-ft car shows the latter to have only 7 sq ft more loading space, or enough for 3 more 70-lb wooled lambs. In spite of these vary small differences in capacity between the two lengths, the "minimum weight" or load for all single-deck cars of 36-ft length is 12,000 lb and for all single-deck 40's it is 13,300. For all 36-ft doubles the "minimum" is 20,000 lb and for all 40-ft doubles 22,100 lb.

Stockmen feel it unfair that the same minimum weight be charged for cars that vary so much in actual loading space. Not only does the shipper run the danger of loss of livestock if he fails to figure actual carrying rates of cars, but he also runs the risk of being charged too heavily for one car as against another unless he takes time to do some figuring. It is probably impossible for the railroads to iron out these differences on cars presently on the rails, but it would seem to their interests to cooperate to the extent that future replacements all be built to uniform length and width standards that are in keeping with their minimum weight charges.

Of course the minimum weight is important only to the shipper whose load will not reach the "minimum" for the car. He pays for the actual net weight of his shipment if it exceeds the minimum, but if it is less than the minimum, he still must pay the minimum, as has previously been noted. Light-weight lambs, especially in the wool (unshorn), and wooly ewes that are thin, usually cannot be loaded heavily enough to reach the minimum, so that an extra fee must be paid.

When should cars be ordered? To ensure that the cars are on hand when the time for shipping arrives, a stock man certainly should confer with his freight agent well ahead of that date. Sometimes cars are scarce in the neighborhood and are difficult to accumulate on short notice. Sheepmen customarily order double-deck 36-ft cars. The freight rate on doubles is less than that for single decks. If 36-ft cars in sufficient numbers are not immediately available, the railroad reserves the right to furnish cars of other descriptions and may supply 40-ft doubles, or singles in either size, to replace the cars ordered. When this is done the sheepman is charged the minimum for the car weights he has actually ordered (in this case 20,000 lb) unless his load surpasses this figure. The shipper should inspect all cars to see that they are in good repair and properly bedded before loading. Usually clean sand is preferable.

If a shipper feels that he may not have enough space, he can order what is called a trailer. This is a single-deck car with a minimum weight of 11,000 lb. If, upon loading, he finds that the trailer wasn't needed after all, his only expense is that charged for sanding.

Making Out the Contract. After the cars are loaded, the freight agent makes out the livestock contract, and it is important in view of unforeseen future exigencies that this be entirely filled in. The agent should be notified *before loading* to count the animals into the cars, and the correct number should be noted in the contract. Charles E. Blaine, who for many years has been traffic manager for the California Wool Growers Association, advises that a shipper should refuse to accept contracts bearing the notation "shipper's load and count" or similar statements. The contract should show the number, kinds, and lengths of cars ordered, and the same data for those actually furnished. The time of loading on the date loaded is important, too. Information on hoof weights furnished by the shipper at the point of origin should be included, or the railroad should be requested to weigh the animals in transit, usually at or near the destination. Such a weighing will provide a low figure for calculation of freight charges.

Feeder lambs or any sheep that are not destined for slaughter within less than thirty days after their arrival at the point of destination are carried by the railroads at a lower rate, and their shipment should therefore be written up on a different contract form. This is important, and the freight agent should be advised that the animals are of this nature.

When animals are purchased as feeder lambs and the intention is to transport them to some feeding center and then later on to market them, still another kind of contract is written. This is called a *feed-in-transit* contract, and the rates beyond the feeding point and to market are much cheaper than the slaughter lamb rate would be.

When a feed-in-transit contract is drawn, it becomes the duty of the shipper to register his freight bill with the freight agent at the feeding point. He then holds the bill through the feeding period and turns it over to the same freight agent when the lambs are shipped to market after being fattened. It should be kept in mind that *feed-in-transit rates must be requested* before shipment from the point of origin and must be a part of the shipping contract.

When mixed shipments are made, the owner may want one or two cars handled in a manner different from the others. For instance, if there are two cars of ewes with lambs, it would be desirable to unload them (at rest and feeding points) into a single corral so that lambs can mother up before reloading. If this request is written into the contract, the railroad will take care of the sheep in this manner.

Feeding of sheep at rest points is very important in avoiding shrinkage and shipping-fever loss. The shipper may request the amount of hay he wishes to have fed per car. It is common practice to feed two bales of alfalfa hay, about 200 to 250 lb *per deck,* unless otherwise ordered. This would amount to about 1 1/2 lb per head (to be cleaned up in about 5 hours) and under ordinary circumstances is enough feed. However, if weather and feeding conditions are not perfect, the sheep may not fill. This is a situation wherein a conscientious attendant to the animals or the owner himself can do the sheep much good. Many rest corrals have no feeding facilities, and hay must be thrown onto the corral floor. Under wet or muddy conditions much of the hay will not be consumed. A good sheepman accompanying the sheep certainly should be able to find ways to fill his charges that could not be expected of a railroad employee.

Get a copy of the contract. The shipper should request that he get the *original and one copy* of the contract. If the sheep are to be turned over to another person (as for feeding and later transport to market), a copy of the car order and the shipping contract should be mailed to him immediately after shipment.

Thirty-Six Hour Release. The law states that all animals are to be unloaded and *fed and rested for 5 hours* or more at feeding points at the end of each 28 hours they are on the cars. However, the owner may, and generally does, give permission that this period may be extended to 36 hours. His written permission is called a "36-hour release." Whether he should sign such a release depends upon several factors. If the shipping point is a considerable distance from a freight terminal where rest would ordinarily be provided, and if many small towns intervene (these demanding stops for switching) and the shipment *goes out on a "local" train, it is usually wise to sign such a release.* Such trains travel slowly and must stop often to drop cars or to pick up others, so that without the 36-hour release it might become necessary for the railroad to unload the sheep at some point where it would be difficult to provide them with experienced care. On the other hand, for some classes of sheep the 36-hour trip could be excessive and cause loss. Such sheep might be weakened ewes or lambs coming from a drought area, or lambs that had been uncommonly exposed before or during shipment. If in the opinion of the shipper there is little excuse for the animals not to make a regular feed yard within 28 hours, he should refuse to sign the 36-hour release.

The Important Man-in-Charge. The sheep owner has the privilege of sending a man along at no extra cost to see that the animals are properly fed and watered at stopping points and to take special care of valuable animals in the shipment. If ewes are lambing during the time of shipment, he can save many lambs by congregating the pairs in one end of the cars behind panels. This will have to be done at the rest points. If valuable rams are being shipped, it may be desirable to provide feeders and waterers in the cars so that they can be fed at the ordinary 12-hour intervals. Perhaps of most frequent occurrence will be the need or desirability of making sure that replacement ewe lambs (generally in feeder flesh only and just off their mothers) have every chance to fill and get watered fully at rest points.

For ordinary shipments, as of big fat lambs that have learned to eat hay or of dry older ewes, a man in charge may not be necessary. The railroads generally have experienced men at their regular feeding yards who do a good job of getting the sheep fed and watered. However, along a route that seldom handles sheep shipments, it is quite likely that the animals will be somewhat neglected. Needless to say, any person sent in charge of a shipment should know what sheep require and energetically go about providing their needs. Certainly the aggregate of losses due to incompetency here totals a staggering sum.

Waybills and Freight Bills. At the point of origin of a shipment the freight agent prepares *waybills* which travel with the animals. At the destination or transit point (for feed-in-transit shipments) the agent uses these to make out his freight bills.

Death or Damage Claims. It is not normal for severe shipping losses to occur, but not infrequently minor losses do and occasionally there are severe losses. If the shipper feels that such losses have been due to carelessness on the part of the railroad, he should *submit a claim for damage.* Accompanying the claim should be the original paid freight bill and the original or a certified copy of the livestock contract. In addition, some real evidence of the value of the animals involved should be provided. This may be the bill of sale or a certified copy of it.

Mr. Blaine, the California Wool Growers traffic manager, states that if animals are short, dead, or crippled, when a shipment is received at a destination, it is highly important that the freight agent make a notation across the face of the freight bill to that effect. A shipper is wholly within his rights to refuse payment for the freight until such time as the agent makes this notation.

How Should Sheep Be Handled before Shipping and During Shipment?

Travel is extremely enervating (even to animals), and every effort should be made properly to prepare any sheep destined for a several-day journey. Even a one-day trip demands some precautions. It is inadvisable to ship just-shorn sheep as they are more likely to contract pneumonia in the moving cars. At least a 10-day pelt is proper, especially if they are to travel through areas where storms may be encountered.

Ewes in late pregnancy are particularly susceptible to car sickness, so that care should be taken to withhold heavy feed for some hours before they are loaded. Ewes that lamb in cars of course are in a very critical condition. If there is chance that any number may produce while en route, a good man should be sent along to care for them.

Fed lambs should have no grain and little hay for two feedings before they are loaded. In such condition, they arrive at commission yards hungry and anxious for a fill whereas, overfull upon loading, they are often carsick and do not fill well previous to their sale and weighing.

Car sickness can be avoided. As already noted, one of the more common mistakes made by shippers concerns *overfeeding before shipping.* This applies equally to train and truck shipments. Ewes or lambs that have been "trailed" to a shipping corral and allowed to fill up on lush feed along the road or about the corral, especially if the weather is warm, are very liable to become sick when shipped. It may also result from overfeeding of hay in the corral. Anything that causes a condition of overheating, overeating, and overdrinking brings on this sickness. Affected lambs show evidence of pain and may kick or bite at their bellies. They may lie down and refuse to rise. Generally the lambs recover soon if they are not disturbed, but some will later lie around a great deal, appear listless, and have humps in their backs and droopy ears—all evidence of injury. Ewes usually exhibit what stockmen call the "blind staggers," acting blind and stumbling about. Later they lie down and refuse to rise, fall into a deep stupor, and die. Gritting of the teeth, groaning, and signs of abdominal discomfort are present, and some ewes tremble and salivate excessively. After shipment the symptoms may be apparent among various animals for several days. Deaths may continue for another week. In general the symptoms are similar to those seen in ewes affected by lambing paralysis.

That car sickness is not limited to pregnant ewes is shown by the following description of a particular case. A small flock of ewes suckling lambs was pastured on green volunteer barley heavily infiltrated with bur clover, a very palatable combination for sheep.

On a very warm day they were driven, in the middle of the afternoon, from shade in the pasture, a distance of three quarters of a mile and toward evening were left in a corral with shade and water. At seven-thirty that evening they were turned into a lush pasture of clover for the night. At seven-thirty the next morning they were grazed slowly toward a gate in the field, crossed a roadway, and were corraled. At nine o'clock a truck arrived and they were loaded and hauled about 70 miles to an auction. For about an hour and a half they stood in the heat in a line of trucks waiting to be unloaded. Two ewes had to be pushed and dragged out of the truck and were in no condition to go through the ring. The others, apparently normal, but very warm and full of feed, went through the ring and were sold within a half-hour. That evening at eight o'clock the sheep were again loaded. Three more ewes were affected and were unable to walk, and it is supposed that they died within the next few days.

In other cases where similar conditions (full stomachs and heat) existed but where hauls were longer, as much as 20% of the shipment has been lost!

This would not be regarded as a disease but appears to be a pretty mortal thing caused by injury to the digestive tract. Nothing so well characterizes a good sheepman as moderation. This applies to many things aside from shipping sheep, and easy changes of feeds or of feeding habits is regarded as extremely good sheep management.

Hot Weather Shipping Advice. Avoidance of car sickness in a case such as that described above would include "trailing" the sheep to corrals during the *evening of the day before* they are to be loaded. This will counter some of the heat effect and give the sheep a chance to rest, void some of their fill, and ease up pressures in their stomachs. Animals coming off dry pastures would rarely if ever be too full to load, but when food along roadways is green and palatable they may easily overeat. If possible, *load the sheep in the cool* of evening or of morning. Sometimes this is difficult because a switch engine is not on hand at the appointed time or the trucks do not arrive. An owner has every right to demand and expect promptness on the part of shipping agencies and should be forceful in his demands.

Can affected animals be treated? The answer to this question is not very heartening, but some instruction may be beneficial. Affected animals should be excited as little as possible and should be left in the shade with (especially) a chance to drink some cool, clear water. A little good hay should be provided, too. It may, and generally does, become necessary to water each sheep from a bucket frequently. If many ewes are affected, it would be good sense to call a veterinarian to recommend the best means of nursing them.

Shipping fever is a constant threat. This disease, technically known as hemorrhagic septicemia, is most often a resultant of shipping and is especially prevalent among lambs coming off the range and being shipped long distances. Ewes also are affected, but lambs much more frequently and disastrously. Such lambs are usually not accustomed to drinking from a water trough or to eating hay. Also they are in strange surroundings at the rest points and to some extent are afraid to eat. The combination results in little real rest for them and in partial starvation. If they are not very well cared for and fed the leafiest of green hay under conditions that are made attractive for them, they usually arrive gaunt and hungry. If they are exposed to storm, wetness, and cold winds en route, they are further weakened. Too, open stock cars are drafty.

Incidentally, one of the most effective agents toward alleviating the condition that the author has seen are the watering troughs provided for lambs in the railroad yards at Klamath Falls, Oregon. Most hauls going to California from the Oregon and Washington ranges are fresh off the range and the lambs are used to drinking from streams. where of course the water is in motion. The original ordinary troughs in the yards were replaced by circular concrete troughs, half of which extend into adjacent corrals under the fence. Each of these troughs has a drain at the center, and water is caused to circulate in the trough by directing the continuous flow from a faucet at the outer edge. Lambs fill very readily and then eat hay well at this yard.

The symptoms of shipping fever generally appear shortly after the lambs reach their destination. Many lambs simply refuse to eat or drink, even after rest. Their eyes are dull or weepy, and often there is a nasal discharge that hardens at the nostrils, causing difficult breathing. They cough lightly and generally exhibit a weak, feverish appearance. Temperatures range from 103 to 108 degrees.

Lambs begin dying very soon if no treatment is given, and sometimes, even with treatment, deaths continue for as long as a month after shipment. Many of the chronic cases show evidence of pneumonia upon autopsy, and those that do ultimately recover have generally lost so much weight while sick that they never reach a suitable (or profitable) finish. Mortality can readily be 10 to 25%.

Shall we vaccinate for shipping fever? Veterinarians are not all agreed as to the benefits of preventive vaccination against this disease. Some recommend vaccination, given 10 to 14 days before shipping, or an antiserum (more costly) given just before shipping or upon arrival. The trouble seems to be that the same causative agent may not be involved in every outbreak. Usually militating against vaccination 10 to 14 days previous to shipping is that lambs are not often available (off ranges) at a convenient spot at such a time. Range owners of course balk at pulling out lambs for vaccination when they have not yet actually been weighed and sold.

Careful handling of lambs before shipping and during the shipment is most effective in avoiding a flare-up of the disease. Upon arrival, too, *immediate* attention to watering and the filling of lambs, preferably on dry or drying pasture or with leafy hay (without molasses) is helpful. Such lambs should be bothered as little as possible and given several days to rest from the trip before being treated for worms, shorn, or fed grain. Any group of lambs that has been on the road for several days should be regarded as just *on the edge of shipping fever* and should be very carefully handled.

A very interesting sidelight on the cause and prevention of this disease is provided by Dr. Arthur C. Rosenberger, a former California Chief State Veterinarian. He has long urged shippers to see that their sheep and lambs are properly fed and rested from the time they leave their home range until they arrive at their new feeding grounds or feed lot. He believes that lack of sufficient feed every day, regularly, has been the most important cause of losses and quotes work of the Colorado Experiment Station in support of this belief:

"From all outbreaks, a member of the *parathyphoid* B group (Salmonella aertryche) was shown to be the cause of the disease. It is believed that this organism is a normal resident of the intestinal tract of some sheep and that it develops excessive virulence under certain predisposing conditions. Hunger was shown to be a strong predisposing cause.

"Since 5 cc. of a bouillon culture of the organism had previously been shown to be fatal to a lamb fasted for 48 hours, it will be seen (in the accompanying table) that even 6 times this amount did not affect a lamb having free access to alfalfa hay. That the organism was necessary in the production of the disease was shown by lamb No. 5 that withstood fasting for 72 hours without showing signs of illness. It appears therefore that two causes operate—first, the organism, and second, fasting.

"Neither is sufficient in itself to cause the disease, but both operating together may result in serious outbreaks.

"Prevention.—Assuming that an organism of the parathyphoid group is present in many flocks, little can be done to prevent exposure. Since animals can withstand considerable doses of the organism if fed regularly, prevention seems to be this simple procedure."

TEST SHOWS RESULT OF EXPERIMENT ON RELATION TO FASTING

Lamb number	Fasted for:	Amount of culture fed	Results
1	24 hrs.	30 cc.	Sick 4th day, died 6th
2	48	30 cc.	Sick 2nd day, died 5th
3	72	30 cc.	Sick 2nd day, died 4th
4	72, watered	30 cc.	Sick 3rd day, died 4th
5	72	none	No illness
6	fed & watered	30 cc.	No illness

Loading Sheep into Carriers

It takes a man who has worked closely with sheep to be a good loader because only such a person understands the timing so necessary to suit the natural urges of the animals. Usually it is best to put 8 or 10 animals into the chute approach, give them a good scare so that they will go up the rise on the run, and then quickly slip back along the side of the other animals, urging them on while they can still see the lead group on the move. In case the leaders stop, it is wise to have a man on the outside of the chuteway with a rather large blunt pole with which to poke the lead animal (and perhaps others), quickly withdrawing as they start moving. If he moves *away from the chute* and back toward the start of the rise, his movement generally causes the followers to keep coming in a steady stream. Loud and continuous shouting on the part of the wranglers is not nearly as effective as hissing or scratching sounds made at infrequent intervals, which startle the group into renewed action.

Often it becomes next to impossible to move a lead group of lambs up the chuteway and away from the main group. Helpful at this time is the practice of pulling a lamb up the chute by one front leg while bleating like a sheep. If other helpers urge a succeeding group up to the entrance while this lamb is on the move, usually they will follow. This works best with a shipment of ewes and lambs, a lamb being used as the decoy. He usually will do his own bleating in this case.

Indian Loading Method. A scratching or rustling sound originating on the ground or near the feet of sheep will excite them into action much more effectively than sounds made at higher levels. A very effective job of loading was noted as accomplished by a crew of Navajo Indians in Arizona, two of whom squatted with their faces almost at the ground near the very bottom of the chute. As each sheep was opposite them they barked like small dogs, causing the sheep to jump into the air and charge up the chuteway.

Similar action can be brought about by scratching the ground with a good-sized stick near the hoofs of a passing stream of sheep or by the emission of a shrill squeak made by the tightly pursed lips of a person standing outside but close to the chute.

A rustling branch—a palm frond is especially good—switched at the feet of the moving sheep excites them beautifully. Evidently the reaction is what one might expect a sheep to show if startled by a rattlesnake at its feet.

Do not lift sheep by the wool. All helpers should be cautioned not to do anything while the loading is in progress that would cause bruises (especially to lambs going to the butcher). Kicking or poking with sharp sticks is to be avoided, and certainly the latter is especially dangerous in loading pregnant ewes. Lifting sheep by the wool to stop or turn them pulls the hide away from the carcass and creates a bloody area on the carcass that requires trimming before a sale can be made. This detracts from the appearance of the carcass and lowers its value considerably.

Other instruments assist loading. Electric prods are used with good effect and are as helpful with sheep as with other stock in breaking up a jam. A man's coat slapped on the backs of a balky group helps just as well as do pieces of canvas, etc. One thing is very certain: Anger or impatience which bring about cursing and kicking on the part of loaders is very ineffectual. Persons who resort to such things haven't had much loading experience.

The tin-can "rattler" described in Chapter 6 makes a useful "dog," very effective in startling lambs. They make a great din when shaken but to be effective they must be used only at intervals and just at the crucial moment to cause a bolt. If the cans are shaken continuously, the lambs soon become used to the noise and disregard it.

A driving canvas is extremely useful in bringing up group after group to the loading chute when small pens or a narrow enough alley are lacking. This is a piece of canvas 3 ft wide and about 20 or 30 ft long with a narrow board or pole attached at each end so that it may be carried by two men. Of course, sheep cannot see beyond the canvas, and they are prevented thereby from running back and out of control. Shaking the canvas makes it flap and scares the sheep toward the chute. If metal eyelets are inserted at the corners of the canvas, when the loading crew is short it may be tied across the alley to hold the sheep. Such a canvas is very useful, too, in bringing sheep up to a shearing lead-in alley and in many other places.

Dogs are not good help at loading. Only the most tractable and obedient sheep dog is likely to be of much help at loading. A dog can be tied at the base of the chute rise and sometimes will bark at the right moment, but generally dogs produce more confusion than is good and they are also likely to cause damage to excitable lambs. The confusion usual at loading causes many working dogs to bite. If a puppy or recently broken dog is used, it may start the biting habit, which will be very difficult to break.

Some sheep dogs will jump up on the backs of a tightly packed group of sheep and bark at the lead, then run back over their backs or alongside the group as it starts to move. Often the dog gets pretty well trampled, and at best, few can be trained to do this trick. About the only place for a dog is at the rear of the main band. There one can do a real service but when closer to the chuteway it causes confusion and fright that slows down the loading.

Belled yearling wethers or goats are used in some places to lead sheep into stock cars or trucks and are very helpful. They can be trained to lead the group into the car, circle around the edge of the car, and come back down the chute ready to lead in another deckload. They are most often seen at stockyards where they lead groups to the scales or onto the killing floors of packing plants.

Night Loading Practices. When it becomes necessary to load animals in the dark, a dim light is preferred to a bright, blinding one. It should be set high and at the rear of the chute, shining up the chute and into the car. For unloading, a flashlight may be wired at the upper end of the chute and shine down the chute just above the level of the sheep's heads. Bright lights blind animals coming out of darkness and once in the bright area they are afraid to go forward into the dark again. Where possible in loading it usually helps to drive a band of ewes out beyond the chute so that the sheep being loaded will hear them and be attracted in their direction.

Sunlight and dust, or night lights and dust stirred up by the sheep, make a very bad loading situation. Sheep are so blinded by the reflection that they have no idea of where to move. Unless the dust can be allayed in some way, it becomes necessary to push the sheep one by one up the chute or even to carry them! This has been done more than once and is surely a difficult procedure. A little planning and preparation can save a great deal of heavy labor when loading.

Unloading of sheep from cars or trucks is generally fairly easy because sheep can see their leaders moving at the lower level and will follow. However, lambs are usually very hard to start. A few may be pushed out of the exit, and if they start, a man inside should very quickly start *turning heads* of others so that they can see the first ones. As in loading, often it becomes necessary to pull one lamb out by one front foot and to bleat to attract others.

Loading Chutes. Figure 102 shows a permanent loading chute for sheep as used on a clover fattening ranch that ships lambs frequently from the fields by truck. This chute is raised and lowered to truck deck levels very easily because it is counterbalanced by a system of weights and pulleys. Its lower edge is not hinged, so that it can be extended or pulled back. The diagram shows one side of the chute approach removed so that the back of the chute and the slide board are visible. An angle iron on the underside of the front end of the chute serves to catch it to the truck. However, to ensure that it doesn't slip as the sheep climb it, it is wise to fix it to the truck with a light chain, too. Although not shown, the floor-way of the chute must be cleated at about 6-in. intervals so that sheep will not slip as they climb (or descend).

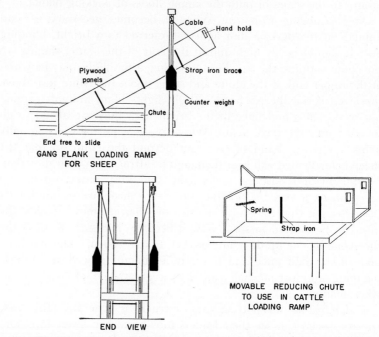

Fig. 102. Devices for loading lambs into trucks at the ranch.

Ordinarily sheep and cattle are loaded from separate chutes. There are dual-purpose chutes, but they are fairly complicated in design and are expensive. It is desirable, however, to have a chute that can be adapted to load all classes of stock.

Combination Cattle and Sheep Chute. Figure 102 also shows a cattle chute containing a small sheep chute to be set up for loading the upper deck or to be used, as shown, for loading the lower deck. Small flap doors are hinged at the back end of the small chute, and these doors are chained back to the side of the larger passageway for cattle to close off the extra space. The ordinary cattle chute is 34 to 36 in. wide, whereas a sheep chute should not be over 14 to 18

in. wide or the sheep will have a tendency to attempt to turn
around in it.

When cattle are to be loaded, of course the sheep chute must
be taken out. Since it must be moved by hand, it should be constructed of light but tough material and be well braced. Three-ply
plywood and 3/4-in. boards are suitable for such lightweight ap-
pliances.

The sliding panel is used to extend the chute sides for the loading
of cattle. Many commercial cattle trucks are equipped with drop
gates, hinged to the trucks, which drop down onto the chute floor
to close the space between it and the truck. If such gates are not
present, 2-in. planks are bolted to crosspieces to make a drop board
that fits into this space. These boards should be cleated, too.

WHAT THINGS SHOULD DETERMINE
WHEN I SHOULD SELL?

The considerations regarding the time to sell milk fat lambs will
differ considerably from those applying to fed lambs, pasture fattened lambs, or other stock, especially in the arid West.

"Spring" lambs (milk fat lambs) represent far the greatest bulk
of sheep movement, and as far as the West is concerned, they go
to market *when they are heavy enough* or when *feed conditions
force them.*

It is natural that a sheep owner should wish to get the largest
number of dollars per head of lamb sold as he can. The high price
generally results from a large number of pounds of lamb per individual rather than from a high number of cents per pound. The
sheep producer who is able to make a great percentage of his crop
weigh many pounds as individuals is far ahead of one who can
command a high price per pound for a small percentage and then
may suffer a low dollar income for many others because of poor
feed, poor management, or other items.

There is a limit of lamb weight, of course, beyond which the
price per pound offered will decrease. Twenty years ago the text-
books professed that a 75-lb lamb was of ideal weight and most
suited to the use of the housewife. This may still be true, but since
the two World Wars it has also been increasingly true that heavier
weight lambs have been used at no lowering of price. This has

encouraged (incidentally) the handling of larger framed ewes and ram breeds that are considerably longer bodied than those used in former years and whose offspring grow at a faster rate.

Most sheep owners do make *more than one shipment* of their lambs, topping out the heavier and generally older lambs early and holding others for more weight or better condition. But when should the first lambs be sold? This decision should properly result

Fig. 103.   Young lamb feeders reap the reward of a "Grand Champion Car-load" award.

from a recognition of feed conditions in relation to market prices and weights of the lambs. One other factor, the "bloom" or finish of the lambs, will affect the decision.

This, then, may be a good guide as to when to ship lambs (before drying spring feed forces the final sale) :

Get them off to the butcher as heavy as possible without having many that are overheavy or commencing to lose bloom (drying out). Thus adequate lamb feed will be left to allow the others to finish, in bloom, before the feed dries and stickers halt further gain.

At present many lambs sired by the large blackface breeds, Suffolk and Hampshire, and out of the crossbred-wool type of ewes or large, smooth Rambouillets, do have plenty of bloom when they are as large as 115 lb if they have come off of bountiful sweet lamb feed. This, however, is a big "if," and no sheep owner should attempt to attain such a weight average where feed conditions cannot maintain the bloom on lambs to such sizes.

The sheep owner in the West is always cognizant of *his position in relation to rainfall.* No series of years presents uniform moisture conditions to keep natural feed in shape, so that what the sheep owner was able to do this year in regard to shipping his lambs is no indication of what he may accomplish next year. One thing is inevitable in the arid West. The feed will dry up. The consequences of this as far as lambs are concerned have been discussed in Chapter 7. If a band of sheep cannot be moved to higher elevations to prolong their freedom from "stickers," they must be shipped or shorn— and most range producers will ship. A lamb will not gain once the sharp awns of these grasses cause them to bite at their legs or kick at their bellies or scratch themselves excessively on the fences.

HOW CAN I GET MOST RETURN
FOR EACH LAMB PRODUCED?

Produce the lambs over a short lambing period, from good uniform ewes and excellent purebred rams, grow them rapidly on natural sweet feeds, supplement the range through creep feeding, get each lamb as heavy as possible but still in "bloom," and sell before stickers slow or stop gains.

HOW SHOULD AGED EWES BE MARKETED?

The sale of aged ewes from the band presents a great problem to sheep owners, many of whom do not find an altogether satisfactory solution. Most range outfits continually operated will have 150 ewes to sell annually out of 1000 breeding females if normal conditions exist. In other words, about 15% of the breeding herd will naturally need to be marketed simply because of age if the normal 7-year age limit holds for the band. Under range conditions (with whiteface ewes) this figure is about correct. Ewes produce first as they near 2 years and have their fifth lamb crop as they approach 7 years of age. Such ewes are often able to produce one or two more crops if they don't have to do so under the rigors of range operations, but they fade away fast if required to produce beyond that number.

This fact may indicate *a good plan for disposing of the aged ewes*. Find some operator who can carry the ewes on soft feed and protect them from the elements. If such a man can be found, he is usually willing to spend a few dollars more for the better aged ewes, at least, than can generally be realized for them from the butcher. This business of handling old ewes on soft feed is a standard procedure in some sections of the West. Of note is the program in the Imperial Valley at the southernmost tip of California. Here every year thousands of aged ewes are lambed in November and December on alfalfa pasture which in these months cannot be cured for hay. In this great irrigated area of practically no rainfall the ewes have an abundance of such feed all "winter" and are fat and in bloom all through the lamb-growing period. (See Fig. 19b). Under these conditions the aged ewes appear to be young and often can produce two or three crops past the 7-year-old stage.

It must be emphasized here, however, that such a program cannot be uniformly successful unless the purchaser of the aged ewes can really provide *plenty of such soft feed and adequate winter protection in areas where the weather conditions are at all severe*.

This latter point is one, then, that does make necessary *the disposal of a large percentage of aged ewes to the butcher*. Here a matter of great import must be considered, and perhaps only the individual sheepman's experience over a period of years can provide the answer to the question at exactly what age of the ewe should he sell her.

These are the facts: An aging ewe may look and actually be in good condition some time after she has recovered from suckling her lamb. In such shape she may pass the cutting gate and go on into the breeding flock for another year. (If no earmarking plan has been used in a band to denote the *actual* age of ewes and a good job of mouthing has not been done, it is very possible to pass many old ewes as being younger than they are.) The next winter or spring when *the usual bad feed period* comes on and this old ewe is suckling lambs again, she will fade very fast and very badly— in fact often become so debilitated that she may die in a short time or never recover and will have to be sold as a "shell." In such shape, ewes have little value for food and have often been shipped without realizing that they would hardly be worth the cost of their freight. It behooves the sheep owner, therefore, to scrutinize his ewe band very closely each summer after the lamb crop has been weaned or sold and to make sure that the aged ewes go. Whether he sells them when they are 6, 7, or 8 years of age will depend on the owner's experience with his particular feed and weather conditions, but it is far wiser to sell a year early when the ewes are fat than to hold them too long.

Another important consideration regarding the old ewes is *just what time of year to sell*. Many ewes go to the butchers when the lamb crop has been gone a few weeks. This strong movement of ewes has a depressing effect on the ewe market, and if it is possible for an owner to market them at some other time, he can generally realize a considerably greater return. For example, ewes that are old (and also younger barren or shy-breeding ewes) and those that did not lamb the past season should go to market perhaps even *before* the lambs are marketed. This will serve a twofold purpose, namely, conservation of feed and the likelihood of a better price per pound for the ewes because of the less congested market. (Where the drop band system of lambing has been used, all such ewes are to be found in the group that lambs last. By all means, these ewes should be kept separate and to them should be added other ewes with spoiled udders or those aged ones, at least, that lose lambs to predators, etc., during the lamb-growing season.)

On the other hand, the aging ewes that have raised their last crop might better be disposed of somewhat later in the fall if they can be fattened somewhat on feed such as good stubble, held particularly for them. The temptation to keep them another year should be strongly resisted, should they fatten well. Grain and hay (dry-lot) fattening is not generally a paying proposition with old ewes.

It is recommended that the annual record of prices paid for old ewes at a sheepman's market be carefully studied, so that marketings may be made to advantage. Of recent years fat, aged ewes have sold at about 140 lb for as much as $0.16 per pound, or for a total of $22.40, whereas at other times of the year "shells" at about 90 lb sold for as little as $0.05 per pound, or $4.50 per head.

Some sheep owners have avoided all chance of such a catastrophe by selling 5-year-old ewes and additionally breeding their ewe lamb replacements to lamb at 14 months of age. If a type of sheep husbandry can be maintained that makes such a program possible, it is certainly desirable, but it is likely to be limited to early-lambing areas where irrigated pastures are available to grow out and flush ewe lambs for such early breeding. Too, a buyer willing to pay extra for the 5-year-old ewes must be available.

In a few spots in the West sheep owners located close to a beet sugar factory have gotten one extra lamb crop by carrying the old ewes through the winter and lambing them under confinement by feeding wet beet pulp. Other similar types of feed, such as silage, can be used.

Chapter 10

Growing Wool, Shearing, and Marketing Wool

Wool growth on a sheep depends to a large extent on how well that sheep thrives. If the flock is losing weight, the wool growth will suffer—perhaps not in exactly direct proportion, but a definite deficiency can easily be noted. On the other hand, when ewes keep on an even keel throughout the year, are not pulled down too heavily by the suckling lambs, and gain toward shearing time, good fleece weights and strong, bright fibers will result. This may mean considerably more income for the sheep owner.

It is not the purpose of this text to discuss wool technically but simply to point out to growers means by which they can grow a maximum product in all respects and gain thereby. Many publications are available that give complete information on the properties of the fiber, but with few exceptions, knowledge concerning these properties is not directly applicable to the farmer's particular interest: how to produce and how to get the most return from his product.

How Valuable Is a Good Clip in Relation to a Plain One?

The answer to this question of course varies with the dollar value of the grades of scoured (washed) wool, but it is simple to hypothesize and easy to give examples of differences in value of well-grown versus poorly grown clips of the same grade. The further enormous difference in values of clips of varying grade is even more startling.

Wool is graded basically on the characters of length and diameter, although another item that does not appear in any description of grade, namely *shrinkage,* may actually have as much or more effect upon price than either length or diameter. If there are any features of wool that a grower should understand in order to get full value for his clip, they are these three.

Diameter of fibers very definitely conditions the value per pound of wool. Usually the finest fibers procure the highest price per pound and the coarsest (carpet wool) the lowest. At times this is not exactly true. The diameter of fibers varies with several things. Foremost, the blood lines of the ewes affect diameter. The Merino sheep have been developed to produce the finest fibers, and the long-wools, such as the Lincoln breed, have been developed with a coarse fiber. It should be kept in mind, however, that a Merino sheep will not necessarily always produce more value per fleece than a Lincoln, but certainly its fleece will practically always have more value per pound.

Secondly, diameter of fiber varies with nutrition. The diameter of a given single fiber on a sheep will often not be uniform in cross section over its length, owing to changes in the nutrition of the sheep through its year. In fact, a section may have as little as one-third the area of another and still not show a "break" to the naked eye. In such condition the fleece is spoken of as being "tender." When a break is apparent to the naked eye, the fibers will have grown for a period so weakly that a definite streak, extending across all the fibers at the same distance from the tip, will indicate the stage when the sheep were really starved (or sick). Such a fleece has much lower value than a uniformly strong-fibered one, and even if it has not reached the "break" stage, a tender fleece will still have less value because it will tear apart in the processing called "combing."

This indicates a point in regard to *length of fiber* of which a wool grower should be aware. Generally, the longer the fiber the better it is (up to a limit imposed by the machines that comb the fibers). Shorter fibers, when combed out parallel to each other in the making of a yarn, will not overlap each other or lay alongside each other for as great a length as will longer fibers. This means that each fiber has less chance to interlock (and the wool fiber is

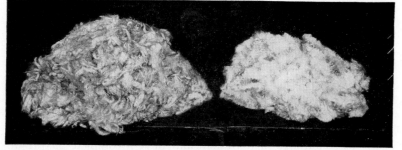

(a)

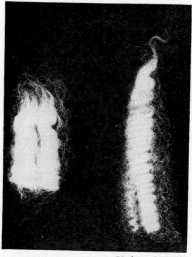

(b)

Fig. 104 (a). Two six-month fleeces produced by the same sheep. On a good ration, weight 8.0 lb; on a poor ration, 2.4 lb.

    (b). Two staples, each grown exactly six months from the same spot on the shoulder of the same sheep, show effect of good and poor ration.

scaled to some extent, fostering a good interlocking character), so that the yarn has less strength and consequently less wearing value than a yarn made of fibers of greater lengths. The grade indication applied to a clip or fleece to denote the length characteristic is either "combing" or "clothing," or for an intermediate length, "French combing." The short form is called "clothing."

Thus if a fleece is spoken of and graded as "3/8 blood combing" or as "64's clothing," a wool man may have a complete picture of its grade. A wool grower should know what these terms mean and further, how they apply to his own clip, because only then can he have any bargaining power in the sale of his wool.

Wool Bureau

Fig. 105. The characteristics of a top fleece: density, brightness, strong crimp, length and low shrink.

The statement was made above that the longer the fiber the better, up to a limit imposed by the combing machines; this statement calls for a moment of consideration. If fibers are too long (in relation to their diameter), the machines built to comb that particular diameter will tear the long lengths into shorter ones. Therefore it is useless to breed sheep to grow wool that is extremely long-fibered in relation to its diameter. This is apparent from Table 6 which shows the minimum lengths that can be combed by present-day machines. It will be noted that the minimums increase as the fibers coarsen. Thus an extremely fine-fibered fleece need not be over 2 1/2 in. long to be combed (and therefore be capable of being spun into valuable yarn), whereas coarser 1/4-blood wool must be longer: 3 1/4 in. (This is partly because the scale on the surface of such wool are larger, and interlocking edges will be farther apart and therefore less strong unless the fiber is longer.) Further, "fine" wool of greater than 2 1/2 in. length has no higher value per pound.

For a sheep owner to be able to judge whether the *price per pound* that is offered him is in line with "the market" (usually Boston), he must know *how his clip grades, what its shrinkage is,* and *how to interpret the terms* under which the values are quoted. For instance, a quotation may state:

1/2 blood clothing, $1.60–$1.70 (clean basis prices)
(Generally several other grades, too, are quoted.)

How can a wool grower know what percentage of his clip may be 1/2 blood or some other diameter, whether it is of combing, French combing, or clothing length, and how much it will shrink, so that he can compare the price of $1.60 (per scoured pound) or some other figure with a figure for wool in the grease at his ranch where someone has offered him 50¢ per pound?

Usually this compound of unknowns is too much for the wool grower and he feels that he has not enough knowledge to make a decision as to the value of his clip; so he takes the best bid he can get and hopes it is somewhere near right. More often, in much of America, he takes whatever price was paid to his neighbor.

All this militates against an incentive to produce a top clip, yet by perseverance and with a few years of experience any intelligent wool producer may become familiar enough with the factors that

Table 6

COMBING-MACHINE LIMITS FOR LENGTH OF FIBERS
OF VARIOUS GRADES OF WOOL

American grades	Bradford counts	Combing	French combing	Clothing
			Approximate length in inches	
Fine	80's 70's 64's	Over 2½	1½ to 2½	Under 1½
½ blood	60's 58's	Over 2¾	1¾ to 2¾	Under 1¾
⅜ blood	56's	Over 3	2 to 3	Under 2
¼ blood	50's 48's	Over 3¼	2¼ to 3¼	Under 2¼
Low ¼ blood	46's	Over 3½	2½ to 3½	Under 2½
Common	44's	Always combing		
Braid	40's 36's	Always combing		

relate to value to enable him to aim toward top production and to realize the maximum return for it.

In order to learn what his clip may actually be worth, he *must know the grades* according to which prices are quoted and be able to distinguish or identify his own wools as to grade. Table 6 shows the grades under the two standards in use in America and the approximate lengths in inches that the combing machines can handle.

In explanation of the "Bradford counts" (the English system), the numbers refer to the number of hanks of yarn that can be spun from one pound of the scoured wool in the form of "tops." A hank is 560 yards, so that a wool grading 80's can be spun so finely that it will make 80×560 yards or over 25 miles of yarn.

The Production and Marketing Administration, U.S. Department of Agriculture, has been supplying weekly quotations of the Boston market to various agencies and including in it further information—translation of the clean basis price into an arbitrary grease value equivalent. This is very valuable in helping a grower determine what his clip should bring if he does have some knowledge of how it shrinks. Table 7 shows a sample of these U.S.D.A. quotations.

Using such a table, a grower who had a reasonable knowledge that of a total 1000 lb of wool, he had 500 lb of fine combing wool that would shrink about 64% and 300 lb of fine clothing that would shrink the same amount, plus 200 lb of 1/2 blood combing that would shrink 54%, could with little arithmetic determine what his clip should be worth in the grease at Boston; then by deducting the shipping cost of 3 to 5¢ per pound (from the West), he could tell whether an offer at his ranch was in line. For example, let us say that he had been offered 50¢ per pound at home. The 500 lb of fine combing would total $500 \times \$0.64$ (average figure) or $320.00. The 300 lb of fine clothing would be worth $300 \times \$0.51$ or $153.00, and the 200 lb of 1/2 blood combing would sell for $200 \times \$0.75$ or $150.00, at Boston. This would total $623.00 or 62.3¢ per pound. If his freight would reduce this by 4¢, the figure would then be 58.3¢ and the 50¢ offer would have been too little.

There are quite a few "ifs" in the above illustration and quite a few uncertainties to be considered. First, can a sheepman know how his clip will be proportioned as to the various grades? Second, how can he be sure of the shrinkage? Third, how much will the

Table 7

DOMESTIC WOOL AND MOHAIR QUOTATIONS ON THE OPEN MARKET AT BOSTON

Week Ending February 1, 1952

Territory Wools

Graded:	Clean Basis Prices	%	Grease Equiv. Based upon Arbitrary Shrinkage Percentages				
				%			%
Fine Combing (Staple)	$1.75–1.80	54	$.80–.83	59	$.72–.74	64	$.63–.65
Fine French Combing	1.65–1.75	55	.74–.79	60	.66–.70	65	.58–.61
Fine Clothing	1.45–1.55	56	.64–.68	61	.56–.60	66	.49–.53
½ Blood Combing (Staple)	1.60–1.65	51	.78–.81	54	.74–.76	57	.69–.71
½ Blood French Combing	1.60–1.70	52	.77–.82	55	.72–.76	58	.66–.70
½ Blood Clothing ..	1.25–1.35	53	.59–.63	56	.55–.59	59	.51–.55
⅜ Blood Combing ..	1.30–1.40	48	.68–.73	51	.64–.69	54	.60–.64
⅜ Blood Clothing ..	1.15–1.25	49	.59–.64	52	.55–.60	55	.52–.56
¼ Blood Combing ..	1.20–1.30	46	.65–.70	48	.63–.68	50	.60–.65
Low ¼ Blood	1.15–1.25	41	.68–.74	43	.66–.71	45	.63–.69
Common and Braid .	1.10–1.20	40	.66–.72	42	.64–.70	44	.62–.67
Original Bags:							
Fine Staple & Gd. Fr. Cb.	$1.70–1.80	57	$.73–.77	59	$.70–.74	61	$.66–.70
Fine Ave. Fr. Combing	1.60–1.70	60	.64–.68	63	.59–.63	66	.54–.58
Fine Short Fr. & Clothing	1.40–1.50	63	.52–.56	65	.49–.52	67	.46–.56

Source: Production and Marketing Administration, U.S. Department of Agriculture.

market change before he gets his wool in the hands of a Boston merchant?

In regard to *proportions of the clip in the various grades,* about the only criterion of value will be previous experience as recorded on the sheet returned to the grower for a clip shipped to be sold on the basis of its grading and shrinkage. If the make-up of the band of sheep has not changed or has changed in a certain known direction, the account sheet of his scoured and graded sale will give the grower a good indication of the make-up of his present clip. As has been indicated, the proportions may be somewhat changed by the condition of the ewes, poor or good nutrition affecting grade to some extent.

For clips that are from bands of very uniform sheep this estimation is relatively easy. There are some (few) producers who grow nothing but fine and 1/2 blood fleeces or an extremely small percentage of any other. Their judgment of the grade percentages can be quite accurate. In fact, there are a few growers with such clips who have learned (pretty much by teaching themselves) the distinction between the two grades they grow and who do actually sort and grade and pack the grades separately. This ability is a goal toward which any wool grower should aspire.

Shrinkage of the clip, and of various parts of the clip, is even more a variable or uncertain quantity than grade. If a grower cannot approximate the shrinkage within 2 to 5% of its actual shrinkage determined when scoured, he cannot hope to argue for a better price or judge properly whether an offer is in line.

The same account (mentioned above) that recorded the grading of the clip previously sold and scoured will have given the shrinkages of the various grades sold. These are probably the best figures a grower can use as a basis for judging shrinkages. It must be borne in mind that because a clip averages a 47% shrinkage one year is no assurance that the same will hold for next year's clip from the same sheep. Many things can change the shrinkage proportion from year to year, but with some experience a wool grower can fairly well tell in which direction and how far the change may go.

Before discussing what factors may change shrinkage, let us investigate what a little difference in shrinkage can do to the wool income check. Referring to Table 7, it will be seen that fine combing quoted clean at Boston at $1.75–$1.80, with a 54% shrinkage would be worth 81.5¢ in the grease, but at a 59% shrinkage it would have a value of only 73¢ and at 64% of only 64¢. A 5% higher shrinkage lowered the grease equivalent value of this particular wool 8.5¢ per pound, and 10% more shrinkage lowered the value 17.5¢ per pound. These figures, applied to a clip of 10,000 lb (from about one band), would mean $850 less for an increase of 5% in shrinkage and $1,750 for a 10% increase.

Some items that change shrinkage are controllable by the sheepowner to some extent, others are not.

Weather variations from one year to the next will change the shrinkage proportion by affecting the amount of dust and dirt that floats into the fleeces. A short, open winter will mean more dry days and more dust than will prevail when the winter is long and damp. An early spring and summer will mean more heat before shearing time and more grease in the wool. It may also mean more vegetable matter in the stickers and burs that matured earlier than usual and

Wool Bureau

Fig. 106. The shearing floor is a busy place. Note holding pens behind shearers, harness on near man to ease his back muscles.

got into the fleeces before the shearing job could be done. On the other hand, a winter of extreme rainfall close to shearing time can wash out much natural grease and yolk and reduce shrinkage. *Heavy winds* during dry parts of the year may drive sand and dust into fleeces, increasing shrinkage.

Changes in feeding grounds can change the shrinkage proportion. Summer and fall grazing in fields where stickers or burs are prevalent, as against feeding in relatively clean stubble, can implant much vegetable impurity in fleeces.

The relative amount of "trailing" of sheep one year and the next can add dust to the fleeces and change the amount of shrinkage. In this regard, farm-flock sheep usually will not suffer as much as herded migratory bands, for they take their time moving in and out from feed and do not stir up so much dust. Even a short trek with a big band of sheep on a very dusty road can raise the shrinkage several per cent.

Postponing the shearing date can greatly affect shrinkage in terms of the amount of grease in the wool. It is always desirable to have enough grease in the wool at shearing time to make the shearing tools cut easily—sheep shearers dislike to shear "dry" fleeces, which slow them down and result in poorer looking work. Of more importance, the wool fiber spins better if it is uniformly coated with its natural secretions previous to being washed. Some portion of the grease penetrates the fiber itself and keeps it soft and pliant through all the processes it undergoes before becoming a fabric. Well-greased fibers are generally thought of as strong, whereas the dry and yolk-starved fleeces are the tender ones.

Therefore, a wool grower should postpone shearing if possible until sufficient warm days have occurred to "bring out the grease" in his fleeces, but often the schedule of the shearers makes it necessary to employ them too early or too late, and great differences can therefore be expected in shrinkage because of the grease content.

Summarizing factors affecting clip value, therefore, it may be said that primarily a high return per fleece is more desirable than a high price per pound. However, the combination of a good weight per fleece and a good price for each pound of it means a maximum of return. High fleece weights—10 lb versus 7 (for range bands)—result from keeping the sheep well fed and the wool fibers well nurtured and conditioned by sufficient natural grease and yolk secretion.

Making sure of a high price per pound depends on reducing shrinkage and keeping the fibers bright and strong—factors which are tied up with good nutrition—plus sufficient knowledge of grades and basic market quotations and their proper interpretation and application to a man's own clip.

It is certainly desirable that every wool grower be able to check his clip for grades, shrinkages, and quality—at some time against an offer made by a wool dealer to be able to establish in his own mind how close the offer comes to the real value of the clip. Often a buyer will have a grading and shrinkage sheet for a man's previous clip and will use it as a basis for an offer. It is to the interest of the grower to have as much knowledge about his clip.

A means of procuring excellent information on the shrinkage of a grower's clip is to have it *core tested*. This recent development has

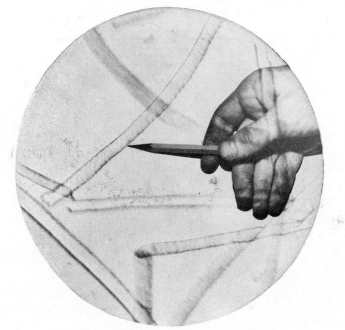

Wool Bureau

Fig. 107. The wool fiber as seen through a microprojector shows the scales clearly in focus.

made possible better prices for some of the larger producers of fine wools and is pretty much limited to such clips. An outline of this system is given at the end of this chapter.

What Is a First-Class Shearing Job?

Other items affect wool value, and among them a reputation for having done a consistently good *shearing job* and *wool-sacking job*

over the years results in better returns. Whether done by the owner himself or by hired shearing crews, a good job of shearing consists of:
1. Removing the fleece in one piece;
2. Making a minimum of "second cuts";
3. Keeping the shorn fleece free of dung and foreign vegetable matter.

There are many excellent sheep shearers who can make large tallies in a day's work and meet all the above requirements reg-

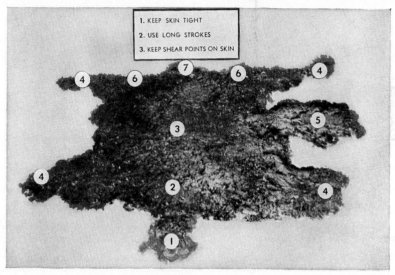

Sunbeam Corp.

Fig. 108.   Cautions when shearing.

ularly. Shearing is difficult to learn and takes much practice. Most shearers are interested in learning the techniques of good men and will listen to their advice and follow their actions because when speed is developed and a clean job goes with it, a day's check is very gratifying. Many good men shear 125 ewes per day, which at the present figure of about 40¢ to the shearer means $50.

The fleece should be removed in one piece and *tied with paper twine* because then, at the mill, it can be opened, laid out on a table, and skirted (separating bellies and less desirable parts) sorted. and graded into portions usable for different types of yarn or fabric. If the fleece is torn apart by violent actions of the sheep due to improper handling by the shearer, or is trod on and pulled apart by the shearer, it is much more difficult to do a good job of grading the clip.

Second cuts should be avoided, or rather prevented, by working no faster than the experience of the shearer will allow him to keep his shearing handpiece close to the hide at every stroke. When he works so fast that his control suffers, he is liable to make a portion of a cut a quarter- to a half-inch away from the hide and then must go back and make a second cut to remove the bit of stubble. (This stubble is called "noil," and a high noiling percentage to a man's clip means a black mark against it.)

The fleece should be kept clean of foreign materials such as:
1. Dung locks or actual fresh manure;
2. Straw or other vegetable matter allowed to blow onto or be dragged onto the shearing floor as the ewe is thrown;
3. Water, either spilled or on the fleece as the sheep come into the shearing pens.

Most ewes are *tagged* before lambing time, as described in Chapter 3. Often this prevents the accumulation of *dung locks* by shearing time the next spring but sometimes not. If dry, hard dung locks do accumulate (and damp ones, too), they should definitely *not* be wrapped up in the fleece as it is tied, but should be separated from it and sacked later. (Many top wool men would tag again to cut out this material rather than take a chance of its being sacked with the good wool.) This material may stain the fleeces and of course means high shrinkage and lower value.

Straw and other vegetable matter allowed on the shearing floor is more difficult to sort or sift out of a fleece than dirt or sand. In fact, much shearing is done on a hard dirt floor with little or no damage to fleeces. When the shearing shed is in close proximity to hay storage or bedding, which may be trailed into the holding pens by the sheep and dragged onto the shearing floor as the sheep are thrown, much such material will end up in the sack with the wool. A help in preventing dung and some other foreign materials from getting to the shearing floor is provided by the use of slatted platforms (elevated) upon which the sheep stand *as they are being held awaiting shearing.*

The elimination of the "bull pen" type of shearing would do much to provide cleaner fleeces worth more money per pound. There are far too many shearing plants so constructed that large groups (20 to 40 sheep) await the shearer in one congested pen and return there after removal of the fleece. This concentrates droppings (on a dirt floor) and causes shearers to drag sheep through filth to a much greater extent than if each sheep is pulled from a smaller pen, with slatted floors, holding only 8 or 10 head, and after being shorn is turned into another pen to be counted. A simple setup of a shearing plant that can keep wool clean is shown in Fig. 111.

Fleeces should be tied with paper twine because it is the only type of tie that does not allow the possibility of a foreign fiber getting in with the wool. Should a cotton or sisal twine be used, it may pull off into the fleece as it is untied for grading at the mill and continue on into the scouring vats, finally being dyed with the wool—an entirely different fiber that takes the dye differently. On the other hand, a bit of paper string is not so likely to become entwined with the wool fibers and usually practically dissolves in the washing processes.

What Is a First-Class Sacking Job?

And, it might be added, why should the fleeces be packed just so? This is all pretty much a matter of marketing effect. A carefully packed box of oranges or cherries is attractive to the consumer. There is a middleman as far as the wool grower is concerned but a sloppy packing job has the same effect and may mean that the buyer will be inclined to offer less money.

Aside from avoiding a shoddy job of packing, different types of wool should be packed separately if full value is to be expected. *Fleeces, lamb's wool, buck wool, black,* and *"off sorts" should not be mixed* if the grower wishes ever to establish in the minds of buyers that he does prepare a uniform bag for which the buyer can offer a price reflecting his confidence that the bag contains only one sort of wool.

How should a bag of wool be sacked then? First, the standard 7-ft burlap bag should be used without turning inside-out. (This exposes the threads along its side seam so that the bag may be opened most easily for display at a warehouse.) Secondly, "ears" should be tied off in the bottom corners by stuffing a handful of wool into each and wrapping string tightly around the base of each.

These "ears" provide handholds to use later in moving the packed bag.

The packing of the fleeces begins after the bag is secured in the sacking frame. If the fleeces are about 7 to 12 lb in weight, the first layer will take just three fleeces. These need be "tromped" very little—succeeding layers, of five fleeces each, will hold the bottom layer snug. In placing the five fleeces a certain order is desirable to shape the bag into its normal oval shape. Figure 109 indicates this order.

The usual procedure is to drop a fleece into the center of the bag, then to place a fleece to each side of it (but *not* at the seam sides) and to tromp them lightly into position. The final two fleeces are placed at the seams, and as they usually are pushed into place with difficulty, they spread the seam sides and cause the bag to take the oval form. Once all five fleeces are in place, tromping begins by placing the foot with the outer

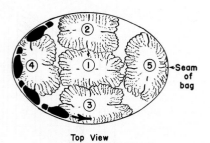

Top View

Fig. 109. A correctly packed and tightly tromped wool bag makes a good impression.

edge of the shoe against the burlap; then with several applications of pressure at each position, the foot is moved in a circle around the bag. Usually two or three complete circlings of the bag will force the fleeces tightly enough into place for another layer to be added.

It is desirable to pack the fleeces fairly tightly so that the bag presents a good, fully packed appearance rather than a loose, sloppy one. Such a bag will weigh 275 to 300 lb when full.

When the last layer has been put in place, some lifting mechanism is employed to raise the bag so that the edges can be removed from the wool ring and the upper edge sewed. It is well to sew the top so that it is closed completely. A lock stitch is employed, which prevents the bag from opening, even though one stitch may later be cut or broken.

The better packed and presented clips go one step further. A *stencil is applied,* indicating the owner's name and the type of wool.

Also another feature is sometimes applied by growers who have a good product and who wish to distinguish it. This consists of *shaping the bag flat* on the two broad sides (away from the seams) by building solid walls in the sacking frame and prying the bag out, after packing, toward one of the seam edges. (See Fig. 110.)

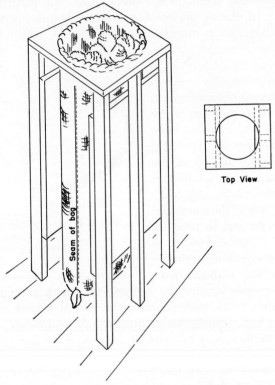

Fig. 110.   A wool bag shaped by solid walls is attractive.

This shape is probably more suited to the packing of small-bulk greasy Merino fleeces (where often nine fleeces are placed to a layer), although the looser fleeces, too, will shape fairly well into a bag of this sort.

What Equipment and Buildings Are Needed for Shearing?

The answer to this question of course depends greatly on the number of sheep to be shorn, and what would be necessary or desirable in one instance would be superfluous and unusable in another.

The essentials only of a shearing setup will be discussed, and these may be adjusted to whatever the wool grower's capacity may require.

If we trace the sheep through the shearing process, all the necessary portions of the setup will be clear. (Follow the diagram shown in Fig. 111.)

Figure 111 (A) indicates that *the dodge chute* may be a permanent structure at the lambing barn (as described in Chapter 5) if the shearing setup is a part of the barn, or it may be in such a position as to be readily accessible to a separate shearing shed so that lambs can be placed where their shorn mothers can pick them up as the job is completed on each.

As illustrated in Fig. 111, the dodge chute separates the lambs, which go to the *mothering corral,* shown at (8) on the diagram, and the wooly ewes, which go into a corral from which they will be forced later into the shearing shed.

In *the forcing corral* shown on Fig. 111, two or more sections separated by temporary (or permanent) paneling may be desirable to help move the ewes toward the lead-in alley and make it easy to keep enough coming to avoid delaying the shearers in their work.

The other main areas of the shearing setup, numbered (1) to (6) on the diagram, are as follows:

(1) The first part of the shed proper is a 3-ft-wide *alley* (usually wooden-floored) under the roof but open to direct light. This light is very important as it is very difficult to move sheep into a dark building from bright sunlight, especially when dust obscures their view. It will be noted that the alley extends beyond the four holding pens shown at (2). The purpose of this extension is to keep a supply of ewes past the last pen so that the gates which allow the sheep to enter the holding pens may swing as shown rather than from the opposite corner. If the sheep are forced to a dead end (as the end of this alley would be), they will tend to turn back and *push themselves* into the holding pens, whereas if the gates opened from the opposite corners, every sheep would have to be pushed in by the wranglers. Sometimes sheepmen tie a decoy sheep at the far end of this alley to facilitate filling it.

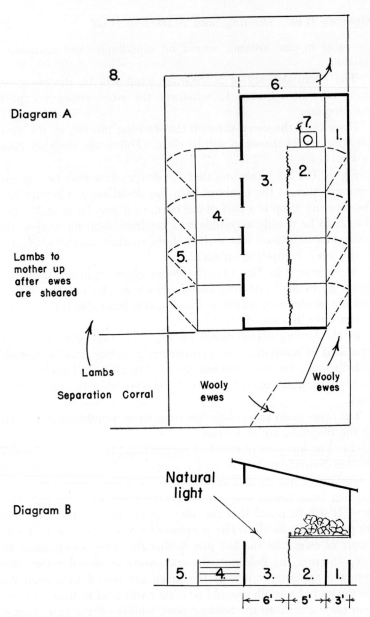

Diagram A

8.

6.

7.

1.

3.

2.

4.

5.

Lambs to
mother up
after ewes
are sheared

Lambs

Separation Corral

Wooly
ewes

Wooly
ewes

Diagram B

**Natural
light**

5. 4. 3. 2. 1.

← 6' → ← 5' → ← 3' →

Fig. 111. A simple shearing plant. A. Plan B. Cross section Numbered
sections described in text.

254

(2) The *holding pens* are about 5 ft square and should prefer-ably have elevated slatted floors made of 2 by 3-in. lumber strips set on edge with a 5/8-in. space between them, as indicated in Fig. 62 in Chapter 5. The gates at the rear of the pen should be the full 5 ft in width so that, when opened, they will shut off the drive-in alley so as to turn the sheep into the pens. The wavy line in the diagram, on the shearing side of the holding pens, indicates a can-vas (or other fabric) false wall (often wool sacks) hung from a beam about 6 ft off the shearing floor. This is sufficient to confine the ewes and allows an easily opened area through which the ewe to be shorn is caught and thrown for shearing onto the shearing floor. As indicated in Fig. 111 (B), a shelf may be conveniently constructed over the holding pens to provide a place where the fleeces may be thrown as they are tied should the owner's program be to sack them later. In such case, the sacking frame is located at the far end of this shelf, as indicated at (7). Naturally, sufficient head space should be allowed in the construction of this portion of the shed.

(3) The *shearing floor* should be wooden and solid. The dis-tance from the curtain to the turnout door should be not over 6 ft. Shearers should not have to travel too far to catch a sheep out of the holding pen and then additionally have to hold onto it and guide it out into a counting pen several feet away from the spot where it is turned loose after shearing. It is much better to have the small door (often only a hole in the wall covered by a piece of burlap) through which the shorn ewe moves to the counting pen, only a step away from where she rises off the floor. The shearer usually will pull the burlap aside, and the ewe will see the other sheep in the counting pen and be attracted out to them.

(4) *Counting pens* may not be a necessity where only one or two shearers work or where the owner does his own shearing, but otherwise they are desirable. Each is generally large enough (5 by 8 to 10 ft) to hold 20 sheep or more, and the owner counts out each man's shear and marks down the tally at the gate of each such pen.

(5) The *alley* leading away from the counting pens guides the sheep to a branding chute.

(6) The *branding chute* is generally not over 3 ft wide and is easy to reach across as the brand is placed on each individual

crowded into it. From the end of this chute the ewes proceed out into the corral where their lambs are waiting to be mothered.

A variation of this shed design seen often in hilly country has the shed built over a slope and a slide down which the shorn ewes slip to the counting pens. This works very nicely and provides a fine setup for eliminating liquid and solid manure from the holding pens.

What Should I Do with My Sacked Wool?

Either of two procedures may be followed:

1. Store it properly, or
2. Ship it to a buyer or handler.

Proper storage of sacked wool can preserve the quality of the fleeces intact and prevent loss of weight and damage by moths, staining, or heating. Briefly, the precautions to be taken are as follows:

Do not allow the bags to stay long in direct sunlight; not only will the bags be weakened by sunburn, but the grease in the fleece will run and will later mat and injure their appearance.

Store the sacks on a wooden floor. If on concrete or dirt they will draw moisture from the ground, and the sacks and fleeces will be stained.

Store under a tight roof as rain and dust injure the appearance and sales value of fleeces.

If there is reason to believe that the bags will need to be stored for a long time, they should be protected from moth damage. This means fumigating under a tarpaulin with paradichlorobenzene crystals or similar agents.

Shipping wool presents no particular problem, and only a hint on loading trucks is deemed essential here. As the bags will weigh in the neighborhood of 300 lb, it will be necessary to use some mechanical means to get bags up three or four layers high on a truck, especially if they must be loaded from ground level. To do this, truckers employ ropes and two long planks, preferably 2 by 8 or 2 by 12 in. in cross section and 16 to 20 ft long. The two lower layers of bags usually can simply be rolled up the planks to the rear end of the truck. As the grade steepens and the upper ends of the planks rest on top of the second and later the third layer of bags, it will be necessary to help roll the bags up by means of a long rope attached to the front end of the truck and extending back to the ground, around under the bag, and up to the hands of a man on the load who pulls it up as shown in Fig. 112. Large stacks of bags are nowadays sometimes loaded by block and tackle, powered by the truck engine.

To Whom Shall I Sell? The myriad of small wool producers who ask this question really have a problem. In the West *itinerant buyers* who visit the small farms and offer to purchase wool are buying because they expect to make a profit. They naturally are en-

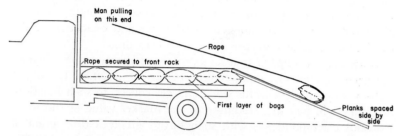

Fig. 112.   Upper layers of wool bags may be rolled onto carrier fairly easily in this manner.

titled to buy for somewhat less than the figure at which they expect to resell the wool. In many instances, aside from taking care of the grower's shipping expenses, this buyer must repackage the wool, put small purchases together, do some sort of sorting and grading, and provide warehousing—and all of this costs money. If the owner has some knowledge of the value of his wool (as outlined early in this chapter), he can decide whether an offer is in line. If he has no such knowledge, it is probably safer to send the wool to a reputable wool handler or buyer's agent, usually located in the bigger cities of the State.

Wool pools offer some advantages, particularly for the small grower, and many such groupings have been organized by local wool growers in many sections. The management of such pools is largely effective in getting full value through the manner in which it presents the bags for inspection and through sealed bids from mill buyers and others interested. As far as possible, bags of wool of varying grades or types need to be grouped separately. Very small offerings from growers need to be grouped and resacked into full bags of one type of wool. Especially good consignments of considerable size, in fairness to the consignor, should be sold separately, although this is not a common practice as the "pool" idea then is defeated. (This has caused various growers who do have exceptional clips to stay out of pools.)

In areas where all sheepmen handle about the same type of sheep and shear at about the same time under good conditions, the offering of wools in a pool should be very attractive to buyers; but where farm flocks are quite heterogeneous and some sheep are sheared under good conditions and others late, so that fleeces are laden with burs and stickers, the pool cannot satisfy the better growers. However, careful segregation of wool types and education of the consignors could smooth this problem out in time.

Wool may be shipped to wool handlers or buyers, some of whom are agents for eastern mills, *located in the larger cities.* Usually, a grower may simply ship his wool, charges collect, to such handlers, and they will pay their estimate of the market value of the wool. Previous correspondence with such buyers giving a description of the type of sheep owned may be desirable in determining a tentative price acceptance.

Why not ship my wool East? If all the uncertainties that exist in the minds of wool growers concerning the true value of their clips are so difficult to resolve, why should not a western wool grower simply ship all his wool to the final handler in, perhaps, Boston, have it sold on a graded and scoured value basis, and not have to worry as to whether he or someone else guessed rightly or wrongly about shrinkage and grades?

The answer to this question is given in terms of the replies of several such wool merchants in Boston who were queried on the topic:

Most were of the opinion that a grower, particularly of the finer grades of 12-months wool, would have some advantage in consigning his clip to the eastern handler. This opinion was qualified, however, by stating that the minimum amount of wool that would bear shipping was 5000 lb and that it was desirable to ship a full carload. This could be the shipment of several persons, such as neighboring sheep owners. Lots under 25,000 lb are commingled with other similar wools, at the warehouses, to make up a line of easily marketable weight.

Further opinion was that if a grower should make up his mind to consign his wool to eastern merchants, he should stay with the plan for at least a five-year period. Owing to the fluctuating character of the wool market, one year he might lose by consigning and the next have an advantage over selling at home. However, more profit would be likely over a period of years as local dealers naturally take a certain percentage of profit if they handle the wool, instead.

It should be kept in mind that fine and half-blood grades, rather choice clips, and large consignments are most suitable for such shipments, and as so much of California wools, especially, are not of this sort, it might be preferable to sell at home for the best price obtainable. The selling of such clips so far from home "often leads to confusion and dissatisfaction for both parties" and handling by reputable local dealers would seem more desirable.

If a consignment is to be made, a grower should contact the State agent for the particular wool merchant he chooses for information or how to ship. He signs an agreement that allows the

U.S. Testing Co.

Fig. 113. Coring wool bags and packing the cores for shipment to testing laboratories.

handler to use his own judgment about selling or that reserves to him the right to reject offers. Advances are generally made on the consignment order.

What Advantages May Core-Testing Provide?

As mentioned earlier in this chapter, this system now in use of removing "cores" of wool from representative bags of a clip, to be scoured as a determinant of the shrinkage of the clip as a whole, has merit and use for some growers. A brief description of what the test entails and what it may avail the wool grower is in order.

Research men and the more progressive men in the wool industry are convinced that this method of determining shrinkage is accurate to within 1% of actual mill shrinkage figures and is far superior in accuracy to the method of visual appraisal (which often is 3 to 8% or more off). Usually, the fine wools are visually estimated to shrink more than they actually do, and the coarser wools (less valuable per pound) are underestimated.

On the basis of Office of Price Stabilization figures on the 1951 American wool clip, every 1% error in shrinkage appraisal affected the average grade fleece profit by 3.38¢ per pound on the clean basis or 1.69¢ on the grease basis. Thus a mistake of 3% could mean a lowered income on a 10-lb greasy fleece of over 50¢, and this multiplied by 1000 of course would be $500 for the wool of one band, if a price was being paid on the basis of the clip shrinking a certain figure.

One thing that has been pretty well determined is that for "original bag wools" (i.e., not graded, before coring) a minimum amount of 10,000 lb is necessary to get accuracy in the test estimate. This is about the clip from the ordinary western "band" of sheep. Graded wools would require less tonnage.

The use of the core-test method on the 1950 clip in the state of Montana, according to a reputable source, "earned the growers an additional million and a half dollars." This is in an area where large holdings are on the fine side as far as grade is concerned.

It would seem desirable to core test every year and to be able to use the resulting knowledge in determining whether to sell to a buyer who estimates visually and who bases his bid on that estimate.

How is the core test made? A fairly laborious process, divided between a field phase and a laboratory phase, adds up to the core test. The United States Testing Company of Boston, Mass., or similar companies do core testing on a commercial scale, and their representatives meet the grower, preferably at shearing time or at a wool warehouse. Then, according to the number of bags of wool, or the number of bags of each grade, a representative number are set aside to be cored, such numbers being determined by the total number in the lot.

The coring itself consists of drilling or punching out "cores" of wool from ten positions in each bag, the cores may vary from 3/8 in. to 3 in. in diameter, the latter resulting in greater accuracy.

These cores are procured by a special coring tube which is often coupled to an electric drill. After the core is withdrawn it is packed with others of the lot in a special airtight container to prevent gain or loss in moisture, and these containers are then shipped to the laboratory for the shrinkage test.

At the laboratory, after the removal of foreign materials, the samples are broken up, blended, and washed, using a soap and washing soda mixture. After drying they are standardized for moisture content and weighed, and the percentage of shrink is determined.

The tests are usually completed and a report is provided the grower within two weeks.

The cost of the core test varies with the amount of wool and has been as low as $5 for up to 50 bags and up to $60 for over 300 bags, for the laboratory test work alone. To this must be added costs for obtaining the cores and labor in moving bags, but generally the total cost has not been prohibitive.

Contacts with State Wool Growers Associations usually will establish the means by which the core test may be instituted by any wool grower.

Chapter 11

Sheep Psychology—Handling Sheep

Many of the operations with sheep are arduous or become quite simple (as an owner gains experience), depending upon how attentive he is to the characteristics of the beast that cause her to react in certain ways.

It is the purpose of this chapter to discuss some of the "psychology" of sheep that the handler should understand in order to enable him to do his work with a minimum of strain and, too, of injury to his charges. Experience usually teaches, but a beginner, equipped with a bit of knowledge, may certainly shorten his training period.

It may be well to consider first a list of sheep characteristics:

1. They are gregarious. This means that they naturally wish to group up, resist being isolated as individuals, and make a strong attempt to rejoin any group from which they become separated.

2. Sheep are fearsome of dark areas. This makes it very difficult to drive them into such spots in barns from a lighted area.

3. They are unwilling to move when they cannot be *sure* of their footing or that other sheep are moving with them. Sheep blinded by direct sunlight or by sunlight on a cloud of dust are "lost." They resist strongly having to step into water or running streams, especially when forced.

4. Sheep respond, in moving, to sharp sounds or quick, darting movements rather than to continued loud noise or slow movements. Thus a slap on the thighs or a sharp hissing sound or a quick movement of a dog is much more likely to get results than continuous loud "hollering."

5. Individuals or small groups of sheep, halted by a gate in an

alley, usually respond violently by quick movement in the opposite direction. Feeling themselves trapped, they will turn about and dash in the opposite direction. A gate that can be snapped quickly across their path takes advantage of this characteristic in making it easy to pen one or a few individuals without having to push them in.

6. Sheep "follow a leader" quite readily. If one of their kind will move, others will follow if they can keep the leader in sight.

Operations with sheep that may be simplified by taking advantage of the nature of the beast are discussed below.

Moving Sheep

Moving sheep on roadways is common practice everywhere, of course, and because it is so feasible and relatively simple when

L. A. Stoddard

Fig. 114. Moving sheep on roadways demands considerable know-how.

handled properly, it becomes a major factor in allowing the owner to make use of pieces of feed at distances from his headquarters.

The job of moving a few head from field to field on a farm is relatively simple compared with the task of trailing 2,000 head or more over county roads and through towns, but even this is easy for some; it is a chore for the unobservant. *Small groups of sheep, especially,* are inclined to "mill" or start to revolve in a circle if not carefully watched when being moved. This milling repeated ad infinitum, could mean a slowing down of the process and a waste of time. The man or men moving such a bunch should observe these few pointers:

1. Watch the leaders (rather than the tail end of the group).
2. Turn the leaders, forcing straight-ahead movement; the others will follow.
3. Do not follow the rear-end sheep too closely or force them faster than the lead moves.

The man who beats the "tail end" and moves with his head and eyes down (watching the tail end) is generally the one who gets into trouble moving a small bunch, and many experienced owners have often been exasperated by the actions of such a helper.

Keep your eyes on the leaders. If they start to one side, be ready with a clod of dirt to throw judiciously or with a quick movement of the arm or a command to the dog that will right the situation. Stay back several yards from the tail-end sheep. They, too, may best be kept going by clods of dirt or handfuls of gravel spotted at their heels occasionally, or by the actions of a dog trained to move back and forth across the rear. If the driver gets too close, there is too much danger of startling some sheep into bolting to the rear and this in turn attracts others to follow.

Do not run after an individual that cuts to the rear from the band. Especially is this true of a lamb. And especially do not allow a dog to attempt to run down such an individual. Stop quickly any movement designed to cut that individual back into the bunch and he will come on his own. Get him excited and he will be very difficult to gather.

Big bands moved on roadways require special handling. Five hundred to two thousand sheep or more represent too large a group to be moved in one mass and need a "lead bunch," pushed along by one man, to keep the whole group moving. Usually, on roads fairly well confined by fencing or natural barriers, one man can keep a hundred or so sheep together in a lead group, prevent them from breaking back, and yet keep them not too far ahead to prevent their serving as decoys for the followers. In very large bands drivers may have to be inserted between other groups of sheep (in addition to those at the rear end) in order to prevent the band from trailing out too far in farming country. The job of the "lead bunch" driver is to keep those few sheep moving so as to entice the leaders of the next group to follow. Therefore he usually will not use a dog or at least the dog must be one that will stay close at heel. The use of dirt clods, sticks that can be scratched upon the roadway, or other instruments that will cause a rustling sound are very effective in preventing individuals at the tail end of the lead bunch from break-ing back. (In the West where, often, palm-tree fronds are available, a real "rustler" is at hand.) The man's coat, occasionally alter-nately raised overhead and then beat against his legs, is effective, too.

To keep the followers coming, the lead-bunch driver must keep watch of the distance between his group and them. Sheep will not be decoyed well if that span is longer than about a hundred feet. Frequent "bleating" by the driver or slackening of the pace of the lead bunch may have to be resorted to.

He must also keep continuous watch of the roadway ahead for side roads, holes in the fence, open gates, etc., and be on hand with a clod of dirt or his dog to prevent the leaders from breaking away.

In any band of sheep there will always be some natural leaders. A few sheep (and the same ones every time) will soon find their way to the lead. Likewise the tail-enders are always tail-enders. There-fore it is wise to start out a band en masse and wait some time for the natural leaders to find their way to the front.

Often owners own old wethers (belled) or goats to use as leaders. A goat is a very excellent leader because he usually carries his head high and can more easily be directed by a quick arm or hand move-ment of the driver than can a sheep.

Streams of water will usually stop a band of sheep completely, and the only way in which they can be made to cross even a nar-row stream is to force a few sheep across and quickly start the remainder in their path. This is often an arduous task and requires quick-moving and energetic men. Sometimes a mixed group of ewes and their lambs can be started by a man carrying a large lamb across the stream and holding it there where it will call its mother.

If and when she starts, men must be ready to startle others into following her, and *continuous movement* of the sheep to the water's edge and across the water must prevail or the whole process will have to be started again. Usually continuous movement is best brought about by standing back, once a few sheep start trailing across the water, but being ready at any instant to startle a hesitant group so that the continuity of the movement is not broken.

Automobiles on the road of course are problems when it comes to sheep driving. The *approaching* car is not so much of a problem as the one that must be put through the band from the rear. On a winding road, of course, a man must be sent out ahead of the sheep to flag down an approaching vehicle. Usually a considerate word to the driver will get his cooperation in making the passage for both him and the sheep safe. Often it is best that he stop and wait until the sheep pass by him, but on wide roads he may hasten his passage by causing a passenger to get out and "part" the sheep ahead of the machine as he moves ahead slowly.

The car from the rear must be "put through" by men handling the sheep. It must be understood that the sheep have the right of way and that the car must wait the convenience of the herders. When many cars are on the road, sheep drivers will usually hold up the "putting through" of a car until several others can follow it closely. Otherwise the task would be very hard. It is generally found best to "put through" a string of cars to one side of the road, turning *all* the sheep toward the opposite side as the cars approach. Here a good dog that will ease up one side of the band is very useful.

If the contour of the roadway makes it necessary to take cars up the center of the road, the sheep will need to be parted by a man who may scratch a stick on the roadway to startle the sheep as he moves along. He should caution the following car to keep closely at his heels to prevent sheep crossing behind him, with the possibility of their being hit by the car.

The Use of Sheep Dogs

Good dogs greatly simplify the movement and handling of sheep, and when well-trained and well-handled they make possible itinerant sheep enterprises that would be impossible without them.

Except where sheep are kept under fence (and even there, occasionally), sheep dogs are an absolute necessity.

No attempt will be made here to describe sheep-dog training but rather to point out, in reference to the nature of sheep, where and how dogs may best be used.

Fig. 115. An intelligent, well trained dog is a great help to the sheep handler.

As was stated in Chapter 6, on lambing, a dog has little if any use at that period because the mother instinct of ewes is so strong that the presence of a dog disturbs them too much to make the movements of individuals or very small groups smooth.

A dog is the most useful with dry sheep and with ewes and their lambs when the lambs are a month or more old. Here, he is most effective when used only at infrequent intervals and when his actions are quick, violent, and startling. A well-trained band of sheep soon learns to respect a dog that startles them and that they know means business, but they are "well broken" only by consistent and determined herding by a well-directed dog. If they are played with by a dog that does not have the strength or willingness to force obedience, they may become a real trial. When the sheep are well "broken," a herder need only whistle, many times without loosing his dog, to make sheep stop or turn.

Usually a dog that is good has been trained to think of nothing but working sheep. He has been taught that playing, being fondled, even eating are secondary to working the sheep, and so he usually is found tied or in his kennel when there is no work to do and is loosed only when the sheep need watching. The dog that plays about the ranch is usually a poor sheep herder.

At the season of the year when ewes are suckling lambs and daily gains are very important, judicious use of the dog is especially necessary. Quiet handling of the sheep puts on gains, and the good herder will walk with his dog to a point where he wishes to turn the sheep rather than send the dog out to wheel them in. The simple presence of the dog with the herder at that spot is enough to cause a well-broken band to stop and turn. Training of the band of ewes should be done in the period when they are dry.

Catching Sheep

Individual sheep often need to be caught for inspection, for treatment, or for other reasons, and small enclosures or chutes that would make the job easier are not always available.

The uninitiated generally will attempt to cut out the one sheep from the bunch (when in a corral or fence corner) and to catch the animal by hand. This is usually just that: an attempt. Alone, or with a helper or two, the best way to catch one sheep out of a small group is to corner all of them (and don't let *one* get away until ready to seize the one wanted). Then, keeping the corners of the group "tucked in" against the fence and one eye on the individual wanted, wait until she is back in the far corner and surrounded by other sheep. Then a quick dash in to catch her, regardless of the others, will be successful because the other sheep hold her from bolting until a hand can be laid on her. Holding *all* the sheep in a corner until ready to catch the individual is necessary because of the sheep's instinct to follow the leader. If one breaks out, all are very likely to try to follow and often cannot be held in a corner without much help.

Sheep may be caught—singled out—by a shepherd's crook, as has been described in Chapter 4, but care must be exercised in the use of this instrument to prevent injury to legs and joints.

The actual act of catching the sheep, by hand, is correctly done in one or two ways. Distinctly not correct is to grab the fleece, although, in desperation, this has to be done at times.

The two best spots to lay hand on the sheep to stop and hold it are under the chin and in the rear flank. A strong ram or a heavy ewe if caught under the chin may still have strength enough to break away if it can get its head low enough; therefore, as soon as the chin is grasped, it is well to pull the sheep's head up as a horse would be reined up.

Lighter sheep can be stopped pretty readily by the grasp in the rear flank. The catch is made and a lift put on the flank simultaneously. This keeps the sheep from using its hind legs to pull away effectively.

Lifting and Throwing Sheep

Individual sheep must often be lifted into trucks or over fences, and heavy ones present quite a task; even the lighter ones may be hurt or the lifter himself be hurt if he fails to observe a few precautions.

When a sheep is to be lifted by one person, his best grip (and chance to do the job easily) is one where both arms are placed around the sheep at the breast as he stands straddled over her and faced toward her head. Then the sheep should be gripped tightly to the operator's chest and as he stands up her hind feet should

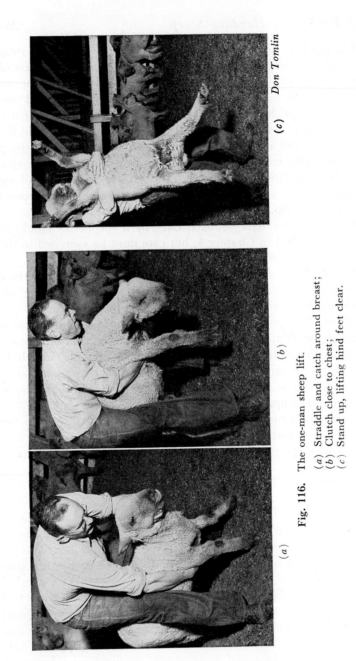

Don Tomlin

Fig. 116. The one-man sheep lift.

(a) Straddle and catch around breast;
(b) Clutch close to chest;
(c) Stand up, lifting hind feet clear.

easily clear the ground. If the sheep is held more loosely or gripped by its forelegs instead of around the breast (behind the forelegs), it is difficult to get her hind legs off the ground.

After the sheep has been so raised, the task of throwing her over a fence or onto a truck may be eased by using the leg (or knee) to boost the sheep as she is swung up.

Don Tomlin

Fig. 117. Throwing a sheep by simultaneous leg pull and twist.

Extremely heavy sheep will need to be lifted by two persons, lest the catcher unduly strain himself. Probably the best means when two persons are at hand is to grip each other's wrists as each stoops at opposite sides of the sheep with one pair of arms extended beneath the breast bone just in front of the forelegs and the other pair reaching beneath the sheep at the rear flank.

Sheep need to be thrown for shearing, tagging, and treatment, and especially in the case of ewes heavy with lamb or of weighty rams or ewes this should be done in such a manner as not to injure the sheep or strain the operator.

Several means of throwing sheep are employed. The usual procedure on large lambs or dry ewes for shearing is to catch the right rear shank of the sheep in the right hand (see Fig. 117) and *as the sheep is being pulled backwards* to reach and grasp the right flank with the left hand and to twist the animal to the left and against the operator's left leg. All this action is in a continued movement. The right hind leg should not be raised too high and the catching of the flank with the left hand and the twisting motion should take place *at the same time* as the pulling to the rear is going on. Then the sheep will drop easily and with little likelihood of injury.

With sheep so weighty that it is difficult for the operator to pull and twist as described above (and also with ewes heavy with lamb), it is better to "nose down" the sheep (out of the shearing holding pen). (See Fig. 38.) In this process the ewe's rear is faced toward the shearing floor and the shearer catches her muzzle in his left hand as he stands at her left side and holds her rear with his right hand on her dock. Then by sharply folding her head and neck back onto her right shoulder she can be made to "sit down" and can then be lifted by her front legs and pulled to the shearing position. She "folds up" much like a steer being "bull-dogged" in the rodeo arena.

Chuting Sheep

Many operations with sheep demand that they be run through various chutes and alleyways. Not only should the chutes be constructed properly, as described in Chapter 5, but also certain actions of the chute attendant are needed to facilitate the movement or penning of the sheep.

At the dodge chute the man operating the cutting gate has to attend carefully to his task of snapping the gate "at the sheep's nose." It is also necessary to have a man on the chute proper to start the sheep going again should their even movement be interrupted. While the sheep move evenly, this man should stand back from the chute a couple of paces so as not to frighten (and consequently stop) any that may not be keeping their eyes on the sheep ahead. At the same time he must watch all the sheep currently moving in the length of the chute and be ready quickly to start up a sheep that stops. This he will generally do best by pinching her tail. As she moves ahead he should then move *back* down the chute, tapping succeeding sheep on the rump until the even flow is going again.

Sheep that occasionally are able to turn around in the chute should be lifted by the head and spun around on their hind feet to get them moving again in the right direction.

At the bagging chute (an alley about 3 ft wide) care must be taken to prevent sheep from backing up, causing a crush, as they are "bagged" and passed by. Sheep naturally tend to back up if they are stopped and cannot turn around. This happens in alleys and pens of all dimensions and can result in such a crush that sheep are injured or killed. So an eye should be kept on that portion of the chute or pen where this may occur. Moving back alongside the congested spot—sometimes just stepping right over and into the crush—is necessary to loosen them up.

At the lead-in alley to shearing holding pens or to jails, advantage can be taken of the escape instinct of sheep to facilitate getting them penned. As has been stated before, a sheep finding herself stopped at the end of an alley immediately bolts in the opposite direction. The gates opening from the alley into jails or shearing holding pens may be swung so as to direct the excited "trapped" sheep (on the run) into the pen—after which the gate may be quickly closed before she realizes she is trapped again and bolts out.

Loading Sheep

The task of loading lambs into trucks or into railroad cars demands some attention to a few details if it is to be done easily.

For lower-deck loading, where the lead-in ramp is not so steep, not too much difficulty is generally experienced if enough help is on hand to keep the flow of lambs coming. In railroad cars, where the entry is at the center of the car, it is best for the man who drives in the lead bunch to stay in the car and to one side of the doorway to direct the lambs to one end until that half of the car is tightly filled. He may have to startle the lambs several times to cause them to jam up fairly tightly. This is necessary because the full deck quota cannot be reached without some forcing of the last few lambs if the major portion (in their helter-skelter positions) are not packed at this point seemingly tighter than they should be. Later, when the lambs get to standing parallel to each other, the pack will loosen considerably.

Upper-deck loading may be especially difficult if the chuteway is steep, if the sun is directly overhead, or if dust is flying. If all three of these factors exist, it is extremely difficult to get sheep to move.

Often in the West sheep are loaded from temporary corrals to which commercial trucking lines bring their own loading chutes. Temporary forcing alleys lead up to the chute and under these circumstances loading can be, and frequently is, a real trial. One of the most trying situations occurs when loading takes place in the middle of the day and the sun is overhead. This combination of light with a cloud of dust means having to push very nearly every lamb or sheep up the chute. The obvious answer to this is to try to arrange early morning loading, with the truck spotted in such a position that the sun is *behind* the sheep. Then too, watering down the immediate loading area will keep flying dust under control. If no forethought is taken in these respects, sheep will be found to be very obstinate creatures indeed.

The immediate entry point into a railroad car or a truck is a spot where the expenditure of a little effort will cause the sheep to pack in tightly and hasten the loading job. If a man can be spotted at this point and startles each sheep, as it is about to step into the car, by a poke in the ribs or better by the intrusion of a rustly tree branch at the feet of the sheep, causing it to jump and charge ahead—then the loading will go fast and smoothly.

Handling at Lambing Time

Many of the fine points of handling the ewes at lambing have been covered in the instruction in Chapter 6 on lambing, but further reference is made here to those characteristics of lambing ewes that should be well understood to make the lambing period easier for the operator.

1. The mother instinct of most ewes is so strong immediately after lambing that the ewe will follow very closely if her lamb (or lambs) is picked up and carried off to the barn. She loses her fear

of being alone in favor of protecting her young. "Bleating" by the man, if the lamb does not, is of help in moving her along.

2. This does not mean that every ewe will so react. Some first lambers and some older ewes are quite frightened and wild when a man approaches and picks up the lamb. In order to move such a ewe and her lamb successfully, most careful watch must be kept on the ewe, and at the slightest indication that she is about to bolt, the lamb must be released for her to see and smell again.

3. Some ewes are so wild that the lamb must be picked up and moved at the end of a shepherd's crook, for if picked up by hand the ewe feels that man is too close. Or some ewes may be induced to follow if the lamb is allowed to stand on all four feet facing the ewe and is pulled along backwards by a grip on its loin.

4. If it is too far to move such a wild ewe to the barn, it may be more desirable to catch her and transport her in some manner. The wild ewe may often be caught by moving the lamb a short distance by the crook (the hook under its ribs) and then, if the ewe will approach and smell the lamb, catching her front foot with the hook slipped out from under the lamb and held still until ready to pounce. This requires considerable dexterity and practice, but most lambing help uses the sheep hook so frequently that catching a wild ewe in this manner becomes fairly simple.

5. A less wild ewe may be caught in the field in another manner. The lamb may be picked up by the loin and moved across in front of the herder at ground level. As the ewe moves in front of the man to follow the lamb it can be dropped quickly and the ewe grabbed.

Chapter 12

Prevention and Treatment of Disease
and Other Sheep Troubles

Some of the troubles of sheep have been treated in the text previous to this point when they tied in closely with the discussion of various steps in a year's program of sheep raising. However, there are other diseases and troubles that are liable to strike sheep at any time of the year, and a further section regarding their prevention or treatment seems necessary.

Diseases and troubles already discussed are listed below with a notation of their locations in the text.

How Healthy Are Sheep?

It is surprising how many people who have had little contact with sheep feel that they are heavily diseased animals. The lists of sheep diseases seen in texts and bulletins certainly would do nothing to allay this feeling, for they are long and filled with frightening words and descriptions.

However, few range men will admit to experience with more than one or two diseases or troubles aside from normal lambing abnormalities, and although it is true that the possibilities are numerous, any one sheepman is very unlikely to experience many in his entire lifetime association with his animals.

Although in America more sheep are now being handled under more confined conditions than those of the strictly range operations of the past, and although such confinement will probably result in a higher percentage of disease, still disease control will never be a major portion of a sheepman's activities.

Who Will Take the Responsibility for Keeping a Flock Healthy?

The answer to this is: the owner, chiefly. Since the individual animal has a relatively low dollar value and the sheepman deals in a relatively large number of individuals, it would generally be too costly to have veterinarians do most of the health-control work for a band or flock of sheep. Veterinarians are not as a rule trained as completely in the treatment of sheep as in that of other more valuable individuals, and because they usually are located in cities and towns at long distances from sheep ranches, they have fewer calls and less experience than with other stock.

Thus it becomes mandatory that the sheepman be the doctor for his flock, and generally only in epidemic outbreaks or where new forms of disease manifest themselves (where State veterinarians are in charge) will the owner call upon someone else to care for his animals.

Are There Any Contagious Diseases of Sheep?

Contagious diseases, where a rapid spread may mean disaster in a big way to a livestock man, are fortunately few among sheep.

In the author's experience the only one that has caused considerable trouble has been *contagious foot rot,* and because of the threat which it presents to the many new sheep operations on irrigated pasture that are coming into existence, a rather complete discussion of it is presented first in the following category.

DISEASES AND TROUBLES PRIMARILY OF ADULT SHEEP

Contagious Foot Rot

This disease is of such nature that a lame ewe carrying the germ in her hoof may impart it to her lamb or lambs two or three days after they are born. It strikes sheep so seriously that they often are barely able to stand or to take a step to reach feed. Under such conditions sheep will fail fast, and deaths may occur as a result of privation. Moreover, because the disease occurs largely in the wet months, little effective control can be brought to bear on it for a considerably long period.

Contagious foot rot is a specific disease of sheep, and although other animals have various foot ailments, the germ that causes this disease will not affect other types of animals and cannot be blamed for "rot" in them when they run with affected sheep.

The only manner in which this disease can spread is for the germ to be implanted in wet, muddy spots (generally) *from the hoof of an infected animal.* In other words, the germ must be brought to the area in the hoof of a sheep and spilled out in a receptive (wet) spot; then it can be picked up on the feet of other sheep. Overwet or muddy conditions in themselves *will not produce* this contagion but may produce another type of foot trouble variously called *foot abscess* or noncontagious foot rot.

The above being true, it can readily be seen that *vigilant observance of lame sheep* and *vigilant isolation of them* until the cause of the lameness can be determined will control the spread of contagious foot rot. The disheartening feature in this control program is that some individuals treated and supposedly cured (no longer lame) may harbor a small pocket of infection in the hoof, become lame much later, and start a complete new infection.

It has been determined that the germ causing contagious foot rot in sheep cannot exist, even in mud, for more than about two weeks. Thus, if all sheep can be removed from such a field, it would seem that the danger would be over. Such is far from the case for the average range sheep operator because of the difficulties in isolating and treating large numbers of infected animals in the months (winter) when the disease manifests itself and spreads the fastest. At this time of the year the sheep of most operators are confined to the lambing grounds, and it is very difficult to find other lands upon which to carry on lambing operations or to grow the lambs. This being the case, an owner must attempt to treat the disease while having to turn the treated animals back into infective pastures, and this is a heartbreaking procedure. Even if the "cured" sheep are isolated and turned back into fields from which sheep have been excluded for two weeks, it seems inevitable that there will be some supposedly cured sheep that will be able to reinfect that pasture. Complete success therefore cannot be obtained until dry weather allows movement of the sheep to dry feed areas where reinfection is not possible.

The symptoms of contagious foot rot are manifest and striking. Extreme lameness in one to all four feet first indicates the disorder. Inspection of the hoof may show a break between the toes or a swelling (and later rupture) about the crown of the hoof. An extremely offensive odor accompanies the infection. (An offensive odor is characteristic, too, of the noncontagious foot abscess but is not so strong.) Later, as the germs progress through the foot, the horn loosens from the killed live tissues (which usually hold the hoof) and a general opening up and splaying of the hoof occurs.

The only effective treatment consists of the following steps:
1. Close hoof trimming (removal of all loosened hoof)
2. Application of a germ-killing disinfectant
3. Disinfection of other exposed feet
4. Reobservation and treatment where necessary

5. Follow-up in the dry months of "cured" sheep that become lame again

Point number five is an absolute necessity if permanent freedom from the disease is to become possible. And, too often, this is the step in the procedure that suffers poorest attention.

What are the details of the treatment outlined above?

(1) Lame sheep should be dodged out of the band and isolated for trimming. The lamest of course will easily be noted as they come through the dodge chute, but it is advisable to look over the "non-

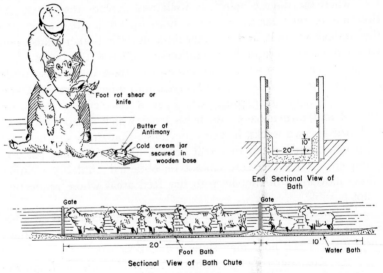

Foot rot shear or knife

Butter of Antimony

Cold cream jar secured in wooden base

End Sectional View of Bath

Gate · Gate

20' · Foot Bath · 10' · Water Bath

Sectional View of Bath Chute

Fig. 118. Treating contagious foot rot.

lame" group afterward to catch others just beginning to show lameness.

Any spot is all right for the trimming but perhaps the preferable place is the shearing shed where parings from the hooves will dry up and where a board floor exists.

The trimming of the hoof must be carefully and completely done so as to uncover every possible spot of infection. Set the sheep on her rump as in shearing and proceed. Underneath the horn of the hoof the live tissue is deeply serrated, and offers an ideal protective setup for the germs, especially at the spots where it is still attached to the horn. It is desirable and necessary to trim back the loosened hoof (preferably with a sharp pocketknife) *until the last cut draws blood*. Only then can the operator be sure that he has removed all the horn that might be covering germs. Do not make the mistake of thinking that a cure can be had without trimming. No sulfa treatment is effective for this disease.

In making the cuts, usually the thin flap of horn *between the toes* is removed first and then the knife is used around the side of the hoof. Often the *entire* hoof cover will have to be removed. Sometimes, even though the sheep is very lame, the hoof will show no loosening from the live undertissue, but generally a swelling will be apparent somewhere (often near the crown); the hoof should be pared off over this and then in a widening circle until the dead tissue is all uncovered.

An area to be careful about in trimming is at the point of the toe where too deep a cut will cause a large blood vessel to bleed badly.

(2) *The second step is disinfection.* For this purpose various materials can be used, but the author has found the most effective material to be butter of antimony ($SbCl_3$), a yellow liquid that can be purchased at any drugstore very cheaply. This is a dehydrating material that very effectually "digs into" the serrations of the exposed live hoof and kills the germs. It is also a very effective cauterant. (It is extremely inadvisable to use weak disinfectants such as sheep dip or a bluestone solution when it is possible with the stronger type to do a complete job the first time.)

The butter of antimony is applied with a swab, which can be made of a bit of wool tied to a small stick. The disinfectant may be put in a small jar fixed to a piece of board set up so that it will not be tipped over but will be within reach of the operator. If so handled, a pint bottle of butter of antimony will suffice for 1,000 hooves or more.

(3) *A foot bath containing bluestone (copper sulfate) solution* should be ready for use after a group of sheep has been trimmed. The kind most often used is a long, narrow trough paneled on each side, allowing the sheep to single-file into it. The liquid should be kept just deep enough (about 2 in) to cover the hooves, and the sheep should be allowed to stand in it while another group is

being trimmed (for perhaps ten minutes). Since much of the liquid may be carried out of the troughs as the sheep file out, a drainage pen at the far end may serve to conserve the liquid.

The purpose of the bluestone foot bath is twofold; namely, to disinfect the feet that did not require trimming and to harden them

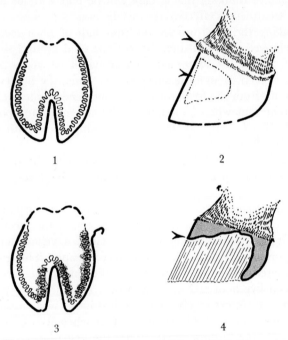

Fig. 119.   Trimming the hoof affected with contagious foot rot.

    1. Cross section indicates deeply serrated live tissue beneath solid hoof in unaffected foot.
    2. Pus breakout may occur at crown of hoof or between toes.
    3. Hoof loosens over affected areas (shaded). Knife should first be used to remove horny flap between toes.
    4. Knife trim continues from removal of between-toe flap to sides of toes and as high as horny material is loose.

or cause them to dry quickly. Such a bath is also desirable for the unaffected ewes if they are brought through muddy gateways or into areas that might be infective.

One undesirable feature of a bluestone bath is that some very lame sheep will lie down in the liquid, and others may jump up on the rear of ewes standing ahead of them. This discoloration of the fleeces (and accompanying drying) is unsightly and is damaging to the wool.

To help prevent sheep from lying down in the liquid, or from crowding each other and causing some to slip, the foot bath should be narrow (about the width of a sheep).

Also of value is a section at the entrance and filled only with clear water into which the sheep first step. This added section is particularly valuable when the entire band is to be walked through the trough for disinfecting and foot-hardening purposes, since it serves to clean the feet before the sheep enter the bluestone section. Also this first part is the section where sheep would most likely slip and fall as they resist entering. If they fall here, they do not soak up bluestone solution into their fleeces.

The troughs may be built into the regular dodge chute, but if large numbers of sheep are to be handled, usually a separate setup is desirable. The troughs may be constructed of redwood lumber properly calked, or they may be of permanent concrete structure.

Preparation of the bluestone foot-bath solution is best accomplished by dissolving the crystals (and they should be bright blue and fresh) by hanging a burlap sack containing them so that only its lower end is immersed in the water filling a wooden barrel. In this manner a full bag of crystals will dissolve overnight, whereas the same crystals, just thrown into the foot-bath water, will take days to dissolve.

The bluestone solution should be fairly concentrated, that is, a pound, at least, to a gallon of water.

A 2% formalin solution may also be used, this amounting to 03. of formalin per gallon of water.

(4) *How fast will the treated sheep heal?* Reobservation and retreatment of some sheep, becomes a necessity no matter how careful the first operation has been. If the trimming has actually been complete and the disinfection effective, a complete new hard hoof will form within a week. Usually half of a trimmed group will show some lameness five to seven days after the first treatment, and it is wise to reinspect and retrim these if any deformity of the hoof is seen or if severe lameness continues. Subsequent observations every five days are desirable. In some instances the germ will enter the ankle proper and cause infection in that joint. These cases are

virtually impossible to cure and should be sent to the butcher. Their menace to other sheep as reinfecting agents should not be overlooked.

(5) *The final cleanup* of the disease must take place in the dry season and because, by then, few lame ewes are seen, this most necessary job is often overlooked. *No sheep owner who has had contagious foot rot in his herd should neglect this final task* as it will mean another winter of infection if *one* holdover case is missed.

Therefore as lame sheep are noted during the summer and fall months they should be caught by the herder or owner and inspected. If they show any swelling or outbreak, they will need to be trimmed and swabbed with butter of antimony, a small bottle of which should be carried by the herder. For these infrequent cases the material may be swabbed on by the operator's finger.

Such sheep may be turned back immediately into the band because there will be no danger of contagion where no mud spots exist.

Foot baths into which all the sheep must step in order to reach the salt troughs have been used effectively in the late fall months to harden hooves and prevent infection. Since the *contagious foot rot germ cannot exist except in the hoof of a sheep* (or, for a short time, in mud after implantation there from such an infected hoof), these foot baths will be effective only in disinfecting feet of sheep whose hooves may have harbored a spot of infection and later have broken open. The use of such foot baths seems a poor substitute for close observation and individual treatments, but various sheep owners attest to its effectiveness.

The foot-bath solution in this case is again usually bluestone. On occasion sheep have drunk from these bluestone vats and been killed, so that it is desirable not to install them until the sheep have been acquainted with another watering place.

Other disinfecting materials may be cheaper and although they do not have the hoof-hardening effect of bluestone, they are as effective in killing the germ. "Roccal" is one often used.

Foot Abscess or Noncontagious Foot Rot

Sheep often become lame as a result of being forced to stay on muddy ground so long that the mud packs small sticks and gravel between their toes. Or lameness may occur simply because some material becomes lodged between the toes. This lameness will occur generally in only one foot or one toe but may affect the sheep very seriously. Transfer to dry ground and removal of the damaging obstruction or mud pack is recommended as the only treatment. *Do not scrape the tender tissues.*

Such cases may show evidence of some infection and an outbreak of pus may occur, but the author's experience has been that it is much safer to do no more than to isolate the affected sheep in a dry location and let nature take its course.

Sometimes trimming and disinfection simply drives the infection in deeper and the time of cure is prolonged. A month or more may be necessary for natural means to bring about a cure, in which time the sheep should be well housed and fed.

The Liver Fluke and Black Disease

The liver fluke, a leaf-shaped flat worm, causes considerable loss in some sections where a particular snail necessary to its life-cycle exists. Losses are due to liver injury and to chronic nutritional disturbance leading to general debility. Also, the immature fluke, in its wonderings through the liver, produces a seat of infection for *Clostridium novyi*, a germ which causes what is known as black disease.

The snail necessary to the fluke's life-cycle is a small mud snail with a sharply pointed shell and rarely exceeds 1/4 in. in length. It is most numerous in stagnant ponds, so the incidence of fluky sheep and black disease would be most likely on lands where such are common. Sheep pick up larvae of the fluke after they have left the snail and are in the water or encysted on grass near the ponds.

Severe infestation of flukes in the liver occurs in the early summer or late spring months, about April or May, and affected sheep are dull and often have a distended abdomen painful to pressure near the breast bone. In a postmortem examination, the liver easily crumbles and shows blood clots under its surface, with many immature flukes (1/8 to 1/4 in. long) present.

The chronic type of infestation results in progressive debility and emaciation accompanied by anemia observable in paleness of the eye membranes and gums. Often, too, a dropsical swelling under the lower jaw is present.

What can be done to prevent or control fluke infestation? Certainly, first, the snail should be eliminated as far as possible. As cattle and rabbits also are subject to flukes, they need protective measures in their behalf.

Weak solutions of bluestone readily kill the active snail but not the snail in its dormant period during the dry season or the eggs of the snail. In March or April, as winter waters start to recede, the breeding grounds of the snail may be treated. For this purpose finely powdered bluestone is mixed with sand (1 to 4 parts) and applied at the rate of 100 lb (of the mixture) per acre. The treatment must be repeated at an interval of four to six weeks and is effective if the breeding grounds (damp or muddy areas) are pretty well defined. Copper sulfate used at this concentration will not kill vegetation but will kill fish. Sheep should be excluded from a treated area until rain washes the powder from the herbage.

Treatment of fluky sheep is best accomplished by individual doses of 1 cc of carbon tetrachloride, provided by biological houses in the form of a gelatin capsule. This drug will not kill the immature flukes that may be in the process of migration through tissues to the liver. Therefore a repeat treatment (or several) may be necessary. Usually the first treatment is given in September and others at intervals of four to six weeks until February or March.

For reasons that are not known, ewes under certain conditions may react unfavorably to treatment and may die. It is therefore recommended that they *not be treated* under the following circumstances:

1. Where a feed change is to be made within three weeks after the treatment. Do not dose and then take the sheep to new feeding grounds.
2. Where a ewe is close to lambing or has just lambed.
3. Where concentrates are fed the week preceding treatment.
4. During cold, stormy weather or after a fatiguing journey.

It is recommended that a trial group be dosed before the entire band is treated.

Black disease, which results from infection caused by the burrowings of the immature flukes migrating through the liver, is controlable by vaccination.

Most deaths that occur as a result of fluke infestation are deaths from this disease, caused by a germ, rather than from the fluke itself, although the fluke, of course, is basically responsible. Deaths are usually preceded by no symptoms.

Clostridium novyi vaccine administered to all the sheep located in an area that has had a bad liver-fluke history will effectively stop losses. It is given in early spring *before* the large multiplication of snails takes place (in California, usually the first part of April). Where losses are occurring and the preventive vaccine has not been administered, vaccination should immediately take place.

A calendar for liver-fluke prevention and control is given below. The dates indicated are for portions of California and should be adjusted elsewhere according to differences in climatic conditions. The bluestone treatment should begin *when winter waters begin to recede.*

When	*What*
March:	Start bluestone treatment of snail-infested waters.
April:	Continue treatment if snails reappear.
April 1–15:	Vaccinate as protection against black disease in event of bad liver-fluke history.
May:	Continue bluestone treatment to destroy snails if they are found.
August:	Treat sheep with carbon tetrachloride for control of mature fluke.
September:	Treat again with carbon tetrachloride to destroy flukes that have matured since last treatment.
October:	Again treat with carbon tetrachloride to destroy flukes that have matured since last treatment.
November, December:	Provide drainage where practical.

Garget (Mammitis) and Blue Bag

A "caked" udder (garget) or one that becomes gangrenous (blue bag) are not uncommon infections met after a ewe lambs. However, few ewes in a band will be affected.

The cause of each of these troubles is often obscure; perhaps they result from injuries of the udder or from chilling as the ewe lies on damp ground. Whatever may be the cause, the result as far as the ewe is concerned is generally very serious, if not fatal, and demands close attention and quick action on the part of the owner.

The first symptoms are that the ewe lags behind, walks in a spraddle-legged fashion, and refuses to allow her lamb to suckle. The infection may be, and most often is, in only one half of the udder. The udder is hot and feverish in garget and causes the ewe much pain. She should be isolated and given penicillin medication.

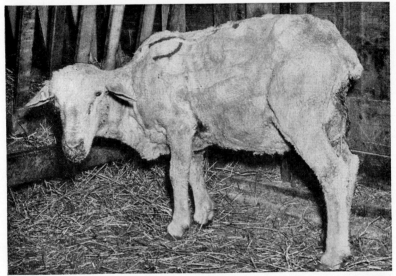

Courtesy ARS-USDA

Fig. 119A.   This ewe, affected with garget or bluebag, shows characteristic depressed attitude.

This consists of injection of 1 cc of procaine penicillin G in oil into the rump muscle. Penicillin also may be syringed into the udder by way of the teat canal.

It is unlikely that many udders are saved by any treatment, but occasionally one caught early enough may be. Hot applications should be made to the udder for some time. The best is a solution of 3/4 cup of Epsom salts to a gallon of water. Stripping of the pus from the teat should be frequent but gentle, and massaging the udder with lard in which turpentine has been mixed will help to relieve the congestion.

In cases where gangrene sets in (blue bag), the pus may be quite contagious and the ewe should be definitely isolated so that germs are not spread. In gangrenous conditions the udder tissues are dead and the teat may be severed to facilitate drainage and drying up of the tissues. Penicillin treatment, again, is very effective in saving the ewe.

Flyblow

The bluebottle fly, which deposits its eggs in meat, raw sores, and filth of all sorts, is an especial enemy of sheep and in "fly time,"

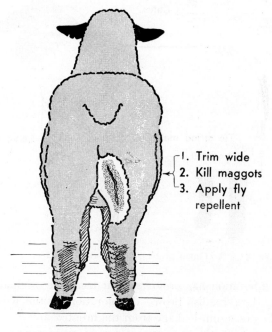

1. Trim wide
2. Kill maggots
3. Apply fly repellent

Fig. 120. Clear a wide margin of dry wool around a maggot-infested wound.

at least, the rear quarters of sheep should be kept shorn or clean of dung and urine stain.

After warm weather in the spring causes the fly eggs to hatch, ewes should surely be tagged (or shorn), lambs should be clean, too, and should not be docked without the application of a fly repellent. Vigilant observation of all sheep stained, or injured at any place on their bodies, should be maintained.

Sheep that are "flyblown" behave very erratically, running quickly for short distances, twitching the dock violently, stamping their feet, or shaking the head in efforts to "get away" from the irritation.

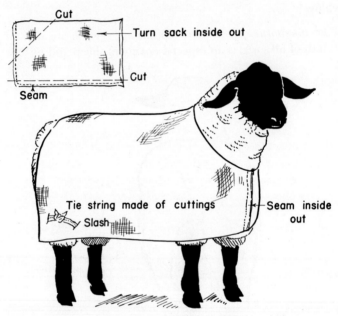

Fig. 121. A blanket protects against the horn fly.

If the infestation has progressed far from the original start near the anus, dark reddish-brown discoloration of the wool or dung locks indicates serum-leakage from the infested area.

In long-fleeced sheep a great patch of maggots may be entirely hidden by the wool, and although maggots may have progressed all the way up over the back, little or no indication will be seen by an uninitiated observer.

Prevention, through keeping the sheep clean, is of course preferable to treatment, but there will be times when treatment is necessary.

Treatment of a patch of maggots (which hatch from fly-deposited eggs in a very few hours in warm weather) consists first of removal of the wool covering the area. *To be sure that the entire infestation is surrounded, shear* all around the sore spot *until clean, dry wool is reached.*

After clearing off the wool close to the hide, removal of the maggots is effected by gently scraping off the larger ones and forcing the others out of their borings with mild sheep dip (1 part to 50). Maggots in deep holes may perhaps better be suffocated by benzol or chloroform.

After removal of the offending maggots, the area must dry fairly well before fly repellents can adhere. Application of a mixture of lard and turpentine has been found most effective by the author. Such a mix does not case over the area as some repllents do. (A repellent material which prevents the air and sunlight from free play on the sore area lengthens the healing time.) No fly will land on a turpentined area. Repellent must be replenished every two or three days until complete drying or healing occurs.

Summer Sores

The small cattle horn fly, often found thick on the backs of cattle and about the base of their horns, occasionally digs into the backs of sheep, setting up intense irritation. The irritation will be alleviated by smearing the area with lard-and-turpentine paste.

Only blackface or open-fleeced sheep are affected, and only certain individuals in a flock may be affected so badly that a large "summer sore" may develop, rather than the often-seen moth-eaten appearance of the wool. The ears and bare areas around the vulva and in the flanks are often badly bitten by this fly.

If a real "summer sore" does develop, it may become a bleeding area six inches or more in diameter as the sheep bites at herself attempting to allay the itch caused by the fly. Ewes that develop a sore of this degree generally will have a sore in the same spot each year. They evidently have a particularly sensitive skin, and it has been noted that their offspring often will be likewise affected. (It might be desirable therefore to butcher such ewes.)

Protection from the fly is desirable. Spraying the backs of the sheep with DDT or BHC (benzene hexachloride) or mixtures of both at frequent intervals can keep down the fly population. Individual sheep can be carried through the summer by keeping them blanketed. Blankets may be made of burlap sacks, but they are easily torn off and must be replaced rather frequently.

In making a blanket for fly protection or for any other purpose, the procedure is to remove the *seam side* of the sack and cut a hole (for the sheep's head) in a corner of the sack on the opposite side. Do not cut this hole too large. Then the sack is fitted over the sheep's head, trimmed if it hangs too low, and tied with a broad strip of burlap (2 to 3 in. wide) around a hind leg above the hock. This tie should not be cinched tightly.

The heavier the sacking material, the longer it will last. It is best to punch two holes in the material, one at the rear flank of the sheep and the other just above the hock, through which the leg tie will be inserted so as to circle the hind leg.

Caseous Lymphadenitis—"Boils"

This disease of the lymph system, usually seen only in very aged ewes, does affect all classes of sheep and has been especially incriminating in regard to rams taken to various ram sales. Rams exhibiting a "boil" may or may not be affected by this particularly insidious disease, but as differentiation between it and whatever may affect the ram is difficult, usually the ram will not be allowed to pass through the sales ring. Research is needed to find a way to make differentiation possible, and care must be taken by sheep owners to prevent the spread of caseous lymphadenitis. Many carcasses are now condemned for slaughter because of it, and in certain areas large percentages of the ewes and rams are affected, although visual evidence is seldom apparent until the sheep are aged.

This is a chronic disease of sheep and goats characterized by cheesy abscesses especially of the lymphatic glands in front of the shoulder and the hip. When the lungs are involved, respiration is rapid and labored and the sheep seems to have chronic pneumonia. Old sheep are generally very emaciated. Large abscesses in the rear flank sometimes occur.

There is much evidence that infection is spread through cuts in the skin, as may be made at shearing time. Therefore, to prevent the entry of bacilli, application of iodine or 5% sheep dip or other suitable antiseptics to wounds may be advisable, but even more practical is the insistence that the shearer allow his handpiece to run for a few seconds in a pan of antiseptic between sheep.

As no treatment for this disease is known, preventive measures such as disinfection of the navel of newborn lambs, docking on clean grounds, cleanup of manure collections in corrals and on bedgrounds, etc., are highly to be recommended.

"Pink Eye"

This type of blindness in sheep has affected isolated flocks seriously but is really very uncommon. Extreme redness of the eye membranes, accompanied by watering of the eye and opaqueness of the eyeball, will make a sheep temporarily entirely blind. He most often recovers spontaneously after four or five weeks and therefore should not be destroyed, but rather isolated and fed carefully.

A review of literature on the disease indicates that the best treatment for it and other eye injuries is pyoktannin blue, a purple dye used in a solution 1 part to 1,000.

After the wool has been trimmed away close to the eyelids and any foreign particles such as stickers or bits of hay have been removed from the eye, the dye is dropped into the corner and allowed to flow over the affected surfaces.

The sulfa drugs are not effective for this disease.

"Milk Fever" (Lambing Sickness)

Aside from lambing paralysis, previously discussed, a similar disease, akin to milk fever in cows but in some ways different, occurs occasionally in ewes.

In cows this disease is due to an acute fall in the concentration of blood calcium and is easily treated by injection into the blood stream of calcium gluconate. Such an injection brings the cow out of her coma in a very few minutes.

Milk fever in the cow appears generally within three or four days *after* calving, but "lambing sickness" sometimes appears *before* lambing, especially if the ewe has been driven heavily or otherwise overexercised. It also appears (as with the cow) *after* lambing, and

the coma that results therefore differentiates the disease from "lambing paralysis," which is never known to occur *after* parturition.

Calcium gluconate, injected into the jugular vein (as with the
cow) brings about an almost miraculous recovery. A ewe in absolute
coma will be on her feet in a matter of minutes and may run off
across the field in full control of herself.

The distinction, then, between the two diseases—lambing paralysis and lambing sickness ("milk fever")—is tied up with exercise.
The former occurs where exercise is nonexistent and always *before*
a ewe has lambed, whereas the latter takes place almost invariably
after forced overexercise and it *may* happen after parturition.

DISEASES AND TROUBLES OF LAMBS

Althought most of the following troubles are associated with
lambs during the growing period or later on in the feed lot, some
of them are also encountered occasionally in the ewes.

Infections Causing Stiffness

Navel Ill and Joint Ill. These conditions occur in lambs from infections at, or a short time after, birth. The infections are of a low
grade and take some days or weeks to build up to a stage where
major symptoms can be seen.

Swellings of the knees or in other joints of the leg indicate local-
ization there. The navel infection generally leads to liver infection
and painful swelling that may cause a lamb to lie down suddenly
and thrash his legs in a spasm. He may die at a week or two of age.

Preventive treatment is to be recommended first and this consists
of application of iodine to the navel shortly after birth, docking
and castrating on clean ground, and general cleanliness of the
lambing setup.

The sulfa drugs and penicillin have given aid in some forms of
the disease. In the author's experience, injections of hemorrhagic
septicemia bacterin or ovine mixed bacterin have brought about
rather spectacular recoveries where the infection was caused by the
erysipelas germs. Lambs so lame that they would take only two or
three steps at a time have responded to 5-cc doses of either of these
materials injected into the armpit. In some cases repeat doses of

3 cc and then 1 cc at 5-day intervals have been necessary, but in others one dose was sufficient to effect a very quick recovery. Veterinarians have stated that the injection of any foreign protein material (such as the bacterin mentioned above) will do the same thing.

Tetanus (Lockjaw) This is usually an infrequent disease affecting especially wether lambs marked in dirty surroundings. The germ that causes lockjaw is found nearly everywhere, but in some locations may be so concentrated that almost any wound can become infected.

As the germ is an anaerobe (does not require air) it can be seen why a male lamb, especially, allowed to lie down on a manure pile or similar filthy bed after being castrated, may be affected. Often lambs pick up the disease from the soil on the grazing grounds.

This disease is usually so infrequent that no one practices protective immunization of all the lambs with tetanus antitoxin. However, in areas where serious outbreaks have occurred, this might be advisable.

Treatment of affected lambs is rarely advisable (because of cost) or effective. A few lambs, given good nursing, will recover, but not many can be saved because the lamb is so helpless. Paralysis of all four legs and of the neck and jaws is almost complete, and only frequent turning, and nursing of the lamb by bottle, can possibly carry him through until immunity is established.

This again, then, is a reason for the maintenance of clean conditions at marking time.

Lamb Stiffness. Several types of "stiffness" of the legs and other muscles of the body are recognized in suckling lambs and have caused many sheep producers no little worry. The cause of some types of stiffness is unknown and no treatments are available, so the producer simply takes his loss or waits for nature to repair the damage done. Other types respond to treatment or may be prevented by measures taken early.

The treatment mentioned as possible for infections of the erysipelas type (as in joint ill) is about the only treatment that has shown any effect upon the various types of stiffness.

White muscle disease of suckling lambs has been reported from all over the United States, usually in farm flocks rather than in range bands where a greater variety of feed has been used. In this disease the hind legs, especially, of lambs are affected, and deaths are usually considered due to inability of the lambs to get about to feed or to suckle. The disease gets its name from whitish areas appearing in degenerated muscle fibers in the legs. The disease is not contagious and is not caused by an infective germ, but seems to be tied up with vitamin E deficiency and is most often noted when farm flocks *are confined longer than usual at lambing time.*

Indications that this disease is brought about by Vitamin E deficiency in the milk of ewes on certain diets have been noted. The feeding of such material to the ewes during the last six weeks of pregnancy did not prevent the disease in the lambs. However, daily oral feeding of 10 cc of cold-pressed wheatgerm oil (carrying the vitamin) was effective in curing the stiff lambs, and this procedure is recommended where there is evidence that this particular type of stiffness exists. Veterinarians are of the opinion that this type of stiffness is not common to the sunnier sections of the sheep-growing areas.

Chronic arthritis has been noted, particularly among purebred sheep. It is a non-pus-forming joint infection that may appear at two or three weeks of age or not until the lambs are several months old. Complete recovery does not occur, but no deaths can be attributed to chronic arthritis. It is considered that this disease is started by entry into the body of germs through the "marking" wounds. The worst cases reported followed docking (in sheds) with an emasculator that crushed the bone of the tail. Hot iron docking and navel disinfection overcame the trouble.

This seems to be little if any different than the type of stiffness described under the heading of Joint Ill.

Feed-change stiffness has been reported under varied sets of conditions. Lambs separated from their mothers in mountain areas have become stiff, but if held on good feed and water for two or three weeks, apparently have recovered completely. Others weaned and changed from a combination of natural grass pasture and milk to pasturage on cultivated oats and vetch have gone stiff but recovered after two or three weeks. Still others, shipped from mountain areas to lowland irrigated pastures, have had a period of stiffness.

It is believed that if the feed change can be made gradually—that is, perhaps with the lamb's mother along so that it may suckle for a time on the new feed—the incidence of stiffness will not be so great.

Although most stiffness in lambs is not yet subject to treatment, *soaking* of the navel in iodine, hot-iron docking instead of the emasculator type, and gradual changes of feeding practices all will help.

Pulpy Kidney and Entero-Toxemia

Each of these diseases is caused by the same germ, *Clostridium welchii* (type D). The former name usually is given to occurrences in lambs, and the latter is used for manifestations in older sheep.

These diseases, sometimes causing severe losses, occur generally on very lush spring feed when the ewe's milk flow increases, this predisposing the lambs to attack. The germ, taken in with the food, flourishes in the intestinal tract and produces a highly lethal poison. In the case of ewe deaths the better pasture is considered the basic cause.

Very few, if any, preliminary symptoms to death are observable, but practically always it will be big fat animals that die. Postmortem examination often shows a very friable kidney and an excessive amount of fluid in the sac surrounding the heart, but a definite diagnosis is generally obtained only by a trained veterinarian.

A vaccine has now been developed that has been found to be very effective in giving animals resistance to this disease, but in some cases the massive production of poisons has apparently been able to overcome the partial immunity conferred by the vaccine.

This suggests that preventive measures in terms of sheep husbandry should go along with vaccination where the trouble occurs. This may consist of corralling in a rough grass lot at night and the feeding of hay of plain variety.

In areas where cases of the disease are on record, *vaccination* is performed on lambs, usually at time of marking. One dose of 5 cc of the vaccine is sufficient if the trouble has previously resulted in low death loss. If the losses previously experienced have been severe, a second dose at a month's interval should be given. Lambs may be vaccinated at any time between birth and three weeks of age.

Founder

Overeating of grain usually is the cause of founder, although a type of founder may result from drinking too much water or from eating some other feeds. Some discussion of the occurrence of founder was given in Chapter 3.

Seldom will any lamb suckling its mother be subject to founder excepting perhaps where creep feeding of grain is improperly managed as discussed in Chapter 7. Ewes, however, improperly herded onto fresh grain stubble, and lambs or sheep of any kind being fed grain in dry lot, are often foundered by accident or by indiscriminate grain feeding.

Founder results in extreme tenderness in the feet due to rupture of the capillaries, and if a sheep does not die it may be made permanently lame as a result of gorging on grain. In a post mortem examination following grain founder the paunch will be found heavily loaded with grain, with very little roughage intermixed.

Quick action on the part of the owner may make possible the saving of sheep on the verge of founder. When it is known that a few head have gotten an overdose of grain (as when it is noted that they have broken into a sack or into a grain bid), the immediate dosage of *all* the suspect animals with oil will save them. However, if the sheep are not found until very sick, oil or any other treatment will be of little avail. A cupful of *raw* linseed oil (boiled linseed oil is poisonous) or of any light white mineral oil for each mature sheep should be sufficient to move the grain through the digestive tract. Epsom salts is not recommended.

The handfeeding of lambs with heavy grains such as corn, wheat, and barley demands a very gradual increase in the amounts fed to ensure freedom from founder. A good practice is to start with very small amounts (less than 1/4 lb per head) and continue at such a rate until *all* the lambs are anxious to eat and come to the grain trough quickly to get their share. Increases then should be made as the lambs indicate they can take more, and this will be indicated when, after an increase, *all* the lambs stay at the trough until *all* the grain is consumed. This same amount should be fed for two or three feedings before a further increase is made. The man who does the feeding should make sure that *all* the animals for whom the grain is intended are present and come to the trough at the same time. He should also realize that high temperatures (or feeding too early in the evening on a warm day) will cause some lambs to eat less than they ordinarily would. This then leaves an excess amount for gluttons to consume, and they may become sick or actually founder. At the next feeding these sick lambs will hold back and the others will overeat and get sick. It is indeed "the eye of the master who fatteneth his flock."

Self-feeding of lambs by means of separate hay and grain bunks is considered risky, although some commercial feeders have successfully mastered this method. However, where an all-in-one mix is self-fed and a reasonable portion of grain is used, no ill effects are noted.

A "lightening" of the grain (corn or barley alone) with oats or various pulps and bran is recommended, especially where novice feeders do the feeding or where lambs are being fed to "show" condition.

Eversion of the Rectum (Piles)

There is some indication that eversion of the rectum (or piles) is due to a hereditary weakness. Groups of lambs sired by one particular ram in a flock have had a high incidence of this trouble.

Most every sheepman has had experience with occasional lambs, and ewes too, that evert the rectum, especially when gorged with feed and sometimes to the extent that it does not revert into place when the sheep is off of feed. The author has found that these cases occur most often in the late spring when feeds were beginning to dry but are still very palatable (and perhaps lack some of the "loosening" qualities of tenderer earlier grasses).

With fat lambs or ewes perhaps the best course is to get them to the butcher quickly. However, valuable purebreds or sheep not in condition to be butchered may be treated.

The usual answer to the question, "What do you do with a sheep with piles?" is: "Nothing." Very little knowledge of treatment is the rule among sheep owners, yet it is possible to cure this trouble, and profitable to pay attention to the few details that must be heeded in order to do so.

Of course, if the animal is not of particular value, it may be as well to slaughter it for meat, but in many cases an owner of a registered ewe or a ram, for instance, would suffer quite an economic loss should the sheep be butchered, and he is anxious to save the affected animal instead.

The sheep owner himself may perform the necessary operation. (It usually falls to the lot of sheepmen anyway to do these things rather than to call in a veterinarian.)

The usual condition is that the rectum is entirely prolapsed and protruding 3 or 4 in. The less usual case is a rectum that protrudes occasionally and then goes back. Most of these cases seem to occur in the late spring when the ewes are getting fat and when the earlier, rather washy feed begins to harden. The rather common procedure in handling these ewes is to take them off the strong, hard feed and to attempt to cause the rectum to stay in simply by starving the sheep. This procedure is sometimes effective but it requires a long time and is hardly the best thing for the ewe. Also, it is time-consuming and uncertain.

It is possible, too, that coughing due to worm infestation is a contributing cause of the protrusion, so that it is strongly recommended that a rigid worming program be maintained with this trouble also in mind. The phenothiazine treatment administered to ewes and lambs in the early spring and through the summer, and to ewes again in the fall, will do much to reduce this coughing.

Now as to the operation for removal of the everted section of intestine. The primary necessity before the operation is to keep the ewe off feed and water, perhaps 18 to 24 hours. It is desirable that little or no feed be passing through the digestive tract. Into the everted rectum will then be inserted either of two different sorts of articles. Perhaps the more preferable is a metal contrivance which veterinarians carry: a tube about 2 in. long and 3/4 in. in diameter with a constriction around its center and a slight taper at the end that is to be inserted into the rectum. When this is inserted, the constriction should be placed just outside the anus and then several turns with a hard string or fishline should be made around the folds of the everted rectum over the constricted part of the instrument. Don't pull the line so tight that it will cut through the rectal walls, but tighten it enough to prevent the metal tube from pushing out. In a few days the everted portion of the rectum will slough off, carrying the tube with it, and the sheep will be cured.

The alternative to using the metal veterinarian's tube is more crude but still effective. It is a piece of garden hose cut about 4 in. long. A "constriction" can be cut into it near its center with a pocketknife. This may be about 1/4 in. wide and just through the outer layer of rubber. It is well to ream out the end of the hose that is to be inserted into the rectum to help funnel feces into and through the hose.

A helper should be available and as one person inserts the hose (the sheep lying on its side) so that the "constriction" is felt through

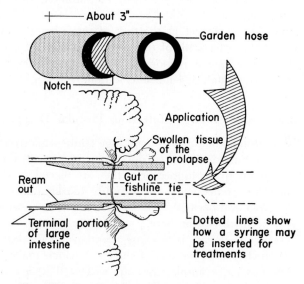

Fig. 122. Rectal prolapse treatment.

the folds of the eversion to be about flush with the body of the sheep, the second person can make the ties. It is well to soak the string used to tie off the folds in iodine previous to applying it and to swab the area also with iodine. Also, because there is some danger of blood poisoning, the sheep should have an injection of procaine penicillin G in oil or a sulfa-drug treatment.

Do not cut off the portion of the rectum outside the tie immediately after tying it. If excessive feces are passing through the sheep and help is not available frequently to prevent, by enema, a build-up of relatively hard manure inside the hose, some sheep will strain so hard that the tie will slip and the hose will be forced out.

If the intestine has previously been cut outside the tie, of course it then is parted and the sheep cannot be saved.

At the point of the tie the intestinal tissues will grow together very rapidly. In fact the author has known a lamb so treated to heal and press out the hose in 24 hours. Usually it will be necessary after about two days to cut the string and to remove the hose and cut off the drying tissue that was left outside the tie.

As mentioned above, frequent enemas (with soapy water) effectively assist the process. They are easily administered through the hose by a dose syringe.

It is advisable too, to get at the task of removing the eversion early, that is, before the walls of the everted portion get thick and leathery. In such a case it is more difficult to tie off the eversion and also to insert a small 3/4-in. hose section.

Sore Mouth ('Dobe Mouth) —Infectious Pustular Dermatitis

This disease usually does not attack range lambs while young and still suckling their mothers, but it does often appear at about the time they are ready to be shipped or as they are placed in feed lots. Because such occurrence may affect future marketings of lambs from a given area and because its *prevention* must occur while they are young, it needs discussion here.

The effect of the disease is to cause eruptions on the lips of the lamb (and sometimes on the bag of the ewe) which make feeding difficult. The lips (in a simple case) are encrusted with scabs that cover violent and tender sores. These are caused by an organism (a filterable virus) that enters minute scratches on the lips brought about by feeding upon browse or rough forage (generally available as the green-feed season ends).

Where this trouble is known to occur each year it is advisable for the flock owner to vaccinate the lambs against the disease. Vaccination is cheap, simple, and effective. Sore-mouth vaccine can be purchased readily, and explicit directions for its use are provided.

When the disease has not been prevented by vaccination, its occurrence may be relatively "tame" or quite virulent, depending upon accompanying circumstances. Cases not complicated by infections caused by bacteria of other sorts will cure spontaneously in about three weeks. In other words, the uncomplicated case is a self-limiting affair and requires no treatment.

However, complications may readily set in, and serious spread of the sore mouth from the lips to the gums, tongue, and even to the lungs, stomach, and liver may occur. Some deaths result, and seriously affected animals rarely recover fully.

It is therefore recommended that sore-mouth crusts be removed by hand and the sores be treated with iodine once a week during the stay of the disease. The scabs should be collected and burned or disinfected unless they are removed in the open where sunlight may disinfect them. It is not well to rely on this, however.

The *virus* sometimes overwinters and may be picked up by ewes lambing in quarters where the diseased lambs were fed. Then the disease appears on and inside the teats of milking ewes and not only is transmitted to the suckling lamb but also renders the udder about useless. Continuous routine vaccination, then, must be practiced, this job being done at marking time.

Ewes and lambs develop an immunity to the disease once they have suffered it or have been vaccinated, so that only new sheep brought to the farm require vaccination. Of course newborn lambs, too, should be treated.

PARTICULAR TROUBLES OF RAMS

The range or farm sheep-raiser has a considerable investment in rams which are liable to certain troubles that are peculiar to the sex and that should be discussed because of the financial losses possible.

Injuries to the Testes

Such injuries are frequent and if severe render a ram useless. Fevers and adhesions connected with the bruise will cause the sperm to become infertile. However, if only one teste is injured, the ram is fertile upon recovery. Therefore help should be given to reduce the inflammation and swelling caused by injury so that the ram can be of service in later years.

Treatment of a ram's scrotum and swollen teste can be nothing more (outside of castration) than immediate action to cause circulation to reduce the swellings. This is done by bathing the scrotum alternately with hot and cold water and is made easy by means of a receptacle which fits loosely over the scrotum and into which the water may be poured. A convenient receptacle can be made from a section of an automobile-tire inner tube about 12 in. long, with one end pinched to closure by a wrap of wire.

The actual treatment demands that the ram be tied in a standing position, and the tube be held over his scrotum (or tied in position by a cord over his back). Then warm water should be poured into the receptacle, soon to be replaced by hotter water. The heat should never be great enough to burn the ram. (When he shows visible evidence of discomfort by stepping about worriedly, the water is at a maximum heat.) Fifteen minutes of hot water should be followed by 15 minutes of cold water, and the whole process should then be repeated.

Such treatment as this, morning and night, for a few days should reduce the swollen teste.

In extremely swollen cases (where the teste seems to be 10 to 12 in. in length) castration of the one teste is indicated and should be accompanied by protection through penicillin injections.

Incidentally, the *prevention* of injuries to the testes is very important. Wherever rams are kept they should find no opportunity to bruise themselves on obstructions and articles lying about. Runways into barns are to be preferred to a setup that requires a ram to jump up into the entryway.

Very careful wrangling of a group of rams is important. These are strong animals, and if they are not controlled by proper paneling and pens, they can very easily strain themselves dangerously.

Pizzle-Rot

When rams are corralled for some time in enclosures that are foul with manure, especially if they are wooly on the belly, the end of the sheath is continuously damp with urine and a "urine burn" causes considerable necrosis and an entry for bacteria that can cause serious distress and death. Every effort should be made to bed rams well and to keep wool shorn from around the sheath whenever they are corralled for any length of time. Sulfa powder or penicillin ointment may help clear up sheath infections.

Index

Abnormal births, 132
Abortions, causes of, 78
    prevention of, 86
Acclimating purchased sheep, 37
Afterbirth, retention of, 144
Aged ewes, age limit to hold, 235
    buying, 37
    percentage replacement of, 233
    selling, 233
Alfalfa pasture, bloat on, 76
    safe usage of, 78
    using, 5
Alfilaria, for grazing, 5

"Bagging out" ewes for lambing, 90, 273
Barley stubble, usefulness of. 9, 69, 79
Barns, needed for lambing, 92
    requirements for lambing, 93
    size requirements of, 109
Bean straw, usefulness, 9
Beet pulp, wet, for aged ewes, 236
BHC (benzene hexachloride) dip or spray, 194
Birth, abnormal, 132, 137
    breech, 135
    Caesarian, 136
    dry, 145
    normal position at, 132
    stillborn, 136
Black disease; see Diseases
Blankets, for sheep, 290
Bloat losses, treatment, 76
Bradford counts (wool grades), 242
Branches of the sheep industry, 10
Branding, chute, 254
    "irons," 106
Breast painting of rams, 60
Breeding ewe lambs, advisability of, 65
Breeding season, length of, 58, 63
    variance with breed, 63
Breeds of commercial ewes as fit locations, 19
Broken mouth ewes, treatment of, 37

Brooders, in lambing pens, 95
Budgeting the sheep year, 44
"Bummer lambs," raising, 146
Bur clover, for sheep grazing, 5
Burdizzo marking of lambs, 187
Buying ewes by ages:
    aged, 34
    lambs, 33
    middle-aged, 34
    yearling, 33
Buying rams, of breeds to suit location, 25
    precautions in, 39

Capacity, carrying of ranges, 8
Castrating lambs, instruments used, 104, 185
    practices, 183
Catching sheep. 268
Characteristics of sheep, 262
Chilled lamb, reviving a, 137
Chutes, loading, 229
    combination, 230
    dodge, 120
Chuting sheep (separation), 272
Clothing wools, 49, 240
Colostrum, analysis of, 147
    for orphans, 147
    when thick, 139
Columbias, as range ewes, 21
    as sires, 33
Combing wools, 49, 240
Contagious diseases of sheep, 278
Core test for wool shrinkage, 247, 259
Corriedales, as range ewes, 21
    as sires. 33
Coyotes as predators, 76
Creep feeding, grains for, 162
    panels, 107
    practices, 160
    results of, 70, 166
Crop size, lamb affected by, 56
Crook, sheep, correct use of, 268

305